BIGGEST Quiz Book Ever

Is your brainbox plugged in and your answering machine switched on? Then you're ready for the biggest, most baffling, mind blowing quiz ever! Dennis, Gnasher and their friends have each picked 10 questions on all of the eight quiz topics shown opposite. Take on your favourite chums in turn and see if you're up to the challenge! There are answers at the foot of each page... but you can add up your scores and fill in the super scoreboard at the end of the book to see how much of a whizz kid you really are!

TOPICS
Geography
General Knowledge
Natural World
Books, Films And TV
Science And Numbers
Sport And Music
History
People

Published 2001 by Beano books geddes & grosset
an imprint of Children's Leisure Products Limited,
David Dale House, New Lanark ML11 9DJ, Scotland.

ISBN 1 84205 034 6

Printed and bound in Europe.

GEOGRAPHY

DENNIS

1. What is the name of the highest mountain in the world?

2. Which country has a dragon on its flag?

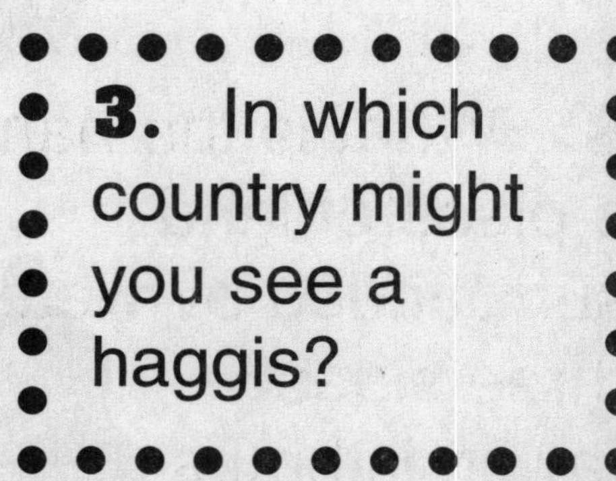

3. In which country might you see a haggis?

4. Where is the Louvre Art Gallery?

5. What is the name of the scale used when measuring the strength of wind?
(a) Beaufort
(b) Celsius
(c) Windward.

6. Kingston is the capital of which Caribbean island?

7. Where is the Acropolis?

8. What is the name of a piece of land surrounded by water on three sides?
(a) an isthmus
(b) a peninsula
(c) an archipelago.

9. In which direction would you travel to reach Alaska from Vancouver in Canada?

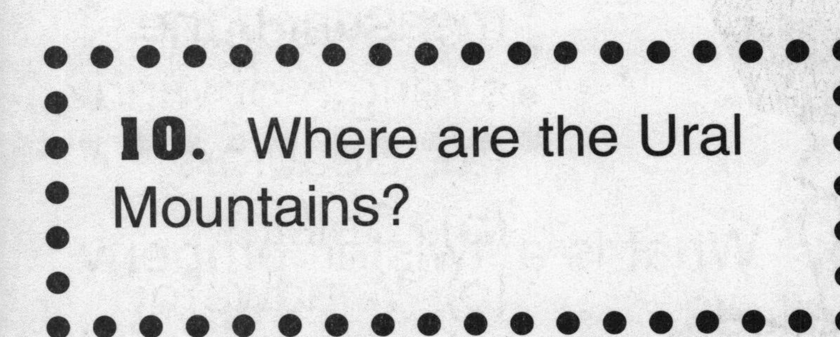

10. Where are the Ural Mountains?

ANSWERS.
1. Mount Everest.
2. Wales.
3. Scotland.
4. Paris.
5. Beaufort.
6. Jamaica.
7. Athens, Greece.
8. Peninsula.
9. North.
10. Russia.

SCORE

MINNIE

1. In Scotland, what is the name for a mountain over the height of 3000 feet?

2. The highest waterfall in the world is in...?
(a) Nepal
(b) Peru
(c) Venezuela.

3. If Minnie went to visit a kibbutz, which country would she be in?

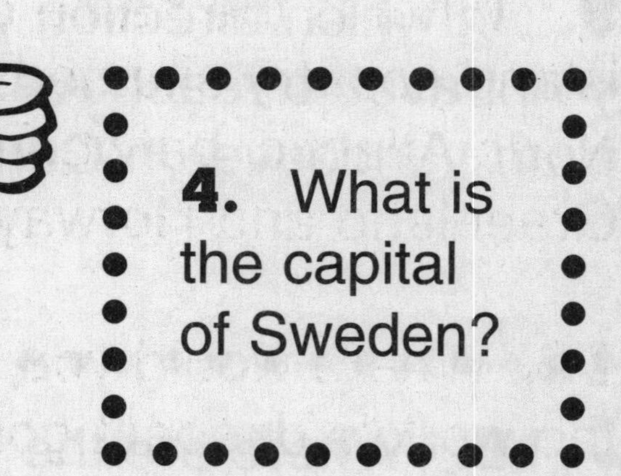

4. What is the capital of Sweden?

5. What is a 'twister' properly called?

6. Where is The White House?

7. In which century was the Colosseum in Rome built?
(a) 2nd Century A.D.
(b) 5th Century B.C.
(c) 1st Century A.D.

8. What is the name of the river that passes through the city of London?

9. What is the name of the island country situated in the North Atlantic, between Greenland and Norway?

10. Where would you find the world's deepest goldmine?
(a) South Africa
(b) Russia
(c) U.S.A.

BILLY WHIZZ

1. What is the name of the volcano close to the city of Naples?

2. Which is the longest road bridge in Britain?
(a) Severn
(b) Forth
(c) Humber.

3. In which country is the Camargue?

4. What flower is associated in song with Amsterdam?

5. What is the name of the cold dry winter wind that blows in the southern regions of France?

6. In which country would you see the Calgary Stampede?

7. What was the name of the architect who designed St Paul's Cathedral in London?

8. Through which European city does the River Seine flow?

9. Is New Zealand to the east or west of Australia?

10. Which city in the U.S.A. is known as the 'Windy City'?

ANSWERS.

1. Vesuvius.
2. Humber.
3. France.
4. Tulips.

5. Mistral.
6. Canada.
7. Sir Christopher Wren.
8. Paris.
9. East.
10. Chicago.

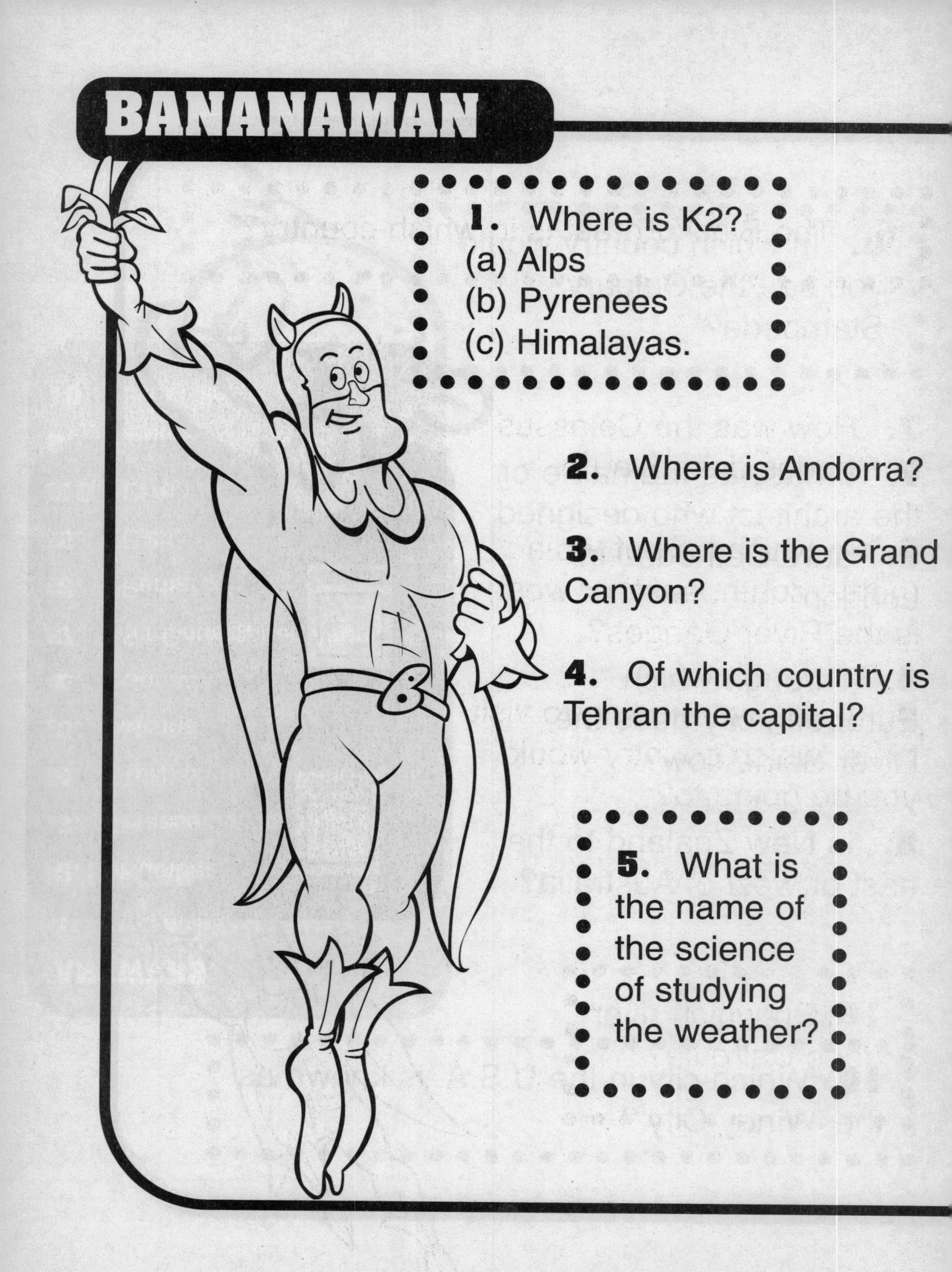
BANANAMAN
1. Where is K2?
(a) Alps
(b) Pyrenees
(c) Himalayas.
2. Where is Andorra?
3. Where is the Grand Canyon?
4. Of which country is Tehran the capital?
5. What is the name of the science of studying the weather?

6. The Black Forest is in which country?

7. How was the Colossus of Rhodes destroyed?

8. In which part of India (north, south, east, or west) is the River Ganges?

9. If you were going to visit Lima, which country would you be going to?

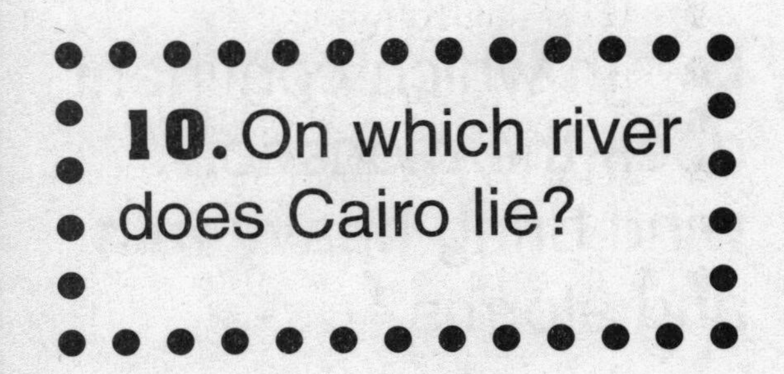

10. On which river does Cairo lie?

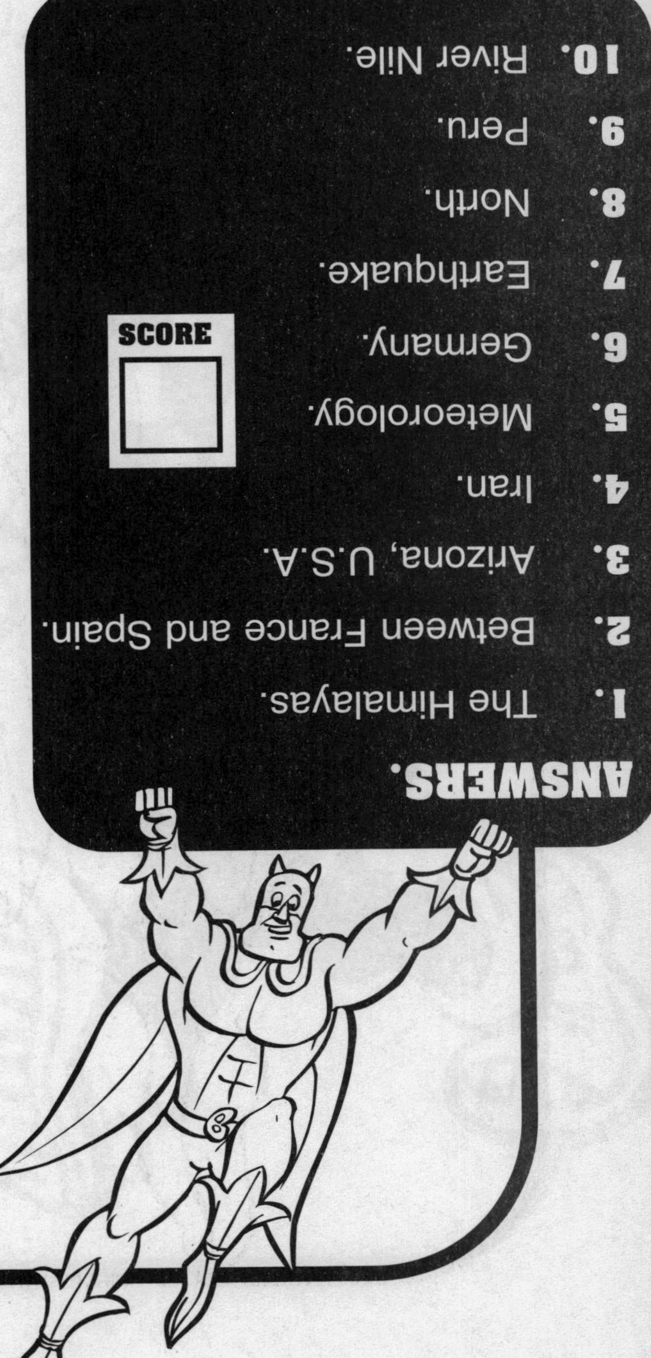

ROGER THE DODGER

1. Where is the Matterhorn?

2. Which African country has the largest population?

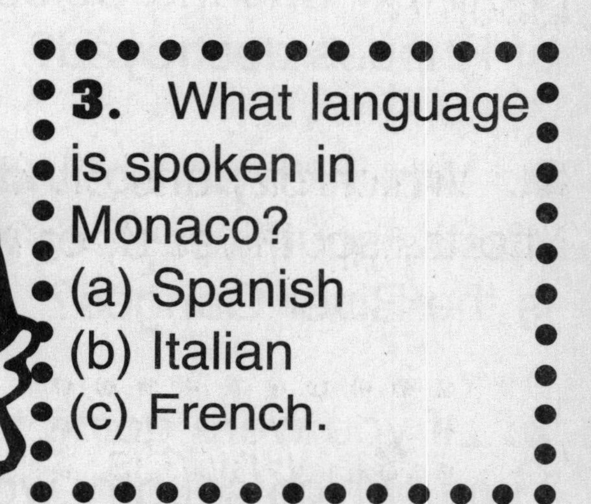

3. What language is spoken in Monaco?
(a) Spanish
(b) Italian
(c) French.

4. What is the capital of Russia?

5. In which continent does the monsoon wind bring heavy rain and storms?

6. Where would you see the Palace of the Winds?

7. Where is the Statue of Liberty?

8. Which city sits on the Mississippi River delta?

9. Which is further North: Calcutta or Madras?

10. On which river does Hamburg lie?

BERYL THE PERIL

1. On which mountain did Noah's Ark reputedly come to rest?

2. The Tasman Sea flows between which two countries?

3. Where is Uluru, formerly known as Ayer's Rock?

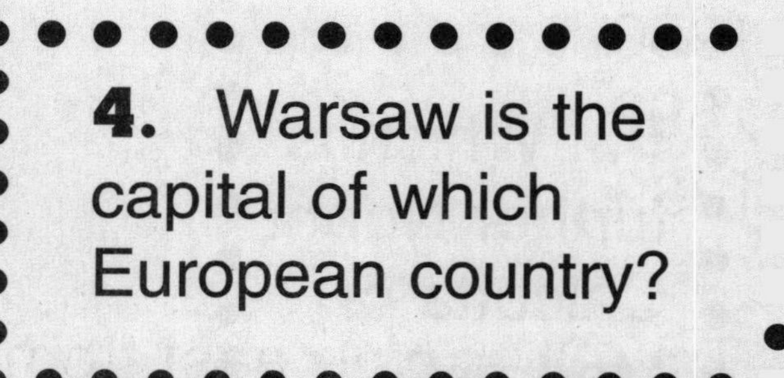

4. Warsaw is the capital of which European country?

5. What is the name given to a wind of force twelve or more?
(a) Tempest
(b) Gale
(c) Hurricane.

6. Can you name the Capital of Mongolia?

7. In which year did the dismantling of the Berlin Wall begin?
(a) 1989
(b) 1992
(c) 1972.

8. When was the Suez Canal opened?
(a) 1950
(b) 1898
(c) 1869.

9. Travelling due east from Brazil across the Atlantic, which continent would you land on?

10. A fjord is a Norwegian mountain, lake or island?

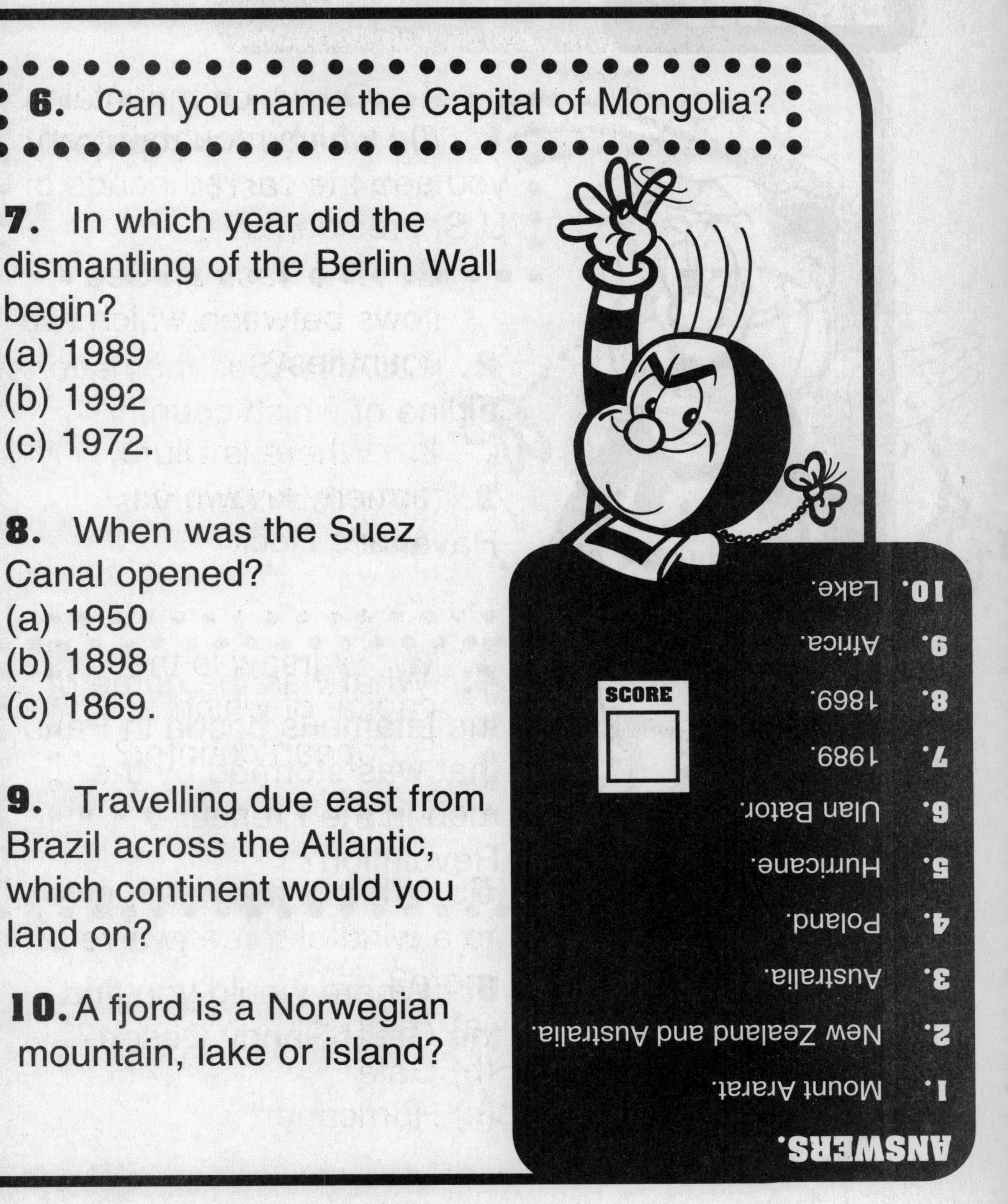

ANSWERS.

1. Mount Ararat.
2. New Zealand and Australia.
3. Australia.
4. Poland.
5. Hurricane.
6. Ulan Bator.
7. 1989.
8. 1869.
9. Africa.
10. Lake.

1. On which mountain can you see the carved heads of U.S. presidents?

2. QUANTAS is the national airline of which country?

3. In which country is Havana?

4. What was the name of the infamous prison in Paris that was stormed by the mob in the French Revolution?

5. Where would you find the Great Sandy Desert?

6. If you were a Walloon, which country would you be living in?

7. Which famous French building was opened in 1889?

8. Name the river common to Bonn and Cologne.

9. Which is closer to London: Devon or Cornwall?

10. Where are the Apennines?

ANSWERS.

1. Mount Rushmore.
2. Australia.
3. Cuba.
4. Le Bastille.
5. Australia.
6. Belgium.
7. The Eiffel Tower.
8. The Rhine.
9. Devon.
10. Italy.

WALTER

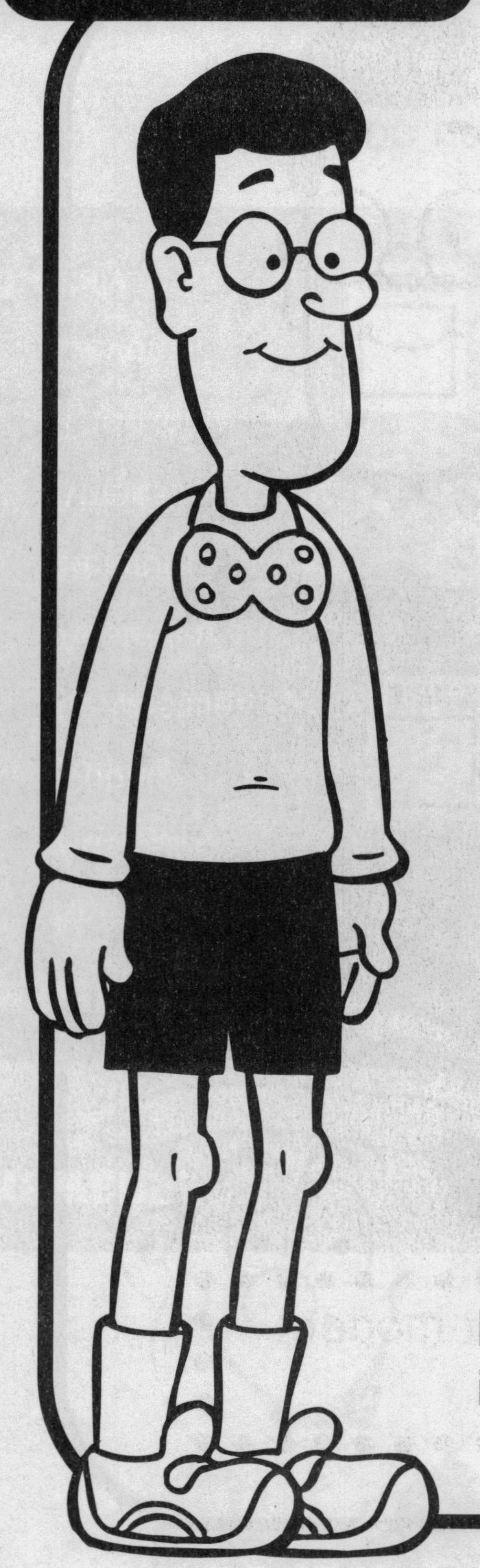

1. In which country is the Massif Central?

2. Where would you find Queen Maud Land?

3. Does the Tropic of Cancer lie to the north or to the south of the equator?

4. What were the names of the twins, suckled by a wolf, who are associated in mythology with the founding of the capital of Italy?

5. What is the name for the rumbling sound that is often heard after a flash of lightning in the sky?

6. In which country would you find Bodrum Castle?
(a) Ireland
(b) Turkey
(c) Holland.

7. Where is Sugar Loaf Mountain?

8. Over which river in Scotland did a terrible railway disaster occur in the nineteenth century?

9. Which is closer to France: Jersey or Guernsey?

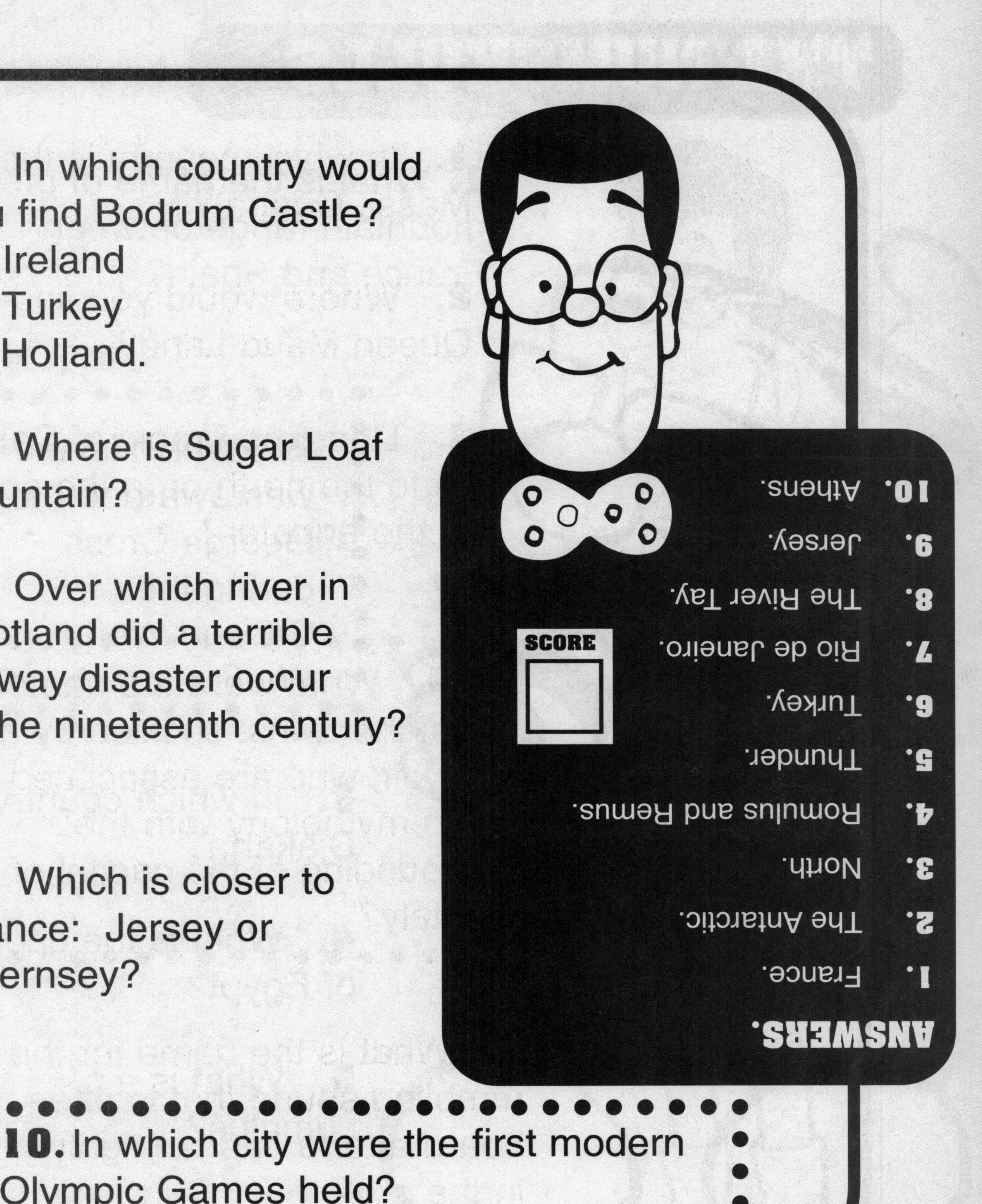

10. In which city were the first modern Olympic Games held?

THE NUMSKULLS

1. What is the name of the mountain range between France and Spain?

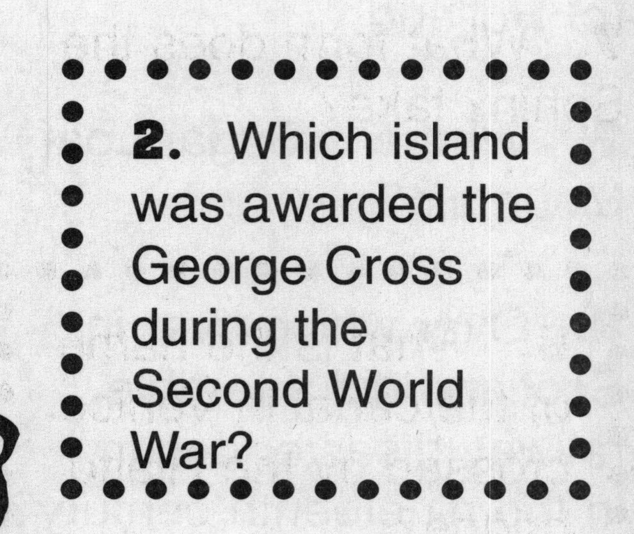

2. Which island was awarded the George Cross during the Second World War?

3. In which country is Djakarta?

4. What is the capital of Egypt?

5. What is a cumulus?

6. On which European island can the ruins of Knossos be found?

7. What form does the Sphinx take?

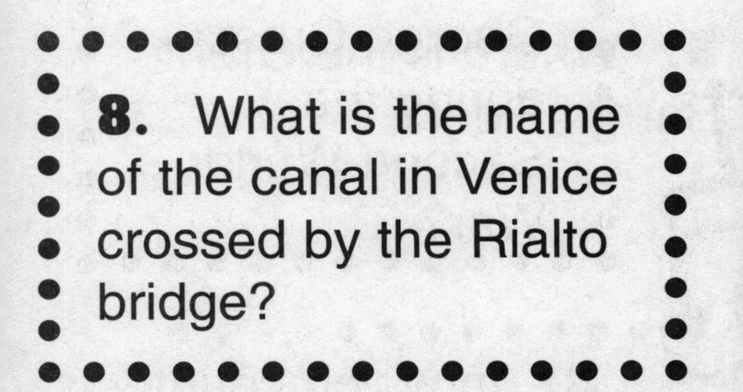

8. What is the name of the canal in Venice crossed by the Rialto bridge?

9. What is the name of the strait between North Africa and Spain?

10. On which river does the Henley Regatta take place?

ANSWERS.

1. The Pyrenees.
2. Malta.
3. Indonesia.
4. Cairo.
5. A type of cloud.
6. Crete.
7. A lion's body with a human head.
8. The Grand Canal.
9. The Strait of Gibraltar.
10. The River Thames.

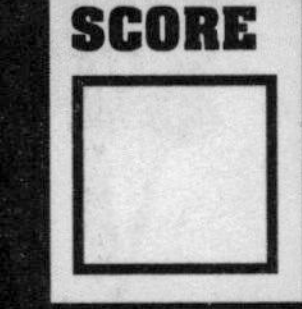

PLUG

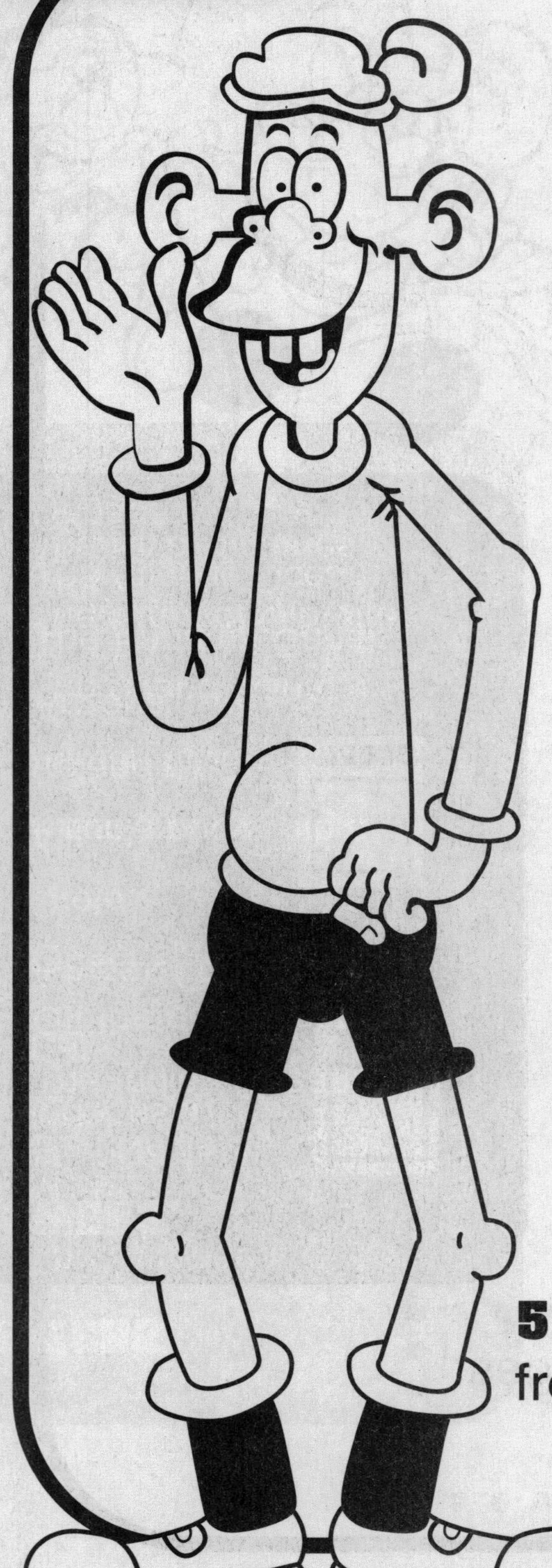

1. What is the name of the highest mountain in Scotland?

2. What is the world's third largest ocean?

3. Where is the Great Barrier Reef?

4. Oslo is the capital city of which country?

5. What is the name given to frozen dew?

6. Where is the Ring of Kerry?
(a) Scotland
(b) Wales
(c) Ireland.

7. In which American state is the town of Phoenix?

8. What is the name of the canal that connects the Atlantic and the Pacific oceans?

9. The Caribbean Sea is part of which ocean?

10. What is the second largest country in the world?

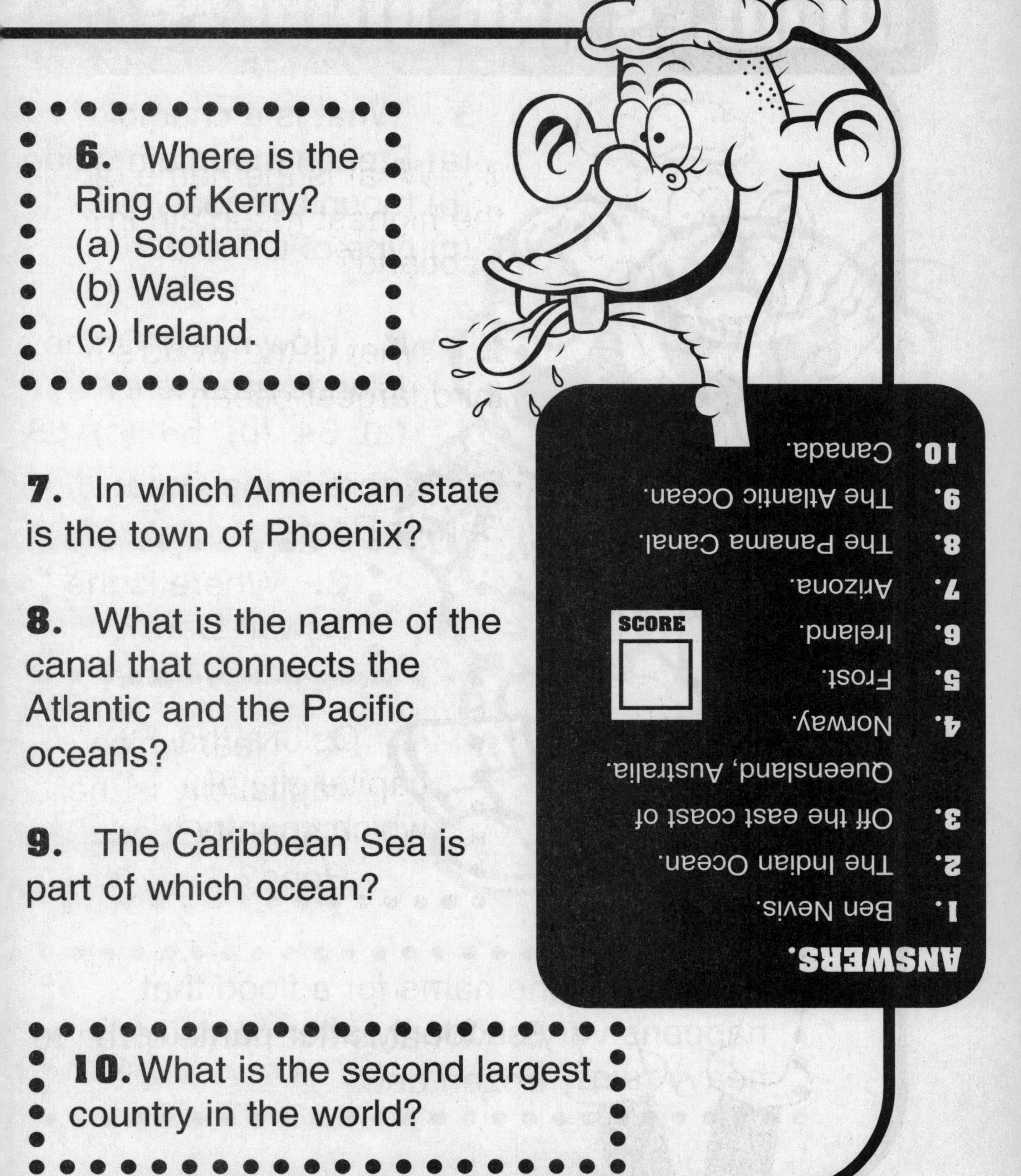

ANSWERS.

1. Ben Nevis.
2. The Indian Ocean.
3. Off the east coast of Queensland, Australia.
4. Norway.
5. Frost.
6. Ireland.
7. Arizona.
8. The Panama Canal.
9. The Atlantic Ocean.
10. Canada.

SCORE

CUDDLES AND DIMPLES

1. What is a chamois?
(a) French mountain guide
(b) mountain goat
(c) type of ice-axe.

2. How many Orkney Islands are there?
(a) 34 (b) 56 (c) 68.

3. Where is the Aswan Dam?

4. Near which capital city is the Cape of Good Hope?

5. What is the name for a flood that happens very suddenly after particularly heavy rain?

6. The volcanic island of Stromboli is off the coast of which country?

7. Where were the 1996 Olympic Games held?

8. Which river flows through the Grand Canyon?

9. In which country is the city of Montevideo?

10. In which country is the Peloponnese peninsula?

ANSWERS.

1. Mountain goat.
2. 68.
3. Egypt.
4. Cape Town.
5. Flash flood.
6. Italy.
7. Atlanta.
8. The Colorado River.
9. Uruguay.
10. Greece.

BALL BOY

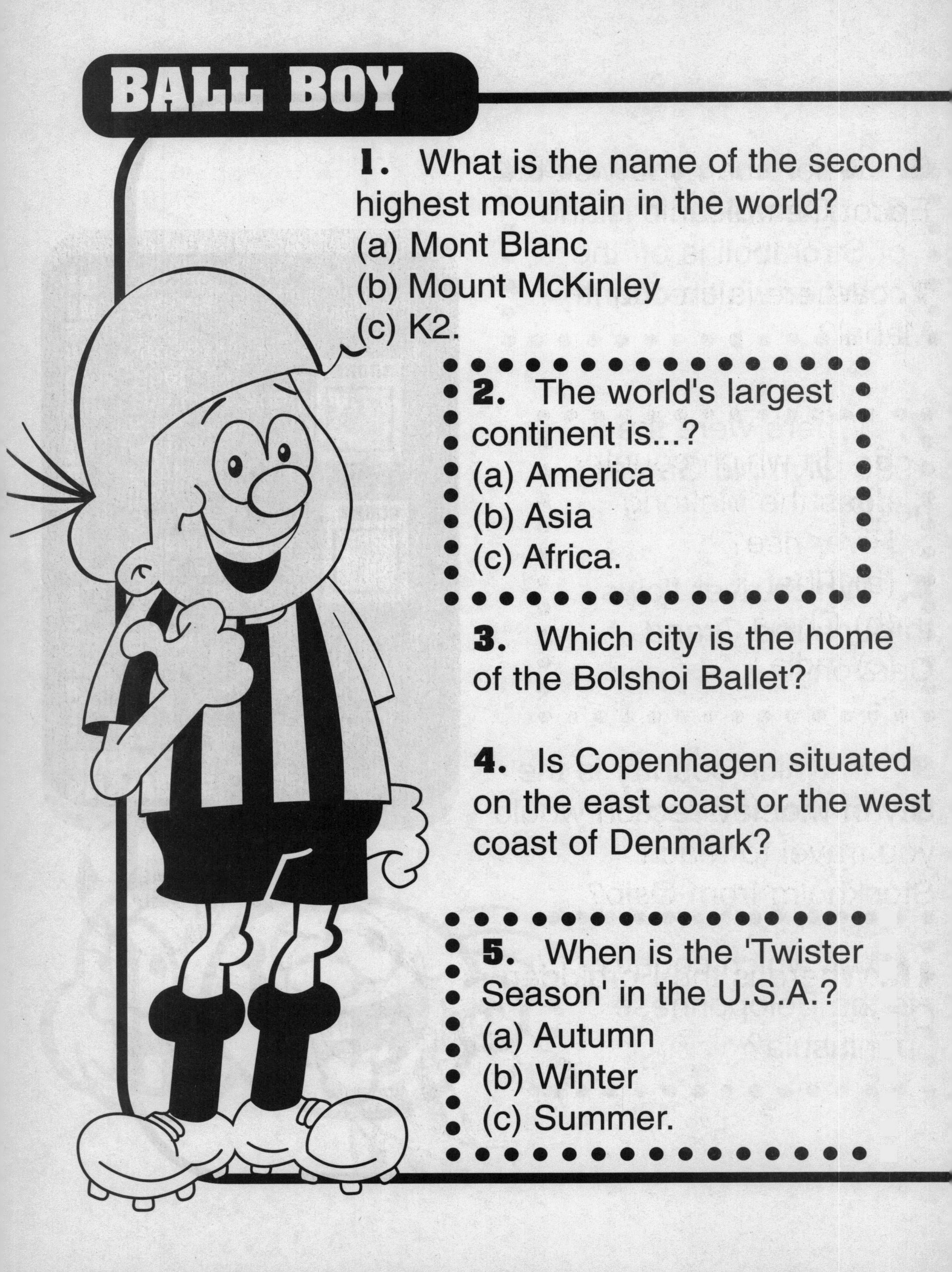

1. What is the name of the second highest mountain in the world?
(a) Mont Blanc
(b) Mount McKinley
(c) K2.

2. The world's largest continent is...?
(a) America
(b) Asia
(c) Africa.

3. Which city is the home of the Bolshoi Ballet?

4. Is Copenhagen situated on the east coast or the west coast of Denmark?

5. When is the 'Twister Season' in the U.S.A.?
(a) Autumn
(b) Winter
(c) Summer.

6. Where can you visit the Epcot Centre?

7. Where is the Taj Mahal?

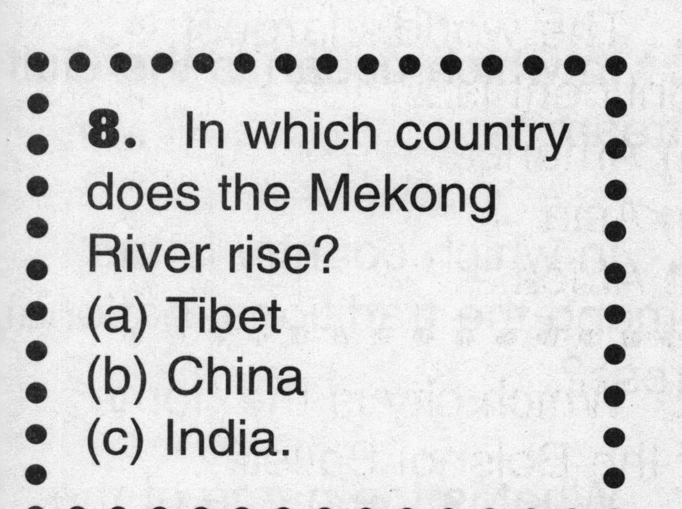

8. In which country does the Mekong River rise?
(a) Tibet
(b) China
(c) India.

9. In which direction would you travel to reach Stockholm from Oslo?

10. Where is the Forbidden City?

MOLLY

1. What is the name of the mountain chain which dominates Switzerland, northern Italy, Austria and south eastern France?

2. In which ocean is the Gulf Stream?

3. In which country is the kimono the traditional national dress?

4. What is the name of the extinct volcano in Scotland's capital city?

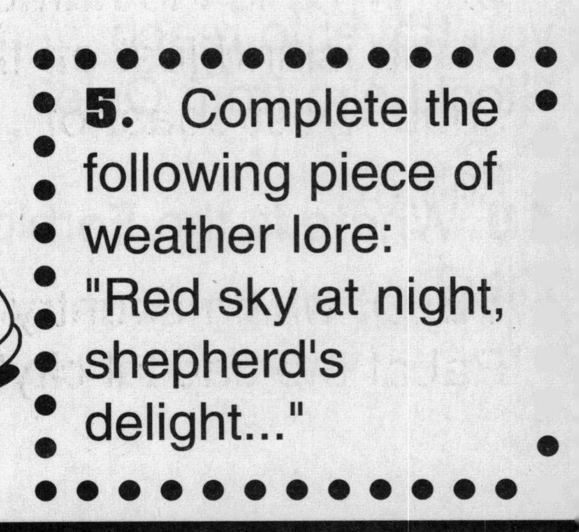

5. Complete the following piece of weather lore: "Red sky at night, shepherd's delight..."

6. Can you name the capital of Malta?

7. Which man-made wonder can be seen from space?

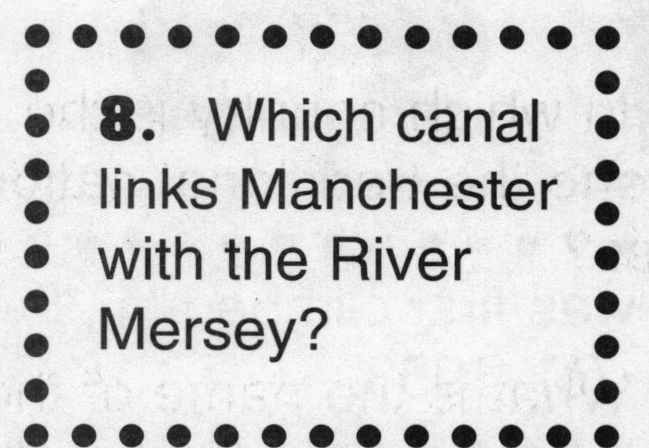

8. Which canal links Manchester with the River Mersey?

9. What is the name of the island just off the south-west coast of Italy?

10. Of which country is Rabat the capital city?

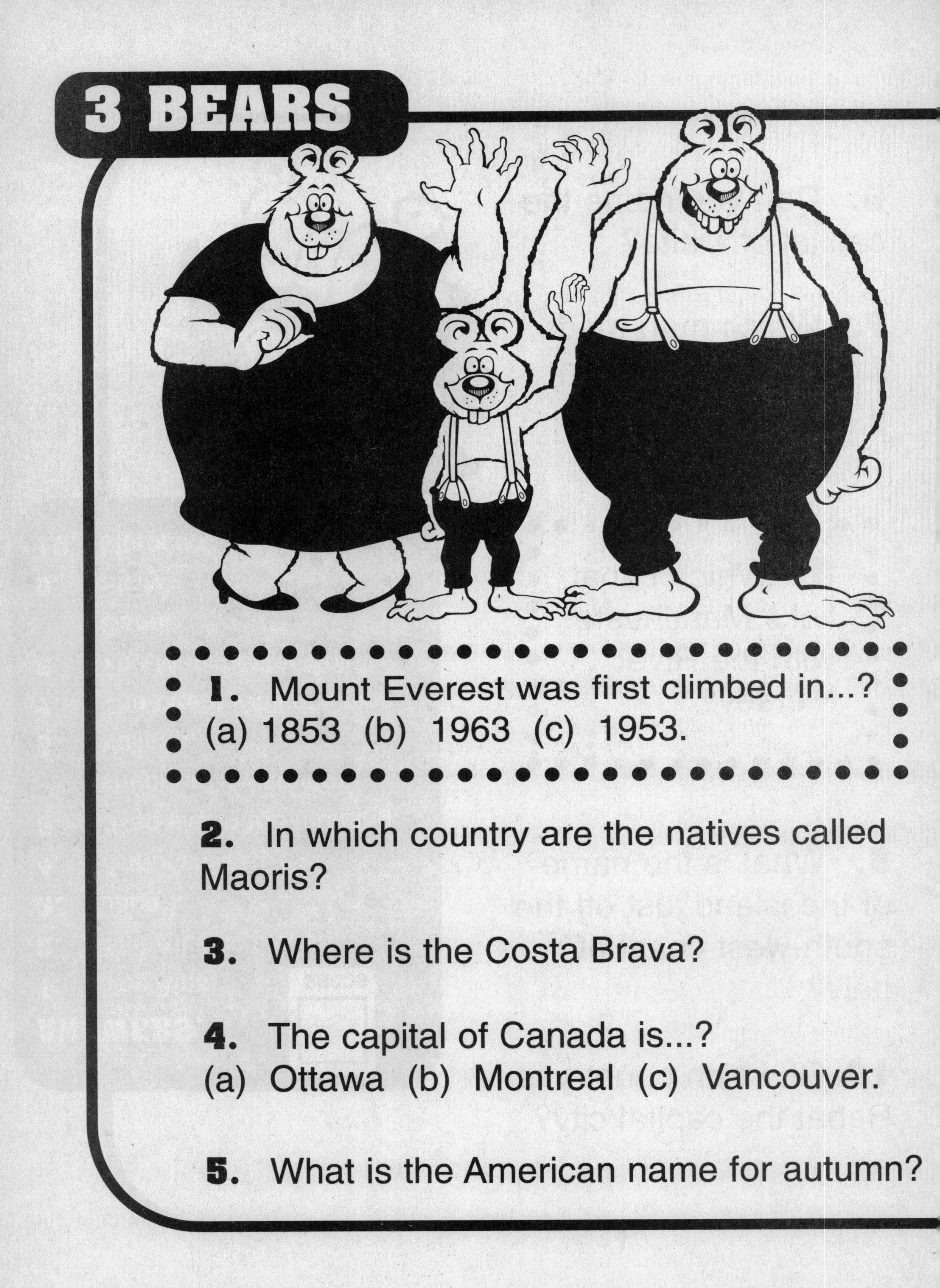

1. Mount Everest was first climbed in...?
(a) 1853 (b) 1963 (c) 1953.

2. In which country are the natives called Maoris?

3. Where is the Costa Brava?

4. The capital of Canada is...?
(a) Ottawa (b) Montreal (c) Vancouver.

5. What is the American name for autumn?

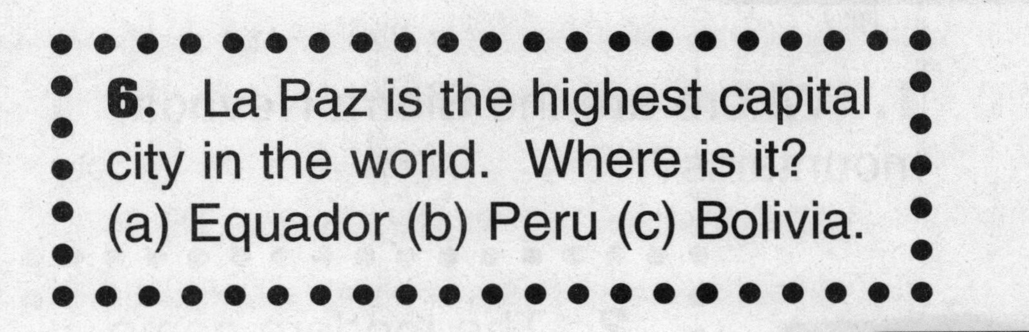

6. La Paz is the highest capital city in the world. Where is it? (a) Equador (b) Peru (c) Bolivia.

7. What is the city of Beijing also known as?

8. Name the longest river in Australia...
(a) Murray
(b) Sydney
(c) Darling.

9. Which is further north... York or New York?

10. By which name was England's capital city known in Roman times?

ANSWERS.

1. 1953.
2. New Zealand.
3. Spain.
4. Ottawa.
5. Fall.
6. Bolivia.
7. Peking.
8. The River Darling.
9. York.
10. Londinium.

SCORE

TEACHER

1. Where are the Sierra Nevada mountains?

2. The modern name for Constantinople is...?
(a) Cairo
(b) Rome
(c) Istanbul.

3. In which country could you take part in an Eisteddfod?

4. Of which Australian state is Sydney the capital?

5. Where might you see a mirage?

6. In which country would you be travelling if you passed through the St Gotthard road tunnel?
(a) Switzerland
(b) Austria
(c) Germany.

7. Name the ancient ruined city carved out of rock in Jordan.

8. Into which sea does the River Danube flow?

9. In which direction would you travel to reach Crete from Athens?

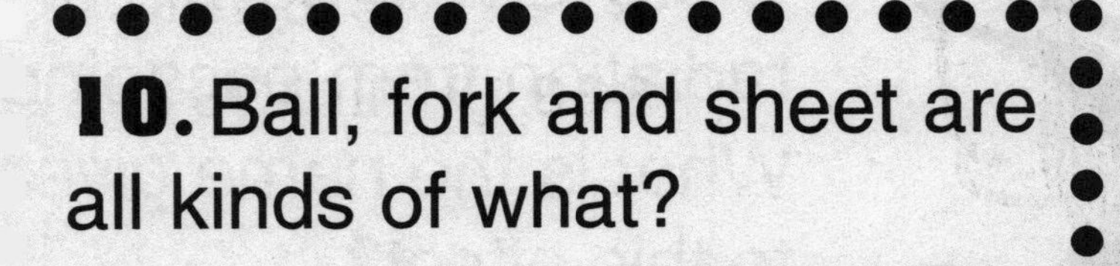

10. Ball, fork and sheet are all kinds of what?

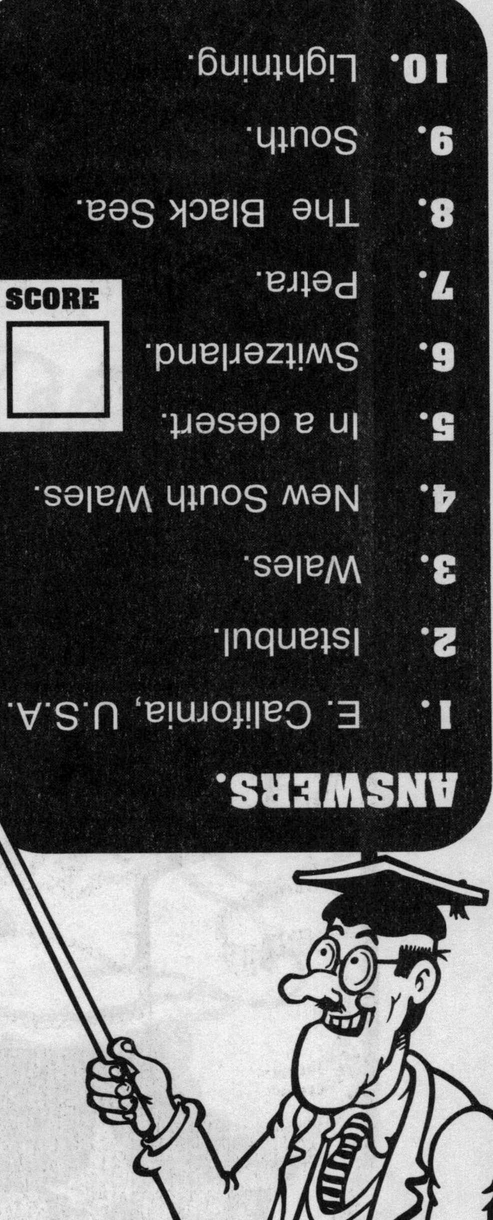

BRAIN DUANE

1. In which country are the Cambrian Mountains?

2. Which county is the 'garden of England'?
(a) Sussex (b) Devon (c) Kent.

3. In which American state is Hollywood?

4. On which island is New Zealand's capital, Wellington?

5. Temperatures on earth are gradually rising because a rise in carbon dioxide in the atmosphere is preventing solar radiation from escaping. What is the name given to this effect?

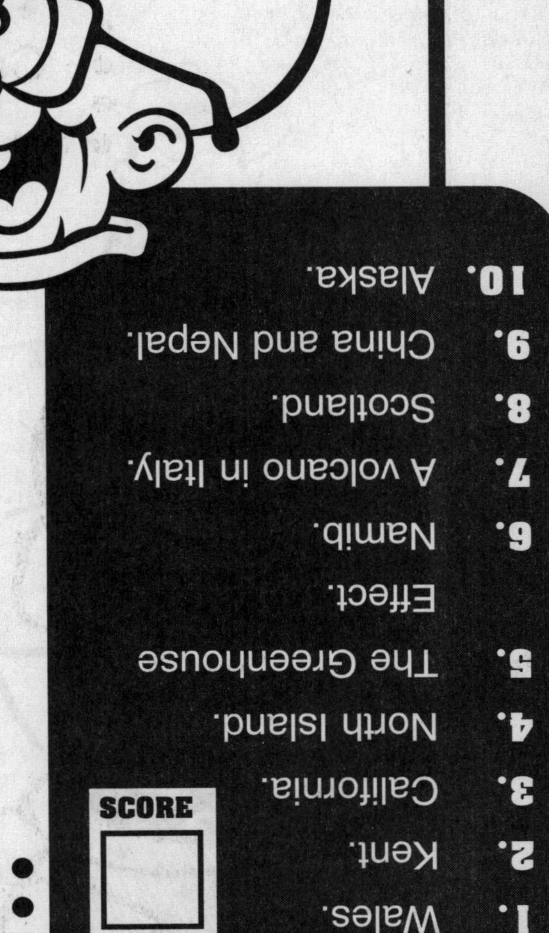

6. Can you name the earth's oldest desert?
(a) Sahara
(b) Namib
(c) Kalahari.

7. What, and in which country, is Vesuvius?

8. In which country is the Caledonian Canal?

9. Mount Everest is on the frontier between which two countries?

10. In which American state would you find Mount McKinley?

DESPERATE DAN

1. Where are the Transylvanian Alps?

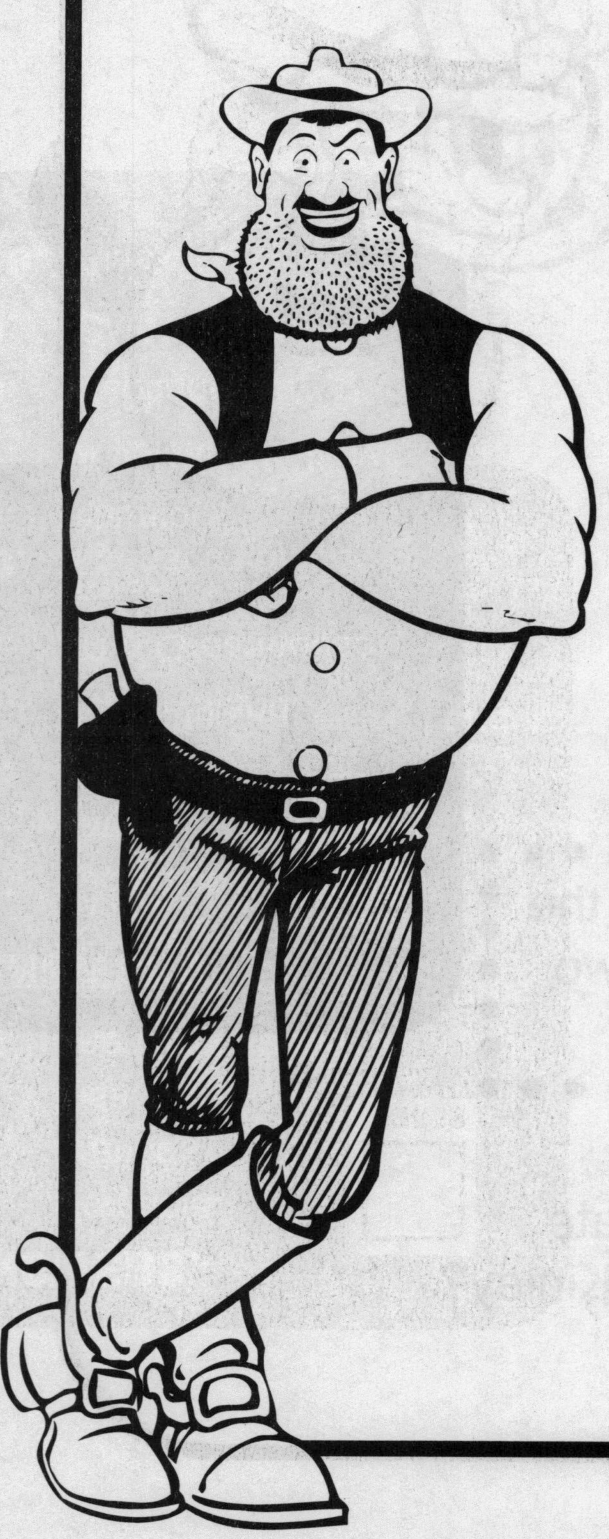

2. Orly airport is in which country?
(a) France
(b) Italy
(c) Spain.

3. Which European city has a leaning tower, and what country is it in?

4. On which river is the capital of Portugal situated?
(a) Rhone
(b) Tagus
(c) Dura.

5. How has space technology helped in the study of the weather?

6. Which is the world's highest lake?
(a) Lake Ontario
(b) Lake Titicaca
(c) Lake Superior.

7. Where is the tomb of Karl Marx?

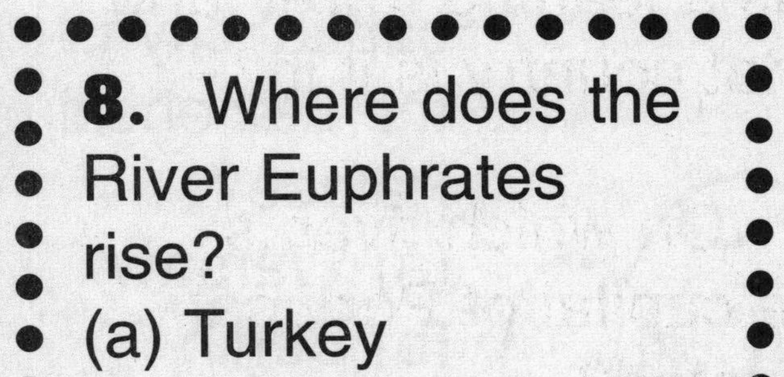

8. Where does the River Euphrates rise?
(a) Turkey
(b) Iraq

9. In which US state is the city of Seattle?

10. What was Devil's Island?

ANSWERS.
1. Romania.
2. France.
3. Pisa, Italy.
4. The River Tagus.
5. Scientists can use pictures from satellites in space to track global weather patterns and changes.
6. Lake Titicaca.
7. Highgate Cemetery, London.
8. Turkey.
9. Washington.
10. A penal colony.

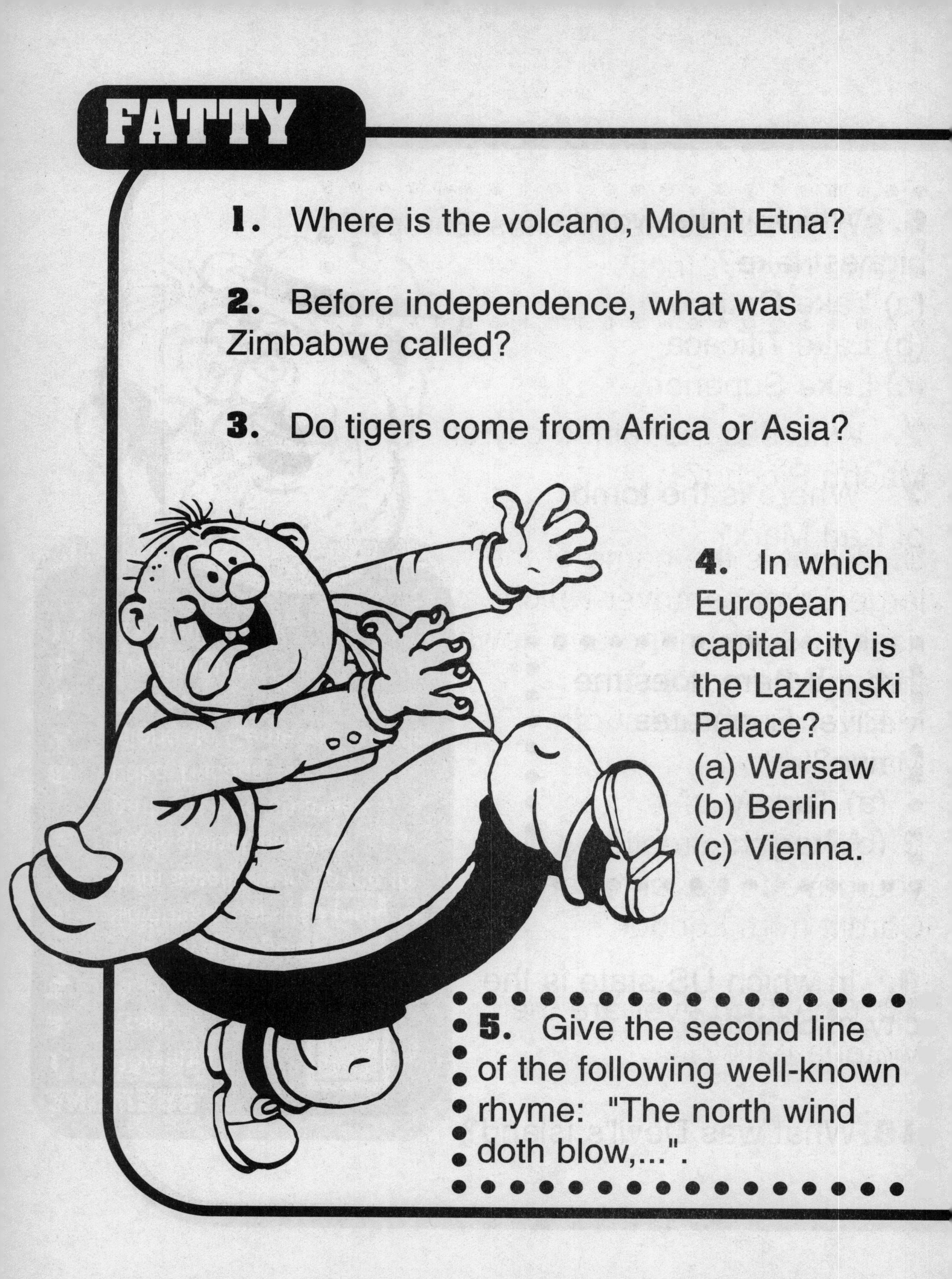

FATTY

1. Where is the volcano, Mount Etna?

2. Before independence, what was Zimbabwe called?

3. Do tigers come from Africa or Asia?

4. In which European capital city is the Lazienski Palace?
(a) Warsaw
(b) Berlin
(c) Vienna.

5. Give the second line of the following well-known rhyme: "The north wind doth blow,...".

6. Which sea separates Europe and North Africa?

7. Where is the ruined city of Machu Picchu?

8. What is the name of the large European river which rises in Switzerland and flows through France to the Mediterranean west of Marseille?

9. In which direction would you have to travel to reach Cardiff from London?

10. On which river are the Victoria Falls?

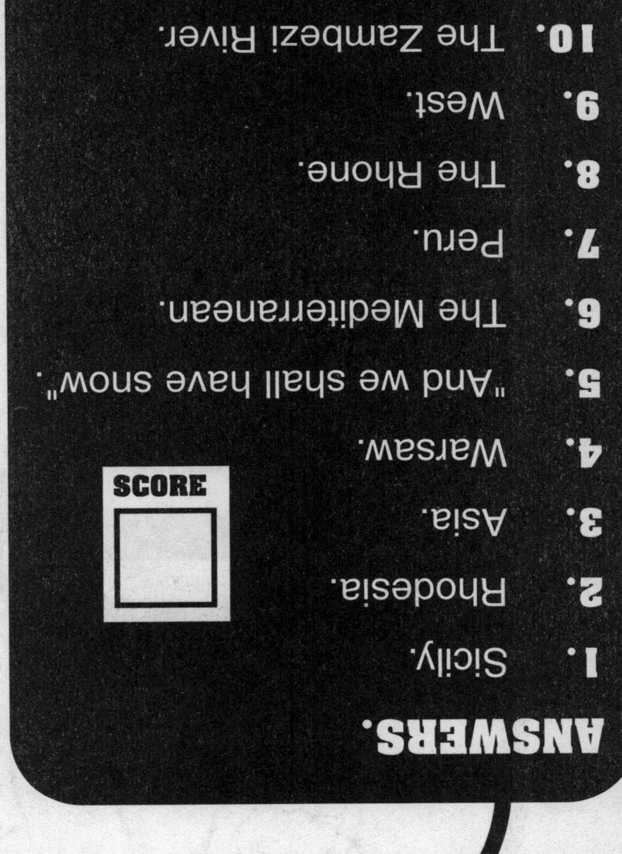

BEA
1. In which country in Africa is Mount Kilimanjaro?
2. In which continent would you find penguins: the Arctic or Antarctica?
3. Where is the Wailing Wall?
4. What is the capital of India?
5. What other name is used for a hurricane?

6. Name Ireland's longest river.

7. What is the name of the city in Saudi Arabia visited by thousands of Islamic pilgrims every year?

8. In which country is the Waitaki River?

9. If you wanted to follow the river Amazon from source to estuary, in which general direction would you be travelling?

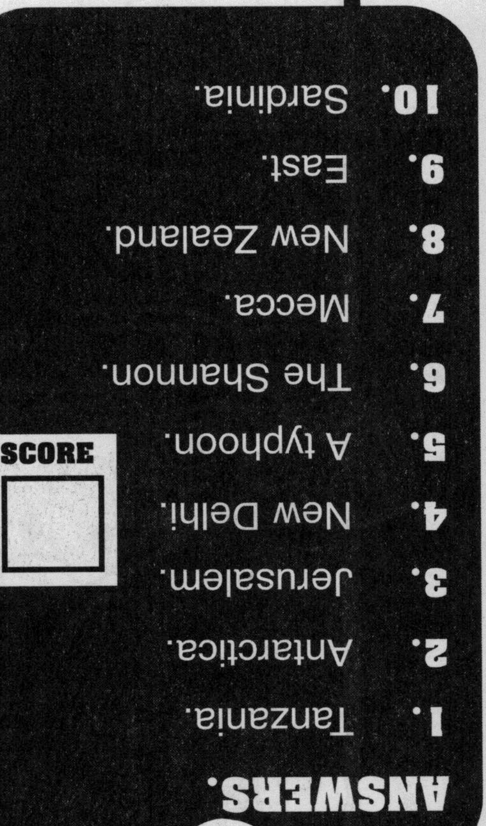

10. What is the name of the Island south of Corsica?

IVY

1. What is the name of the mountain range that dominates much of Morocco?

2. Which country's flag is called the 'star-spangled banner'?

3. In which country is the Antonine Wall?

4. In which capital city is the headquarters of the European Economic Community?

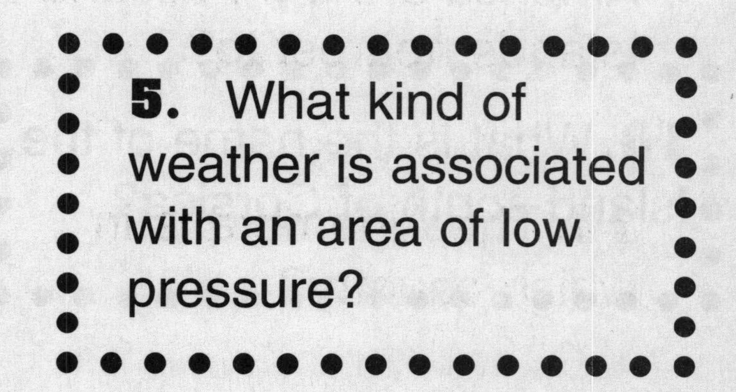

5. What kind of weather is associated with an area of low pressure?

6. In which sea would you find the Cayman Islands?
(a) Baltic
(b) Mediterranean
(c) Caribbean.

7. What is the name of the official residence of the President of the United States of America?

8. In which city in Holland is the Amstel River?

9. Which country in South America are the Falkland Islands nearest to?

10. The Alhambra is in which country?

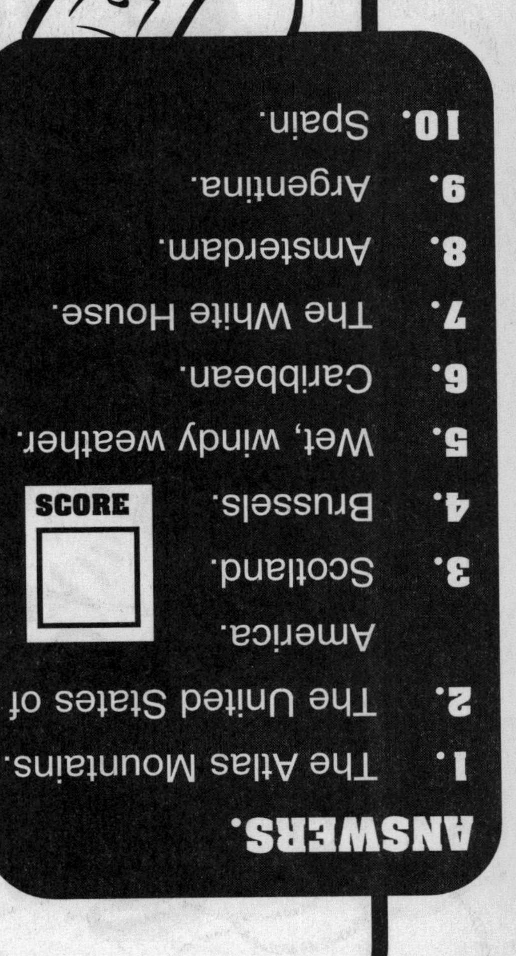

1. What is the name of the highest mountain in Wales?

2. Which country produces most of the world's rubber?

3. Where is the Gobi Desert?

4. What is the capital of Eire?

5. Which is the correct name for a giant wave?
(a) Bora
(b) Titan
(c) Tsunami.

6. Can you name the largest lake in Africa?

7. In which European city was the Millennium Dome built?

8. Which river in Scotland was once the centre of the shipbuilding industry?

9. On which island is the city of Colombo?

10. What is 'Old Faithful'?
(a) a volcano
(b) a geyser
(c) a waterfall.

ANSWERS.

1. Mount Snowdon.
2. Malaysia.
3. Mongolia.
4. Dublin.
5. Tsunami.
6. Lake Victoria.
7. London.
8. The River Clyde.
9. Sri Lanka.
10. Geyser.

BLINKY

1. What is the highest mountain in England? (a) Scafell (b) North Peak (c) Skiddaw.

2. Wild pandas can only be found in which country?

3. Where is the Giant's Causeway?

4. In which European capital city is the Prado Museum?

5. What is the name for a light frost that only freezes the surface of the earth?

6. Mount Fuji is the highest mountain of which country?

7. In which Scottish loch is a monster said to live?

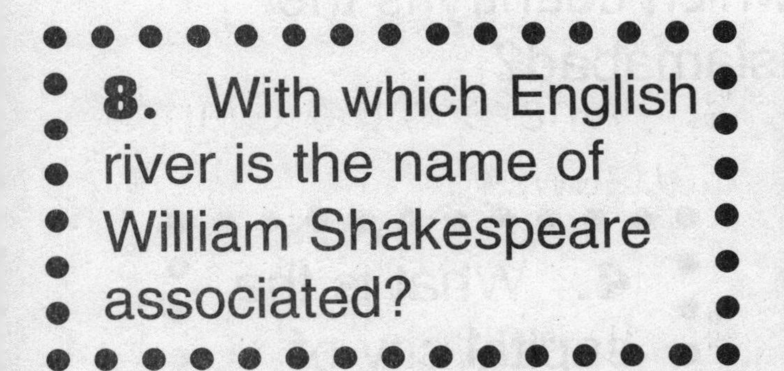

8. With which English river is the name of William Shakespeare associated?

9. What is the name of the town in the centre of Australia?

10. Which country is famous for its cuckoo clocks?

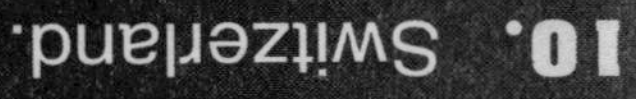

ANSWERS.

SCORE

1. Scafell.
2. China.
3. Northern Ireland.
4. Madrid.
5. Ground frost.
6. Japan.
7. Loch Ness.
8. The River Avon.
9. Alice Springs.
10. Switzerland.

GNASHER

1. What is the name of the great mountain system in the west of South America?

2. In which country would you see Sumo wrestlers?

3. In which country is the city of Islamabad?

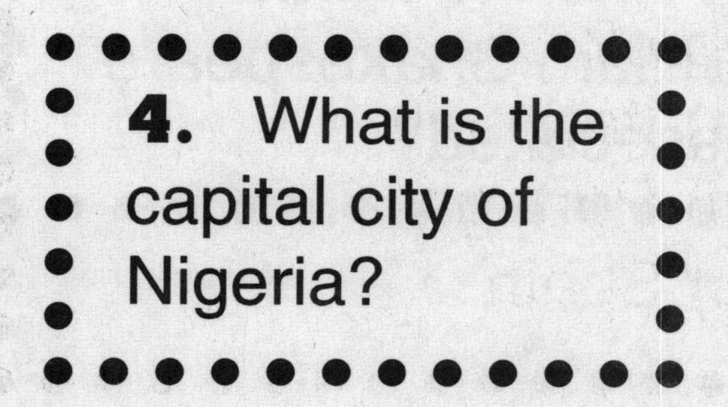

4. What is the capital city of Nigeria?

5. What is the name given to the level on some hills and mountains above which the snow never melts?

6. Where would you find the Appalachian Mountains?

7. In which U.S. state is Cape Canaveral?

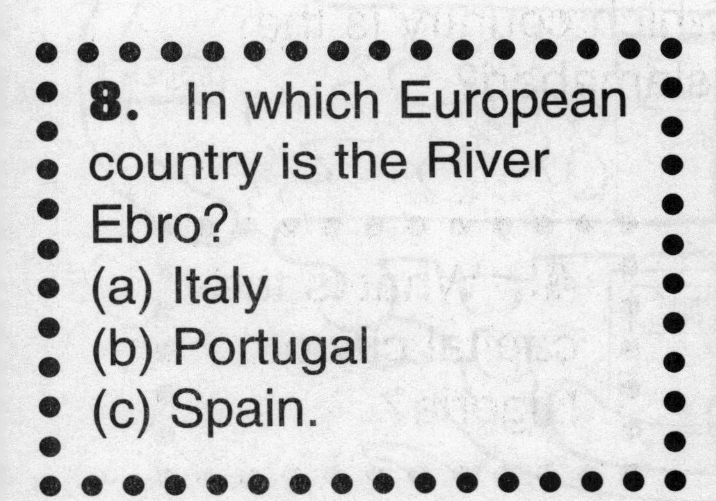

8. In which European country is the River Ebro?
(a) Italy
(b) Portugal
(c) Spain.

9. What is the name of the largest state in the U.S.A.?

10. Where can you see The Angel of the North?

ANSWERS.

1. The Andes.
2. Japan.
3. Pakistan.
4. Lagos.
5. The snow line.
6. U.S.A.
7. Florida.
8. Spain.
9. Alaska.
10. Newcastle.

SCORE

GENERAL KNOWLEDGE

DENNIS

1. What is the capital of the Ukraine?

2. Who succeeded Gerald Ford as president of the U.S.A.?
(a) Jimmy Carter (b) Ronald Reagan (c) Richard Nixon.

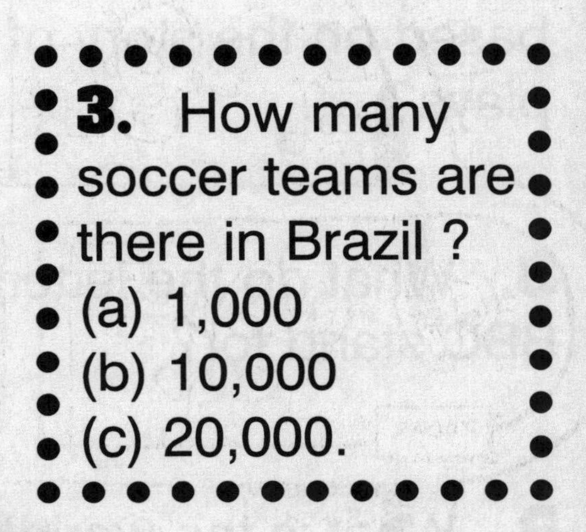

3. How many soccer teams are there in Brazil ?
(a) 1,000
(b) 10,000
(c) 20,000.

4. How many players are there in a Rugby Union team?

5. When was the Forth Road Bridge opened?
(a) 1948
(b) 1897
(c) 1964.

6. Where is the headquarters of the United Nations?

7. The musical 'West Side Story' was loosely based on the story of which of Shakespeare's plays?

8. What do the letters BBC stand for?

9. What is the world's largest city ?

10. What does ALLEGRO mean when it appears on a piece of sheet music?
(a) lively
(b) soft
(c) loud.

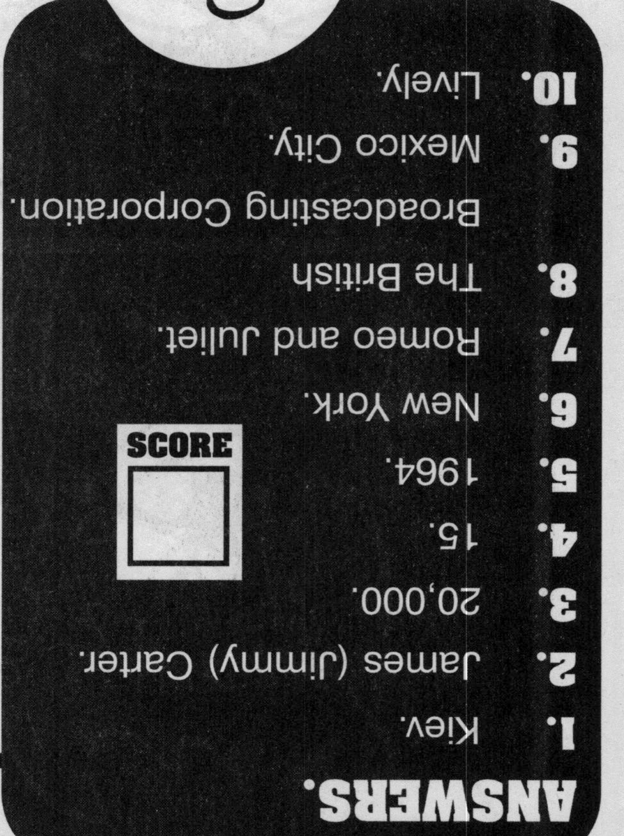

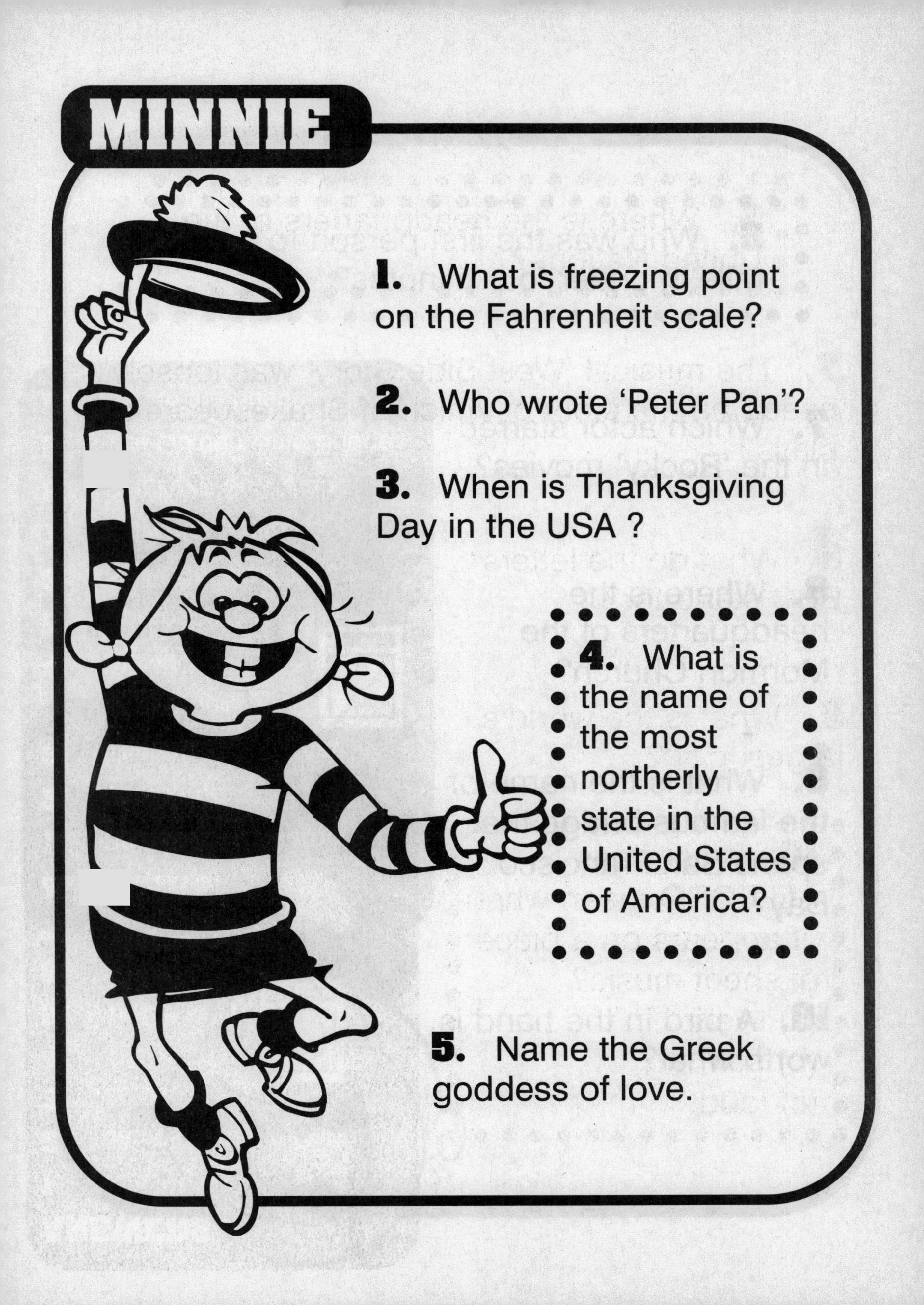
MINNIE
1. What is freezing point on the Fahrenheit scale?
2. Who wrote 'Peter Pan'?
3. When is Thanksgiving Day in the USA ?
4. What is the name of the most northerly state in the United States of America?
5. Name the Greek goddess of love.

6. Who was the first person to run a mile in under four minutes?

7. Which actor starred in the 'Rocky' movies?

8. Where is the headquarters of the Mormon Church?

9. What is the name of the famous bridge that spans San Francisco Bay?

10. A bird in the hand is worth what?

ANSWERS.

1. 32 degrees.
2. J.M.Barrie.
3. The fourth Thursday in November.
4. Alaska.
5. Aphrodite.
6. Sir Roger Bannister.
7. Sylvester Stallone.
8. Salt Lake City, Utah.
9. The Golden Gate Bridge.
10. Two in the bush!

BILLY WHIZZ

1. What is seismology?

2. In which part of the human body are the hammer, the anvil and the stirrup?

3. Name the largest planet in the solar system.
(a) Venus
(b) Mars
(c) Jupiter.

4. What is arachnophobia?

5. What is scrumpy made from?

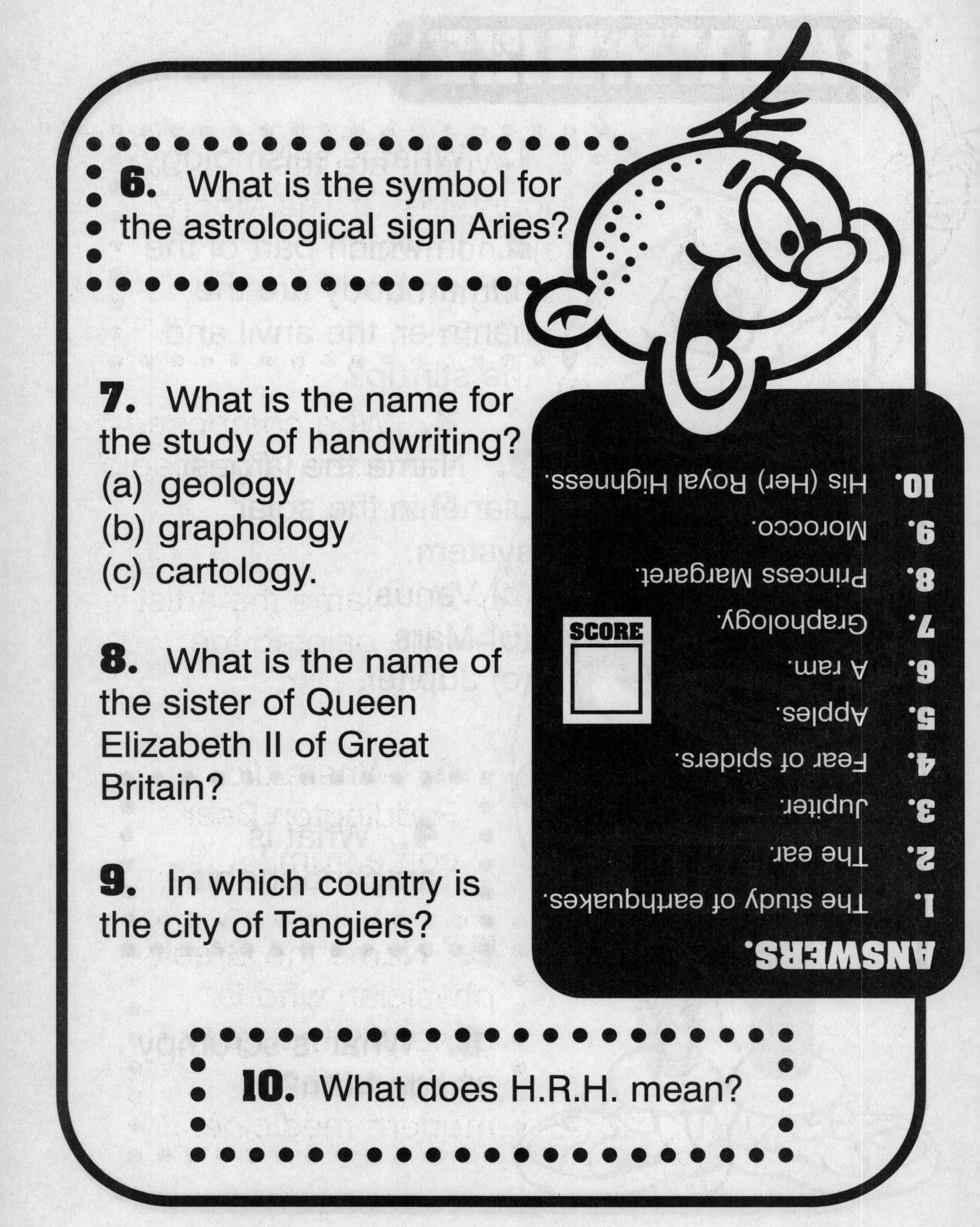

6. What is the symbol for the astrological sign Aries?

7. What is the name for the study of handwriting?
(a) geology
(b) graphology
(c) cartology.

8. What is the name of the sister of Queen Elizabeth II of Great Britain?

9. In which country is the city of Tangiers?

10. What does H.R.H. mean?

ANSWERS.

1. The study of earthquakes.
2. The ear.
3. Jupiter.
4. Fear of spiders.
5. Apples.
6. A ram.
7. Graphology.
8. Princess Margaret.
9. Morocco.
10. His (Her) Royal Highness.

SCORE

BANANAMAN

1. Where are the Mountains Of The Moon?
(a) The moon
(b) Uganda
(c) Chile.

2. Who composed the opera 'The Magic Flute'?

3. Name the artist who painted the 'Mona Lisa'.

4. Where did Paddington Bear come from?

5. Name the Greek physician who is generally thought of as the father of modern medicine.

6. Which country is the biggest producer of bicycles ? (a) China (b) Taiwan (c) Korea.

7. What are cardamom, turmeric and coriander ?

8. Which King of England had six wives ?

9. What is the name for the underground railway system in Paris?

10. If a book is described as 'autobiographical', what does this mean?

ANSWERS.

1. Uganda.
2. Mozart.
3. Leonardo da Vinci.
4. Peru.
5. Hippocrates.
6. Taiwan.
7. Spices.
8. Henry VIII.
9. Le Metro.
10. The book is about the author's own life.

SCORE

ROGER THE DODGER

1. What is cayenne pepper made from ?

2. Which husband and wife team, studying radioactivity, were jointly awarded the Nobel Prize for physics in 1903?

3. What is the name for the stretch of water separating Denmark and Sweden?

4. What is the name for the branch of medicine which deals with children?

5. What does 'amen' mean?

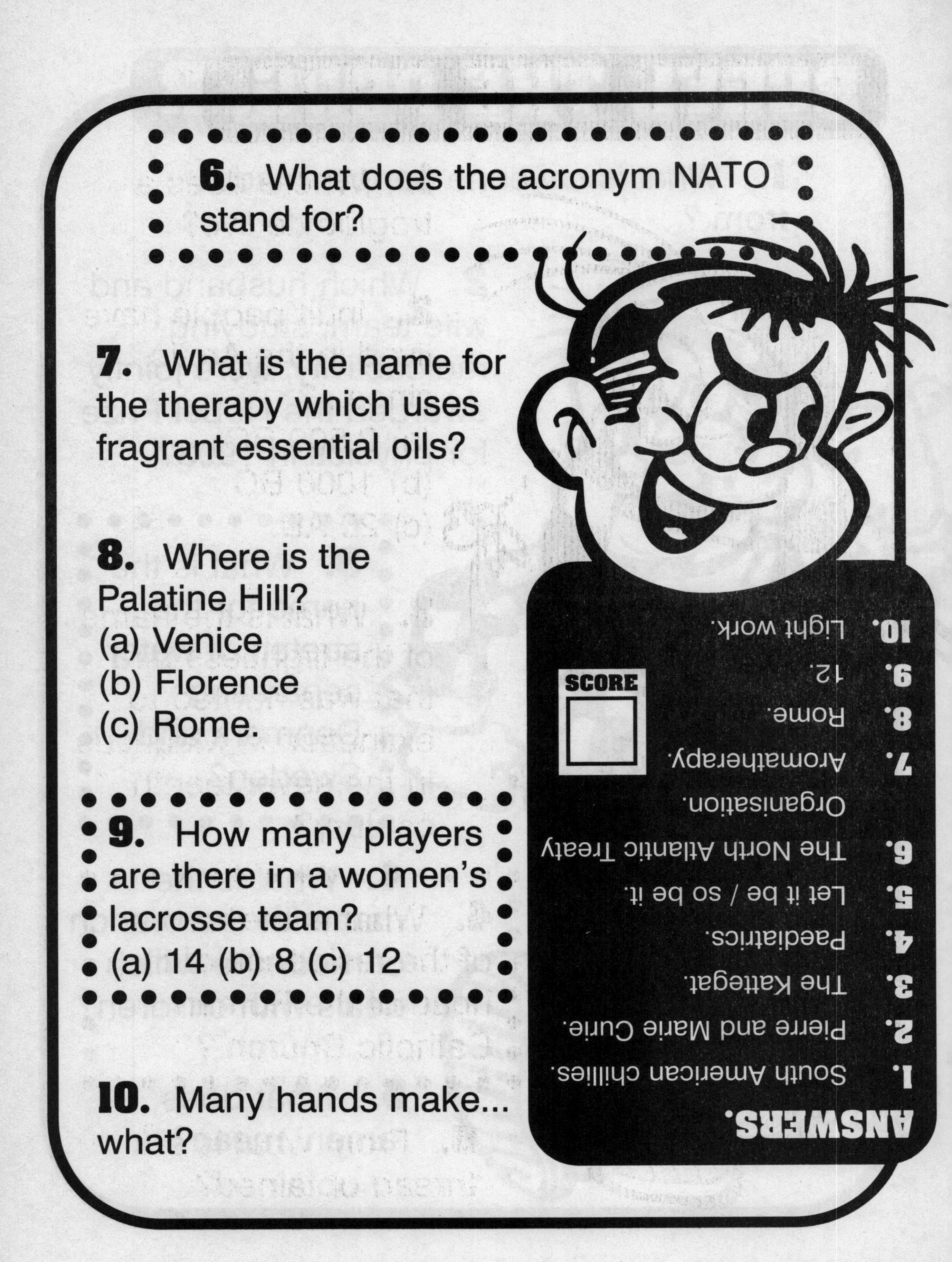

6. What does the acronym NATO stand for?

7. What is the name for the therapy which uses fragrant essential oils?

8. Where is the Palatine Hill?
(a) Venice
(b) Florence
(c) Rome.

9. How many players are there in a women's lacrosse team?
(a) 14 (b) 8 (c) 12

10. Many hands make... what?

ANSWERS.

1. South American chillies.
2. Pierre and Marie Curie.
3. The Kattegat.
4. Paediatrics.
5. Let it be / so be it.
6. The North Atlantic Treaty Organisation.
7. Aromatherapy.
8. Rome.
9. 12.
10. Light work.

SCORE

BERYL THE PERIL

1. Where does a troglodyte live?

2. Inuit people have lived in the Arctic since...?
(a) 2,500 BC
(b) 1000 BC
(c) 20 AD.

3. What is the name of the flightless bird that was hunted to extinction in Mauritius in the seventeenth century?

4. What is the name of the residence of the head of the Roman Catholic Church ?

5. From what is silk thread obtained?

6. What is the name of the first book in the Old Testament?

7. How many colours are there in the French flag?

8. What is an oasis?

9. What date is Guy Fawkes night celebrated each year in Great Britain?

10. If you described someone as being 'tight-fisted', what would you be saying about them?

ANSWERS.

1. In a cave.
2. 2,500 BC.
3. The Dodo.
4. The Vatican.
5. From the cocoons spun by the larvae of the silkworm moth.
6. Genesis.
7. Three. Red, white, blue.
8. A watering hole, or a place where water can be found, in the desert.
9. November 5th.
10. You would be describing them as mean.

SCORE

DANNY

1. What does Desperate Dan like to eat ?

2. Who befriended Man Friday?

3. In which fairy tale did the wicked queen ask the mirror on the wall who was the fairest of them all?

4. People in China and Japan use these implements for eating and cooking. What are they?

5. What were the gifts that the three wise men brought to the infant Jesus?

6. Which country is home to the International Red Cross?

7. John Brown was a close friend and confidant of which British ruler?

8. What is the name of the miser in Charles Dickens' book 'A Christmas Carol'?

9. What do you call a person who comes from Moscow?

10. What does the word 'hirsute' mean?
(a) greedy
(b) hairy
(c) strong.

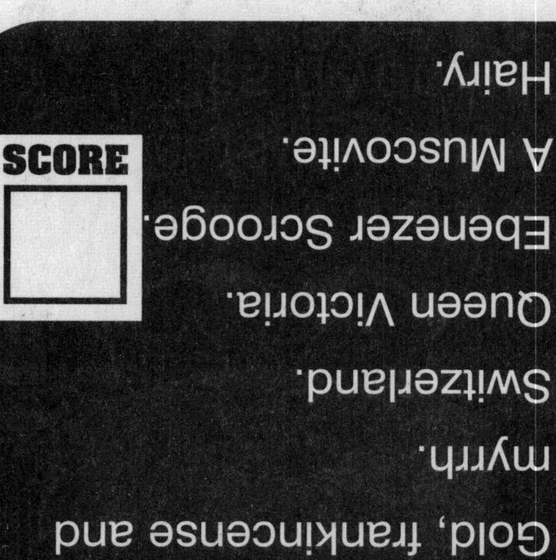

ANSWERS.

1. Cow Pie.
2. Robinson Crusoe.
3. The story of Snow White and the Seven Dwarfs.
4. Chopsticks.
5. Gold, frankincense and myrrh.
6. Switzerland.
7. Queen Victoria.
8. Ebenezer Scrooge.
9. A Muscovite.
10. Hairy.

SCORE

1. What are pince-nez?

2. What is the name of the very first cartoon character created by Walt Disney?

3. What are the only trees that can grow in salt water ?
(a) mangrove
(b) palm
(c) pine.

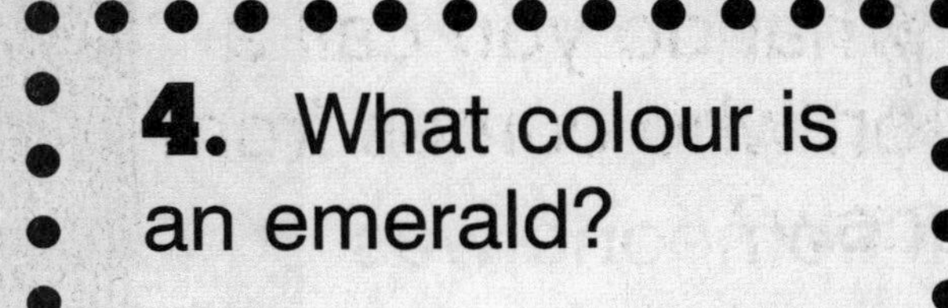

4. What colour is an emerald?

5. Who were the 'Peelers' and after whom were they named?

6. How many stripes does a sergeant in the army wear?

7. If a couple are celebrating their golden wedding anniversary, how many years have they been married?

8. Who is the patron saint of Wales?

9. If someone was described as having porcine features, what would they look like?

10. In Roman numerals what number is represented by XIX?

ANSWERS.

1. Spectacles which have no 'legs', but instead simply balance on the nose - literally translated, "pinch-nose" from the French.
2. Mortimer or Mickey Mouse.
3. Mangrove.
4. Green.
5. They were members of the early police force in London, named after Sir Robert Peel.
6. Three.
7. Fifty.
8. St David.
9. Like a pig.
10. 19.

THE NUMSKULLS

1. Which one is the odd one out: macaroni, tagliatelli, spaghetti, zabaglioni ?

2. What is an abacus used for?

3. How many teeth should a grown adult have?
(a) 28 (b) 36 (c) 32.

4. What is the name for the sign of the zodiac represented by a set of scales?

5. How many characters are there in the Greek alphabet?
(a) 20 (b) 24 (c) 32.

6. What is the soup, Borscht, made from ?
(a) potato
(b) tomato
(c) beetroot.

7. What was the Jolly Roger?

8. Who, or what, was Black Beauty?

9. When was the first issue of the Beano printed ?
(a)1938 (b)1947 (c)1953.

10. You are reading the 'Articles for sale' column in a newspaper and you see the letters o.n.o. after the price of one item. What do they stand for?

ANSWERS.

1. Zabaglioni is a dessert, but the other three are kinds of pasta.
2. For arithmetical calculations.
3. 32.
4. Libra.
5. 24.
6. Beetroot .
7. It was the black and white skull and crossbones flag, flown on pirate ships.
8. A (fictional) black horse.
9. 1938.
10. Or nearest offer.

SCORE

1. Who wrote the plays 'Julius Caesar' and 'Anthony and Cleopatra' ?

2. Which actor played Captain Kirk in the world-famous television series 'Star Trek'?

3. Where would you find a stern, boom and halyard ?

4. Which European country is shaped very like a boot?

5. Where did Kabuki theatre originate ?
(a) China
(b) Japan
(c) Thailand.

6. What is the state capital of Queensland in Australia?

7. What is the name given to people who belong to the Society of Friends?

8. What is 'The Old Lady of Threadneedle Street'?

9. What was the name of the little girl whose secret diary told us so much of the terrors of life for the Jewish people during World War II?

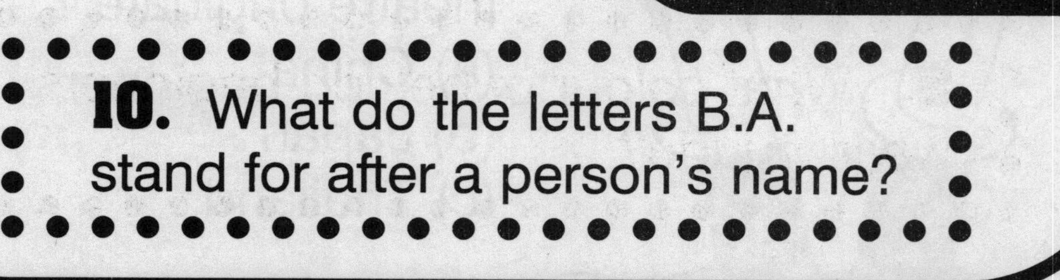

10. What do the letters B.A. stand for after a person's name?

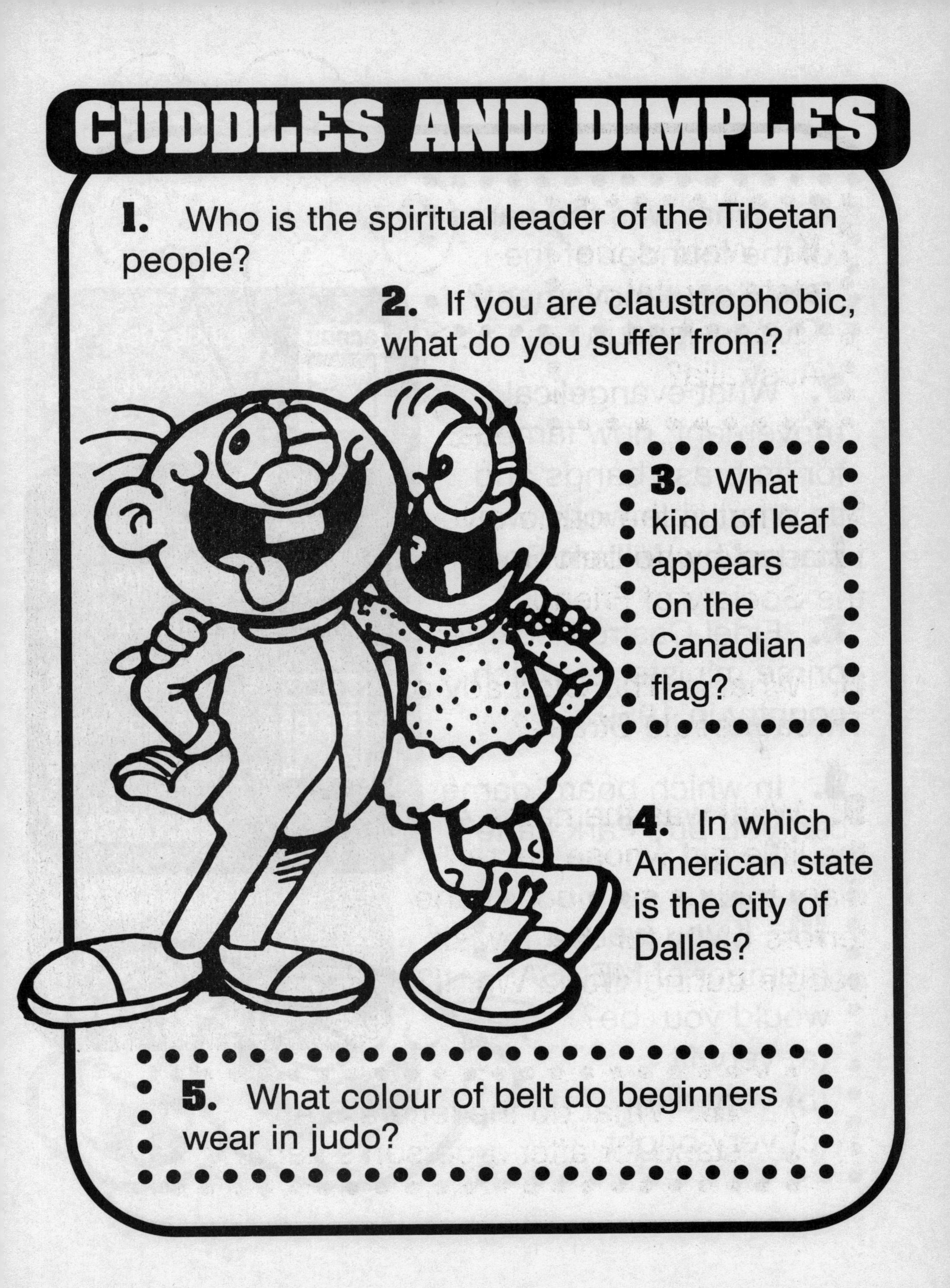
CUDDLES AND DIMPLES
1. Who is the spiritual leader of the Tibetan people?
2. If you are claustrophobic, what do you suffer from?
3. What kind of leaf appears on the Canadian flag?
4. In which American state is the city of Dallas?
5. What colour of belt do beginners wear in judo?

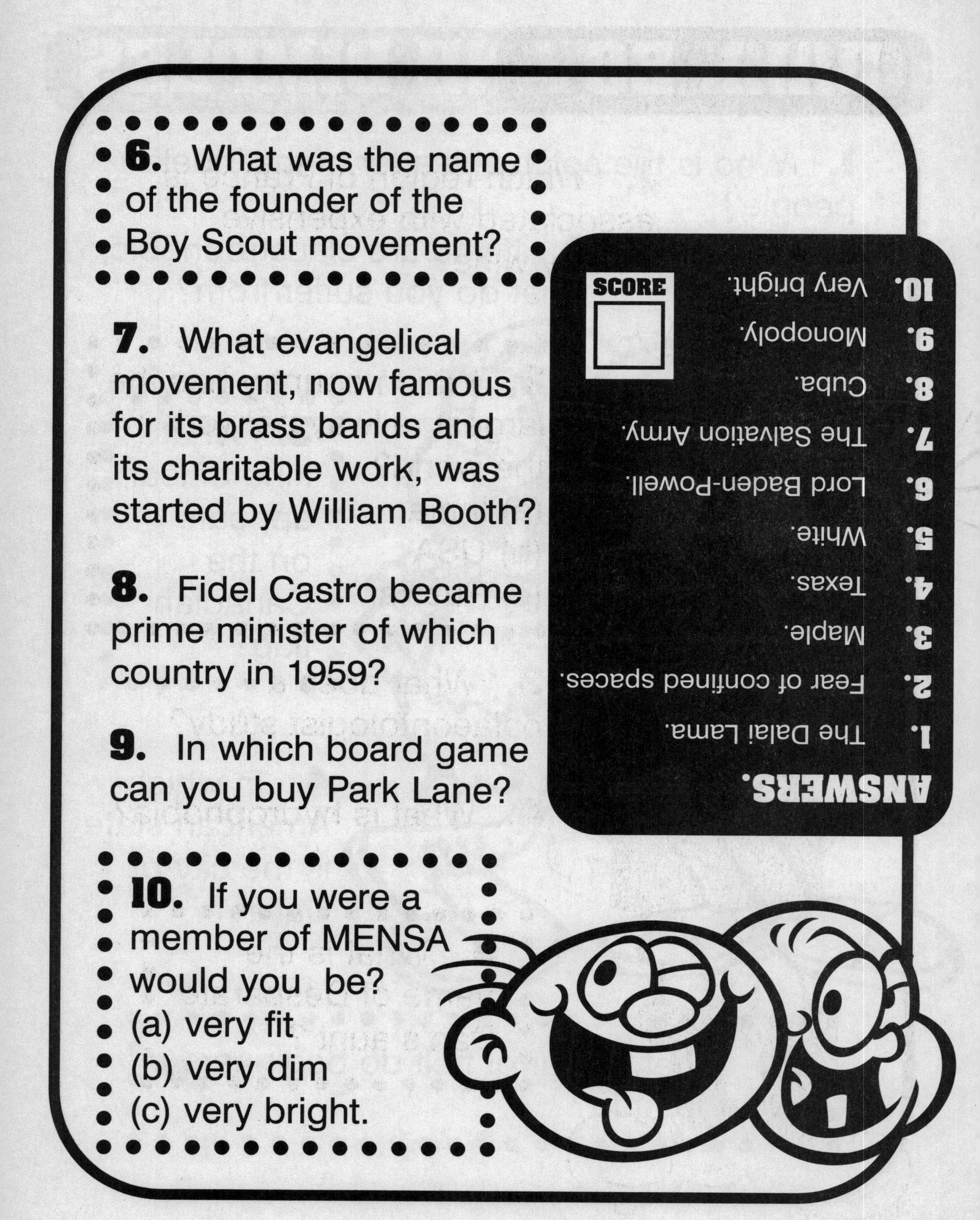

6. What was the name of the founder of the Boy Scout movement?

7. What evangelical movement, now famous for its brass bands and its charitable work, was started by William Booth?

8. Fidel Castro became prime minister of which country in 1959?

9. In which board game can you buy Park Lane?

10. If you were a member of MENSA would you be?
(a) very fit
(b) very dim
(c) very bright.

ANSWERS.

1. The Dalai Lama.
2. Fear of confined spaces.
3. Maple.
4. Texas.
5. White.
6. Lord Baden-Powell.
7. The Salvation Army.
8. Cuba.
9. Monopoly.
10. Very bright.

SCORE

BALL BOY

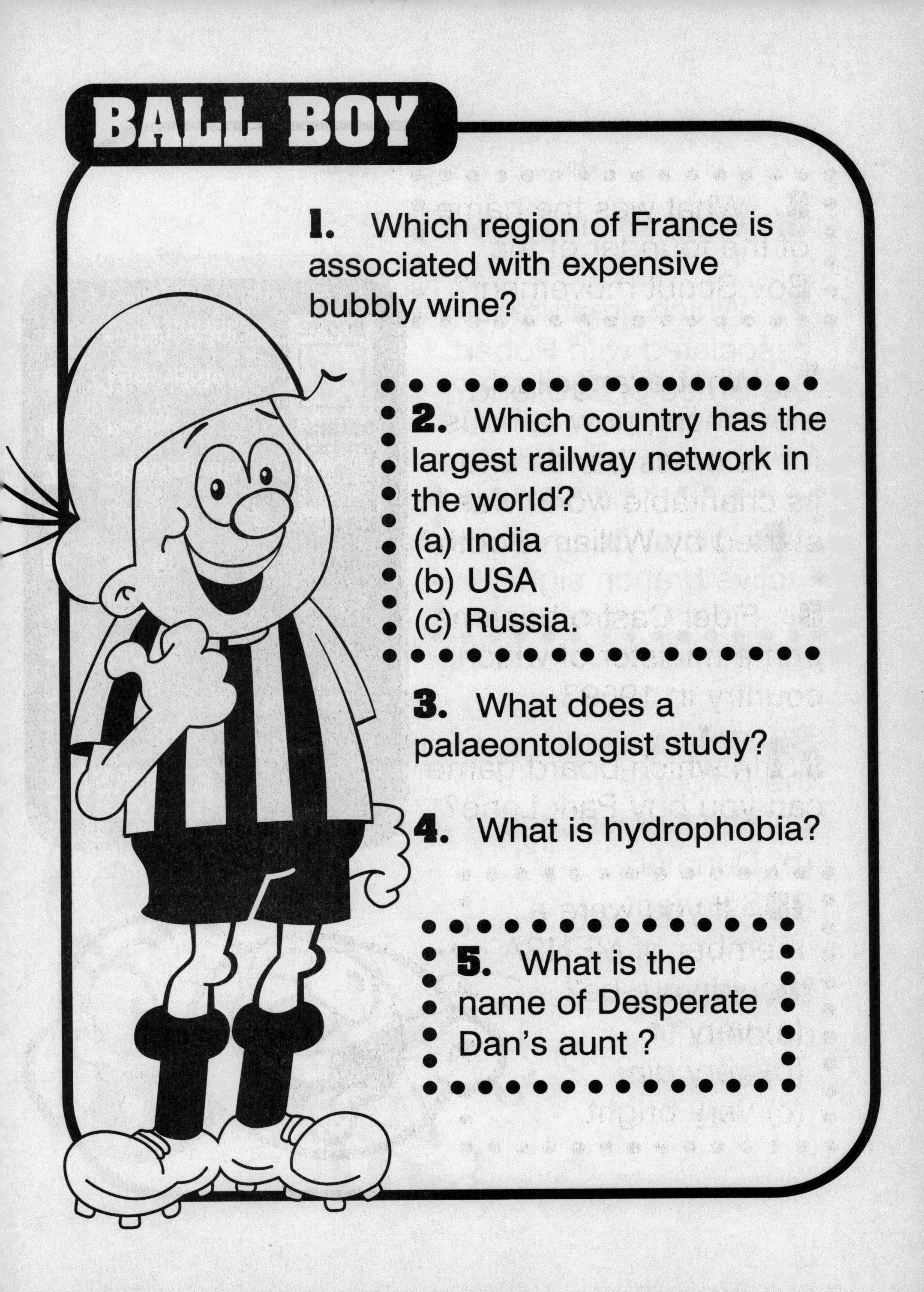

1. Which region of France is associated with expensive bubbly wine?

2. Which country has the largest railway network in the world?
(a) India
(b) USA
(c) Russia.

3. What does a palaeontologist study?

4. What is hydrophobia?

5. What is the name of Desperate Dan's aunt ?

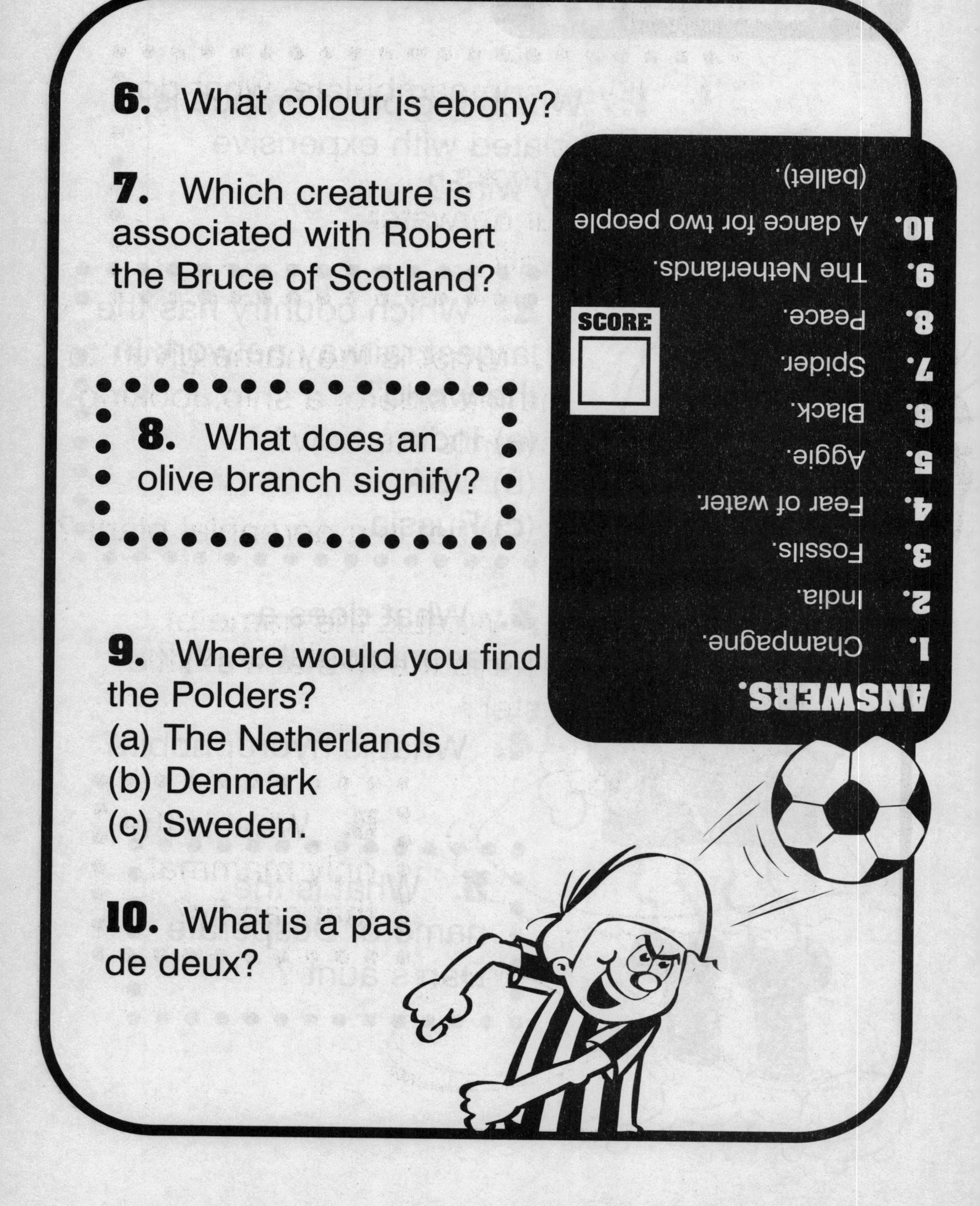

6. What colour is ebony?

7. Which creature is associated with Robert the Bruce of Scotland?

8. What does an olive branch signify?

9. Where would you find the Polders?
(a) The Netherlands
(b) Denmark
(c) Sweden.

10. What is a pas de deux?

ANSWERS.
1. Champagne.
2. India.
3. Fossils.
4. Fear of water.
5. Aggie.
6. Black.
7. Spider.
8. Peace.
9. The Netherlands.
10. A dance for two people (ballet).

SCORE

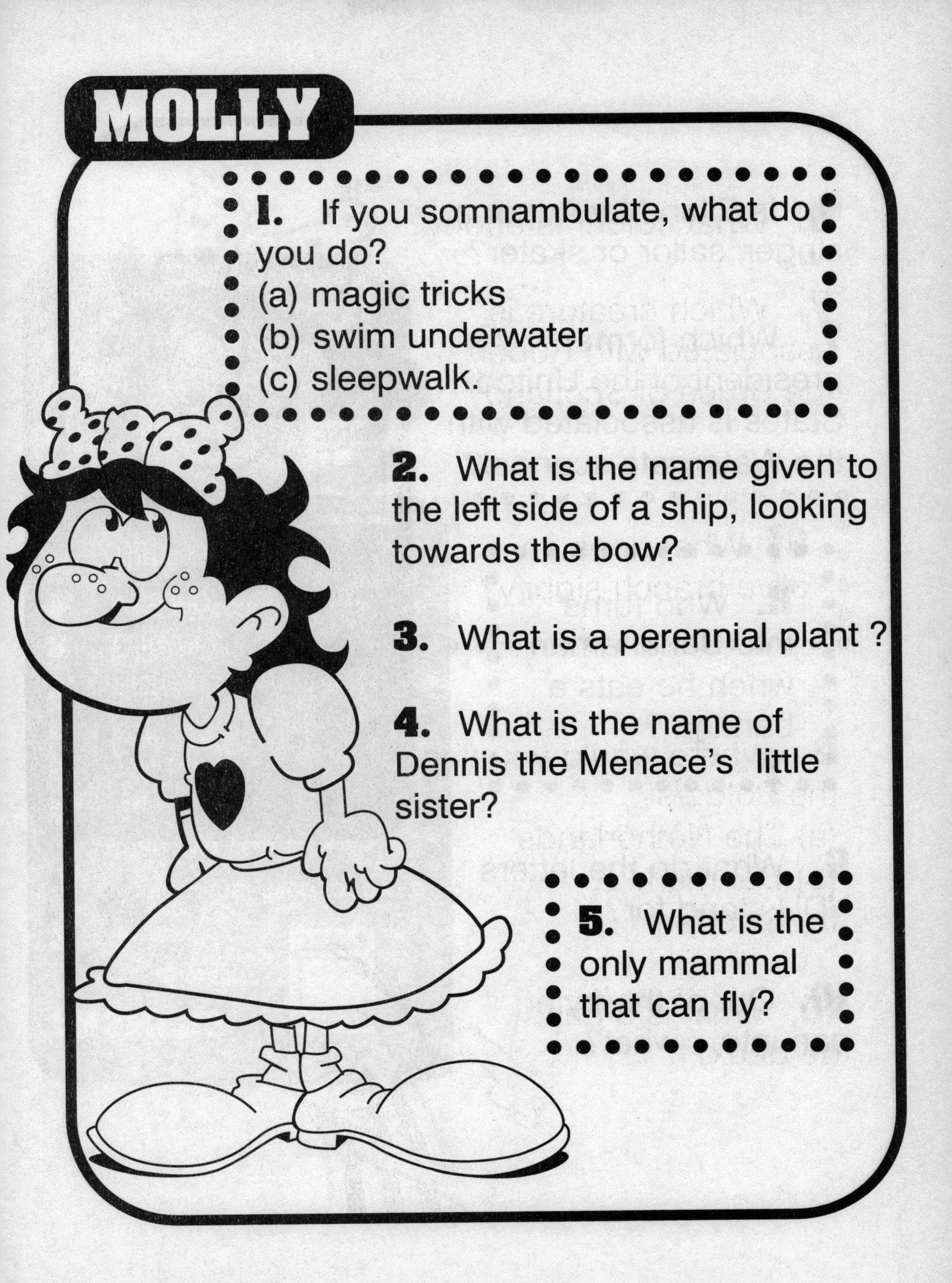
MOLLY
1. If you somnambulate, what do you do?
(a) magic tricks
(b) swim underwater
(c) sleepwalk.
2. What is the name given to the left side of a ship, looking towards the bow?
3. What is a perennial plant ?
4. What is the name of Dennis the Menace's little sister?
5. What is the only mammal that can fly?

6. Is Ellen MacArthur a singer, sailor or skater?

7. Which former president of the United States is associated with the Watergate scandal?

8. Who turns into Bananaman when he eats a banana ?

9. What do the letters VDU stand for?

10. Out of the frying pan into... what?

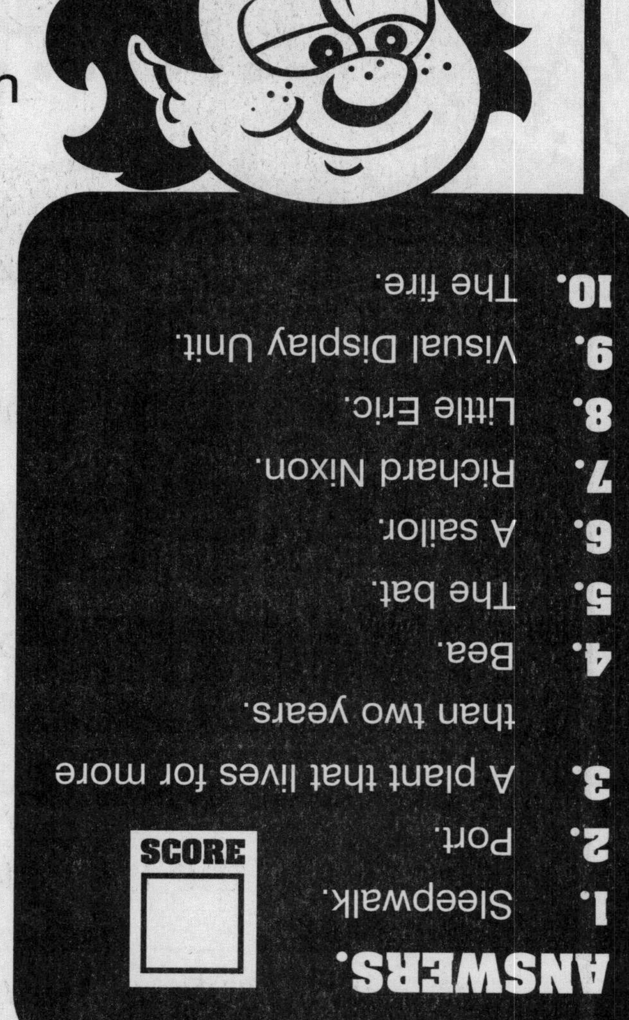

3 BEARS

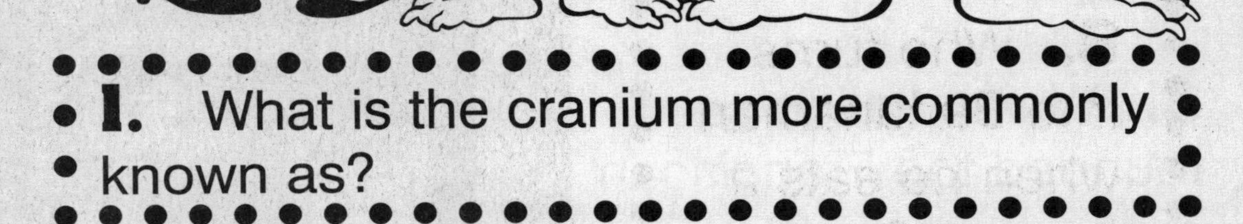

1. What is the cranium more commonly known as?

2. What was the surname of the English brothers, who established the town of Bournville near Birmingham, England?

3. Whom did Tony Blair succeed as leader of the Labour Party in Great Britain?

4. In which year was Nelson Mandela released from imprisonment by the South African Government?
(a) 1988 (b) 1990 (c) 1992.

5. Which British king abdicated to marry Wallis Simpson?

6. What is sodium chloride more commonly known as?

7. What is the name for the cutting teeth at the front of the mouth?

8. Which Italian saint founded the Franciscan order of monks?

9. What does a prestidigitator do?
(a) write poetry
(b) do conjuring tricks
(c) play in an orchestra.

10. All work and no play makes Jack... what?

TEACHER

1. What was a Benz Velo ?
(a) the first car sold to the public
(b) an airship
(c) an ocean liner.

2. Which parts of the body are affected when someone is suffering from arthritis?

3. What is the Italian town of Gorgonzola famous for?

4. Where are the Balearic Islands ?

5. With which political movement is the name Emmeline Pankhurst associated?

6. Which English poet wrote 'Paradise Lost'?
(a) Milton
(b) Shelley
(c) Keats.

7. Where is the headquarters of the All-England Lawn Tennis Club?

8. Name the artist who painted the Sistine Chapel frescoes.

9. Where is the Sonora desert ?

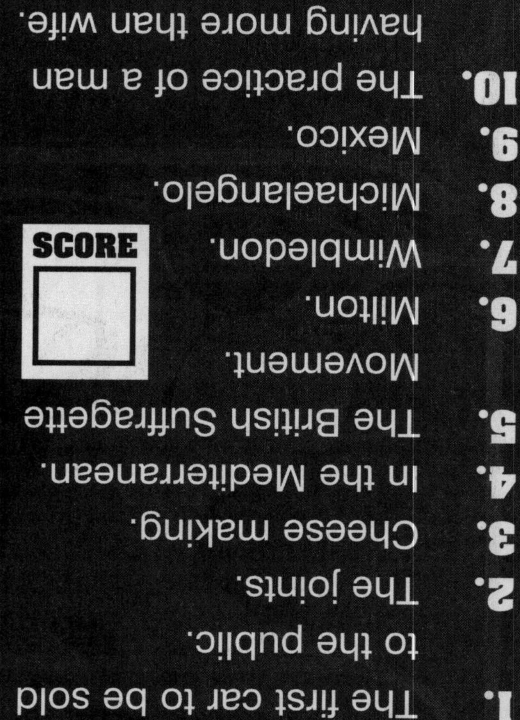

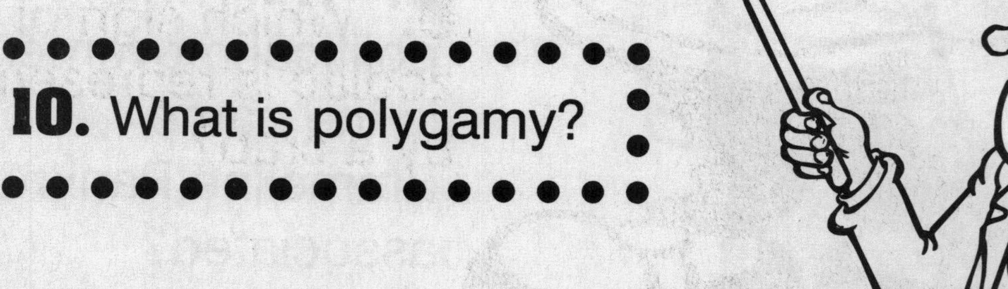

10. What is polygamy?

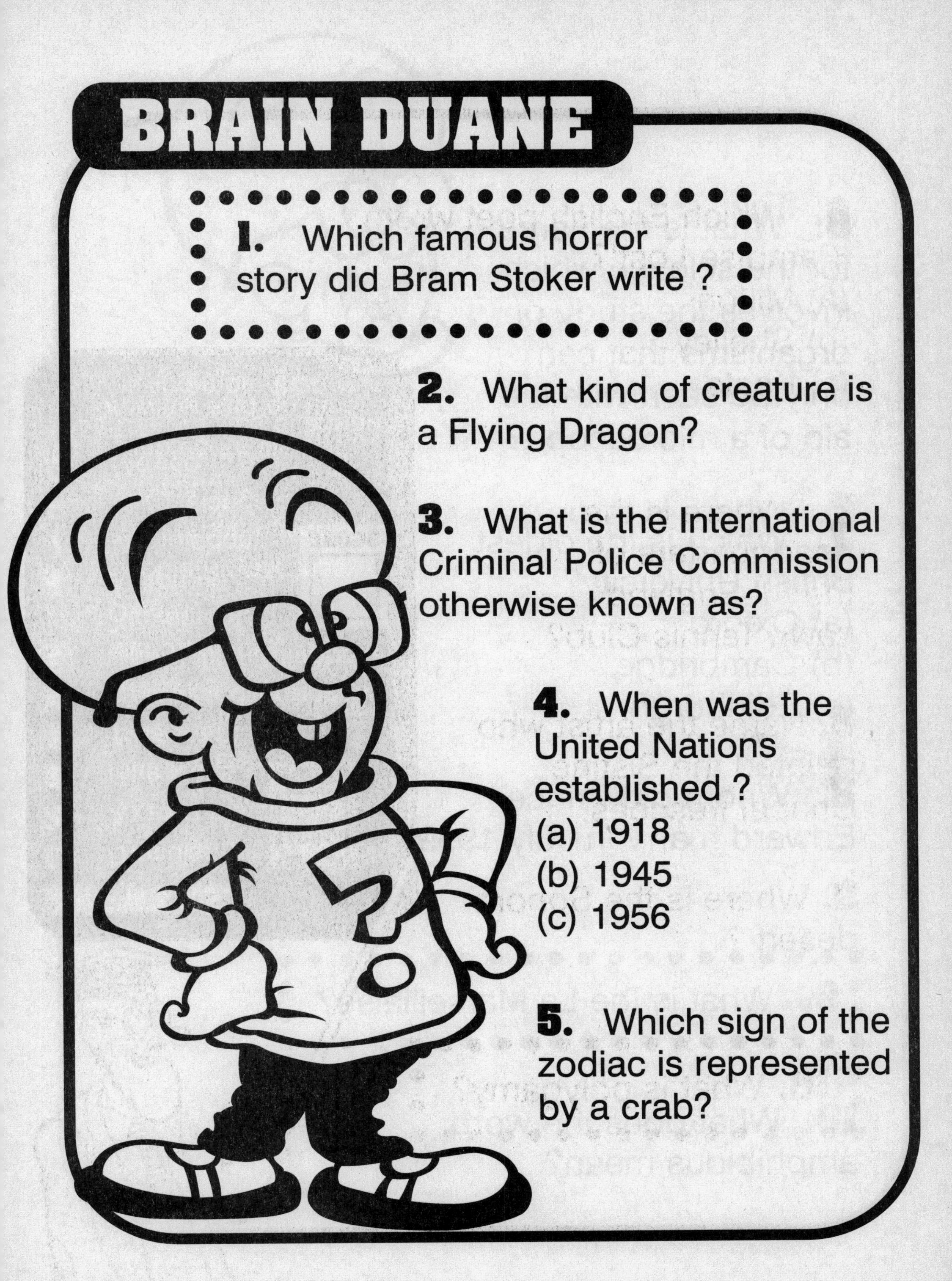
BRAIN DUANE
1. Which famous horror story did Bram Stoker write ?
2. What kind of creature is a Flying Dragon?
3. What is the International Criminal Police Commission otherwise known as?
4. When was the United Nations established ?
(a) 1918
(b) 1945
(c) 1956
5. Which sign of the zodiac is represented by a crab?

6. What is the name for the science which involves the study of organisms that can only be seen with the aid of a microscope?

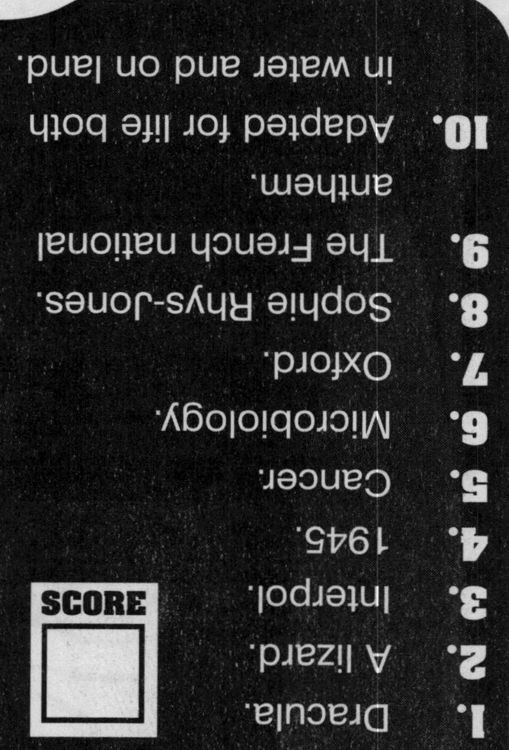

7. Which is the oldest British University?
(a) Oxford
(b) Cambridge
(c) Edinburgh.

8. Whom did Prince Edward marry in July 1999?

9. What is the La Marseillaise?

10. What does the word amphibious mean?

DESPERATE DAN

1. Where is St Basil's Cathedral ?

2. What was the underworld called in Greek mythology?

3. Which volcano in the USA erupted for the first time in 450 years in 1980?

4. What is the name of the largest lake in England?

5. Which country is the world's leading producer of computer software ?

6. Which planet is farthest away from the sun?

7. What is the name of the longest river in Europe?

8. Which language is spoken by the greatest number of people in the world?

9. What is the name of the largest island in the world?

10. Which is the biggest continent?

ANSWERS.

1. Moscow.
2. Hades.
3. Mount St Helens.
4. Lake Windermere.
5. USA.
6. Pluto.
7. The River Volga.
8. Chinese.
9. Greenland.
10. Asia.

SCORE

FATTY

1. What is the name of the highest mountain in Africa?

2. What is the name of the largest ocean in the world?

3. Which planet in the solar system is closest to the sun?

4. Which insect is responsible for the most human deaths?

5. What is the fastest land animal in the world?

6. Which bird has the longest wing span of any bird living in the world today?

7. Which song is the most frequently sung of all?

8. In which city is the world's largest railway station?

9. How many letters are there in the alphabet ?

10. What does 'lachrymose' mean?

(a) tearful

(b) happy

(c) angry.

ANSWERS.

1. Kilimanjaro.

2. The Pacific Ocean.

3. Mercury.

4. The malarial mosquito.

5. The cheetah.

6. The albatross.

7. 'Happy Birthday'.

8. New York.

9. 26.

10. Tearful.

SCORE

BEA
1. What is the fastest speed at which it is legal to drive on motorways in Great Britain?
2. What is the name of the most northerly town in the world?
3. Where is Beanoland ?
4. What is the largest mammal in the world?
5. Who was the first man to set foot on the moon?

6. Which city has the longest underground train network in the world?

7. What is the name of the most northerly point on Great Britain's mainland?

8. What was a boneshaker ?

9. What is the name of the largest Protestant church building in the world?

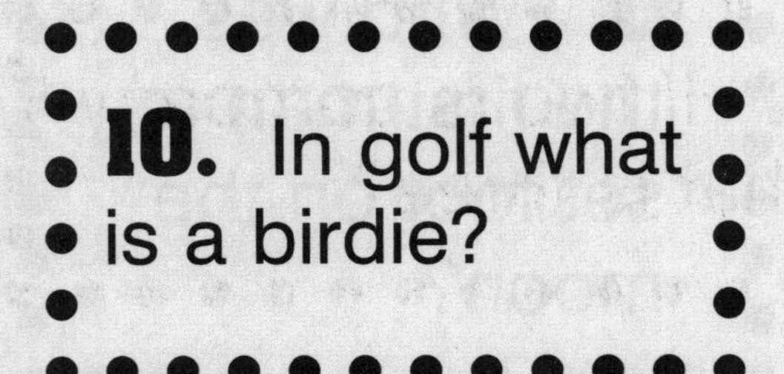

10. In golf what is a birdie?

ANSWERS.

1. 70 mph.
2. Hammerfest, Norway.
3. Chessington.
4. The blue whale.
5. Neil Armstrong.
6. London.
7. John O' Groats.
8. An early type of bicycle.
9. St Paul's Cathedral.
10. One stroke below par.

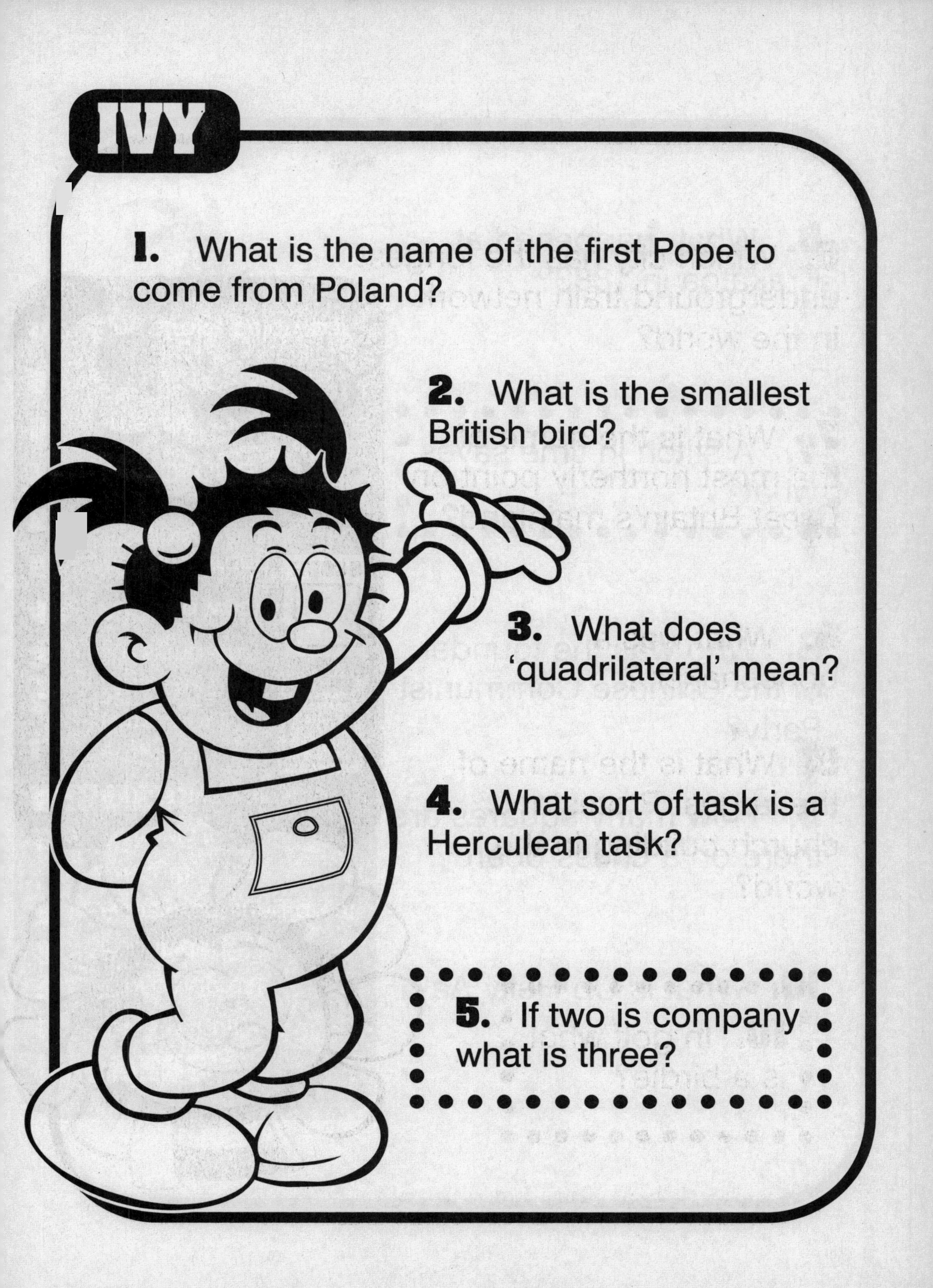
IVY
1. What is the name of the first Pope to come from Poland?
2. What is the smallest British bird?
3. What does 'quadrilateral' mean?
4. What sort of task is a Herculean task?
5. If two is company what is three?

6. What happened at Krakatoa in 1883?

7. A stitch in time saves what?

8. Who was the founder of the Chinese Communist Party?

9. How many squares are there on a chess board?

10. What is Up Helly Aa?

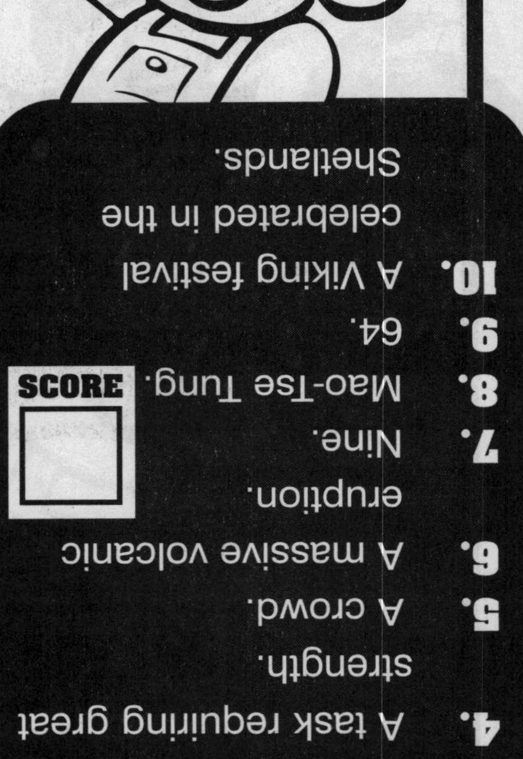

ANSWERS.

1. John Paul II.
2. The goldcrest.
3. Four-sided.
4. A task requiring great strength.
5. A crowd.
6. A massive volcanic eruption.
7. Nine.
8. Mao-Tse Tung.
9. 64.
10. A Viking festival celebrated in the Shetlands.

SCORE

1. Which country was once ruled by Tsars ?

2. What is Mulligatawny ?

3. What does AWOL mean ?

4. With which famous football team is Sir Alex Ferguson associated ?

5. If you mix yellow and blue, what colour do you get ?

6. Which is the odd one out?
(a) homburg
(b) jodhpurs
(c) sombrero.

7. What was Moby Dick ?
(a) whale
(b) dolphin
(c) shark.

8. What colour is a ruby ?

9. In a pack of playing cards what are the two red suits?

10. What does pride come before?

ANSWERS.

SCORE

1. Russia.
2. Soup.
3. Absent without leave.
4. Manchester United.
5. Green.
6. Jodhpurs. They are trousers. The others are hats.
7. Whale.
8. Red.
9. Hearts and diamonds.
10. A fall.

BLINKY

1. Which animal represents the star sign Taurus ?

2. Name the largest country in Africa.

3. What kind of building is used to store aircraft ?

4. Who was Mowgli ?

5. Which fruit is named after the Moroccan port of Tangiers ?

6. If you eat "al fresco", where would you be ?

7. What are triceps ?

8. Who was Boadicea?..
(a) a Roman empress
(b) a British queen
(c) a Greek goddess

9. Where is Pravda published ?

10. What do the letters K.B.E. after a person's name stand for?

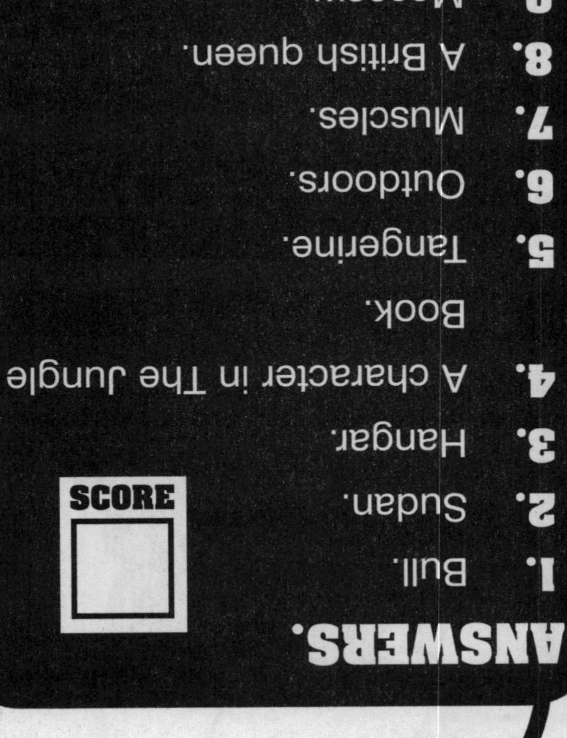

ANSWERS.

1. Bull.
2. Sudan.
3. Hangar.
4. A character in The Jungle Book.
5. Tangerine.
6. Outdoors.
7. Muscles.
8. A British queen.
9. Moscow.
10. Knight of the British Empire.

SCORE

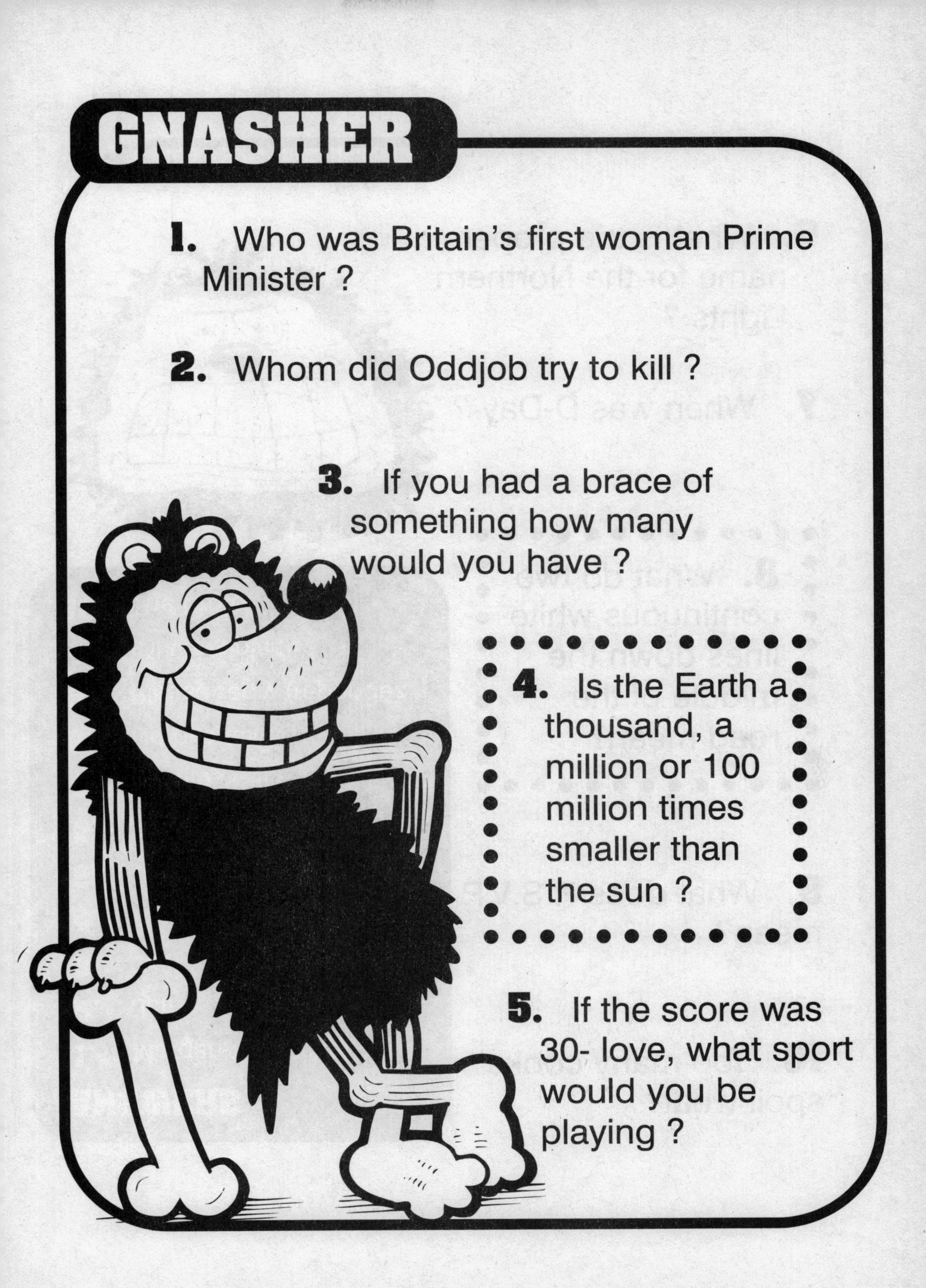
GNASHER
1. Who was Britain's first woman Prime Minister ?
2. Whom did Oddjob try to kill ?
3. If you had a brace of something how many would you have ?
4. Is the Earth a thousand, a million or 100 million times smaller than the sun ?
5. If the score was 30- love, what sport would you be playing ?

6. What is the proper name for the Northern Lights ?

7. When was D-Day ?

8. What do two continuous white lines down the middle of the road mean?

9. What does R.S.V.P. mean?

10. Too many cooks spoil what?

ANSWERS.

1. Margaret Thatcher.
2. James Bond.
3. Two.
4. A million.
5. Tennis.
6. Aurora Borealis.
7. June 6 ,1944.
8. No overtaking.
9. Please reply (repondez s'il vous plait).
10. The broth.

BOOKS, TV & FILMS

DENNIS

1. Who had to let down her hair to let her sweetheart climb up to see her?

2. Which popular TV series features Mulder and Scully?

3. Albert Square is the venue for which TV soap?

4. James Van Der Beek is the star of which popular TV show?
(a) Hollyoaks
(b) Roswell High
(c) Dawson's Creek.

5. Which Disney animated film features the song "Hi-ho, Hi-ho, It's Off To Work We Go"?

6. Which American city was under threat in the film Godzilla?

7. Which superhero works at the Daily Planet?

8. Who wrote Oliver Twist?

9. Which famous scientist wrote A Brief History Of Time?
(a) Charles Darwin
(b) Albert Einstein
(c) Stephen Hawking.

10. Before what time was Cinderella told she must leave the ball?

ANSWERS.

1. Rapunzel.
2. The X Files.
3. EastEnders.
4. Dawson's Creek.
5. Snow White.
6. New York.
7. Superman.
8. Charles Dickens.
9. Stephen Hawking.
10. Before midnight.

SCORE

MINNIE

1. What did Snow White's wicked stepmother make her eat which caused her to fall asleep?

2. In which TV sci-fi series does a Ferengi called Quark appear?

3. Which soap features the characters, Ashley and Bernice?

4. Which TV show, set in California, is based on the books of Francine Pascal?

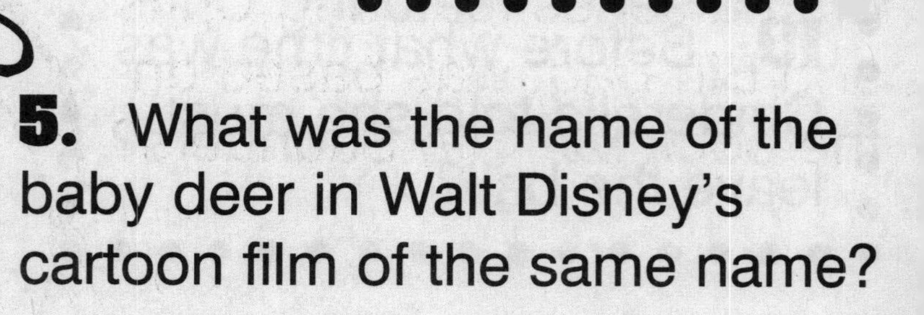

5. What was the name of the baby deer in Walt Disney's cartoon film of the same name?

6. Will Smith starred in which Fourth of July blockbuster?

7. Which of these films did not have an animal star:- Flipper, Flubber or Skippy?

8. Which famous book by Kenneth Grahame features Mole, Ratty, Toad and Badger?

9. In the book by Henry Williamson, what kind of animal was Tarka?

10. Which popular BBC drama series featuring Chris and Bin Bag, was based on the book by Kate Saunders?

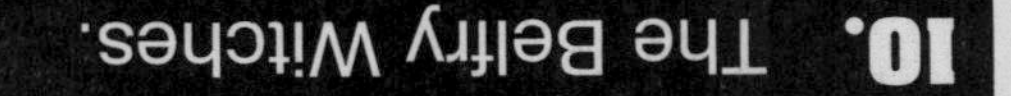

ANSWERS.

1. A poisoned apple.
2. Star Trek: Deep Space Nine.
3. Emmerdale.
4. Sweet Valley High.
5. Bambi.
6. Independence Day.
7. Flubber.
8. The Wind In The Willows.
9. An otter.
10. The Belfry Witches.

SCORE

BILLY WHIZZ

1. How long did the Sleeping Beauty remain asleep?

2. Can you name Buffy the Vampire Slayer's best friend?
(a) Willow
(b) Holly
(c) Rowan.

3. Kylie Minogue was a regular in which Australian soap?

4. Charlie Dimmock is a member of which popular TV team?

5. In which city does the star of Home Alone 2 have to spend the weekend?

6. What was R-2 D-2?

7. Which popular carrot munching character starred in the film, Space Jam?

8. Who wrote Lord of the Rings?

9. Who ran the den of thieves in the novel Oliver Twist?

10. Seth Armstrong is a character in which long-running soap?

ANSWERS.

1. 100 years.
2. Willow.
3. Neighbours.
4. Ground force.
5. New York.
6. A robot in Star Wars.
7. Bugs Bunny.
8. J.R. Tolkien.
9. Fagan.
10. Emmerdale.

SCORE

BANANAMAN

1. In the book, who was the strange little man who didn't want his name to be guessed?

2. Which BBC series featured a police box that could travel through time?

3. Which long-running soap celebrated its fortieth year in December, 2000?

4. Which long-running TV show features the characters, Elmo and Big Bird?

5. Who played the starring role in Braveheart?

6. Which film featured Princess Amidalla?

7. What game did the toons have to play in the film, Space Jam?

8. Name the fictional character who attends a trainee school for wizards?

9. In which novel does the character Long John Silver appear?

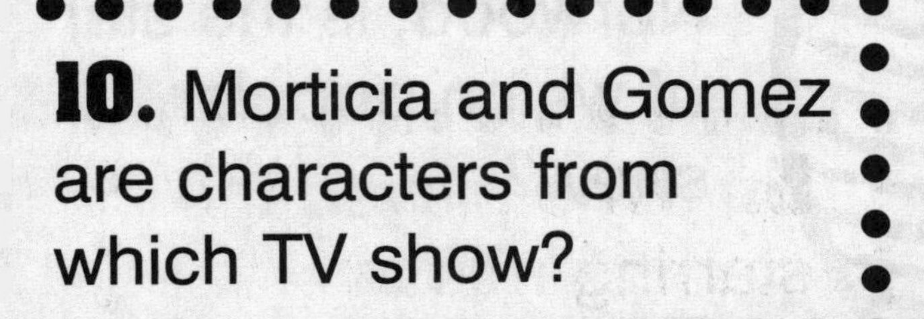

10. Morticia and Gomez are characters from which TV show?

ANSWERS.

1. Rumpelstiltskin.
2. Dr. Who.
3. Coronation Street.
4. Sesame Street.
5. Mel Gibson.
6. Star Wars Episode I.
7. Basketball.
8. Harry Potter.
9. Treasure Island.
10. The Addams Family.

ROGER THE DODGER

1. Which animal surprisingly beat the hare in a race?

2. Which of these characters is not a captain in the various Star Trek series :– Kirk, Picard, Chakotay, Sisko?

3. For sixteen years, Michael Starke played the part of which Brookside character?

4. Singer, Brandy Norwood, is the star of which popular TV show?

5. What was Jaws?

6. In which Star Wars film did Luke Skywalker meet Yoda?

7. Who is the partner of Gotham City's superhero?

8. Christopher Robin and Piglet are friends of which famous character?

9. Who wrote Gulliver's Travels?

10. Name the little elephant with very big ears in Walt Disney's cartoon of the same name.

ANSWERS.

1. The tortoise.
2. Chakotay.
3. Sinbad.
4. Moesha.
5. A shark.
6. The Return Of The Jedi.
7. Robin.
8. Winnie The Pooh.
9. Jonathan Swift.
10. Dumbo.

SCORE

BERYL THE PERIL

1. What were Cinderella's slippers made of?

2. Which character did Leonard Nimoy play in the original Star Trek?

3. Which popular soap is set in and around Ramsay Street?

4. The Fresh Prince of Bel Air made which, now famous, actor a household name?

5. Which American actor starred in Big?

6. Which fun film starring Bob Hoskins was based on a computer game?

7. In which film would you find a scarecrow, a tin man and a lion?

8. Who were writers, Emily, Charlotte and Anne?

9. The tale of Les Miserables was set in which period of history?

10. In which blockbuster film does Bruce Willis save the world from destruction by a meteor?

ANSWERS.

1. Glass.
2. Mr Spock.
3. Neighbours.
4. Will Smith.
5. Tom Hanks.
6. Super Mario Bros.
7. The Wizard of Oz.
8. The Bronte Sisters.
9. The French Revolution.
10. Armageddon.

DANNY

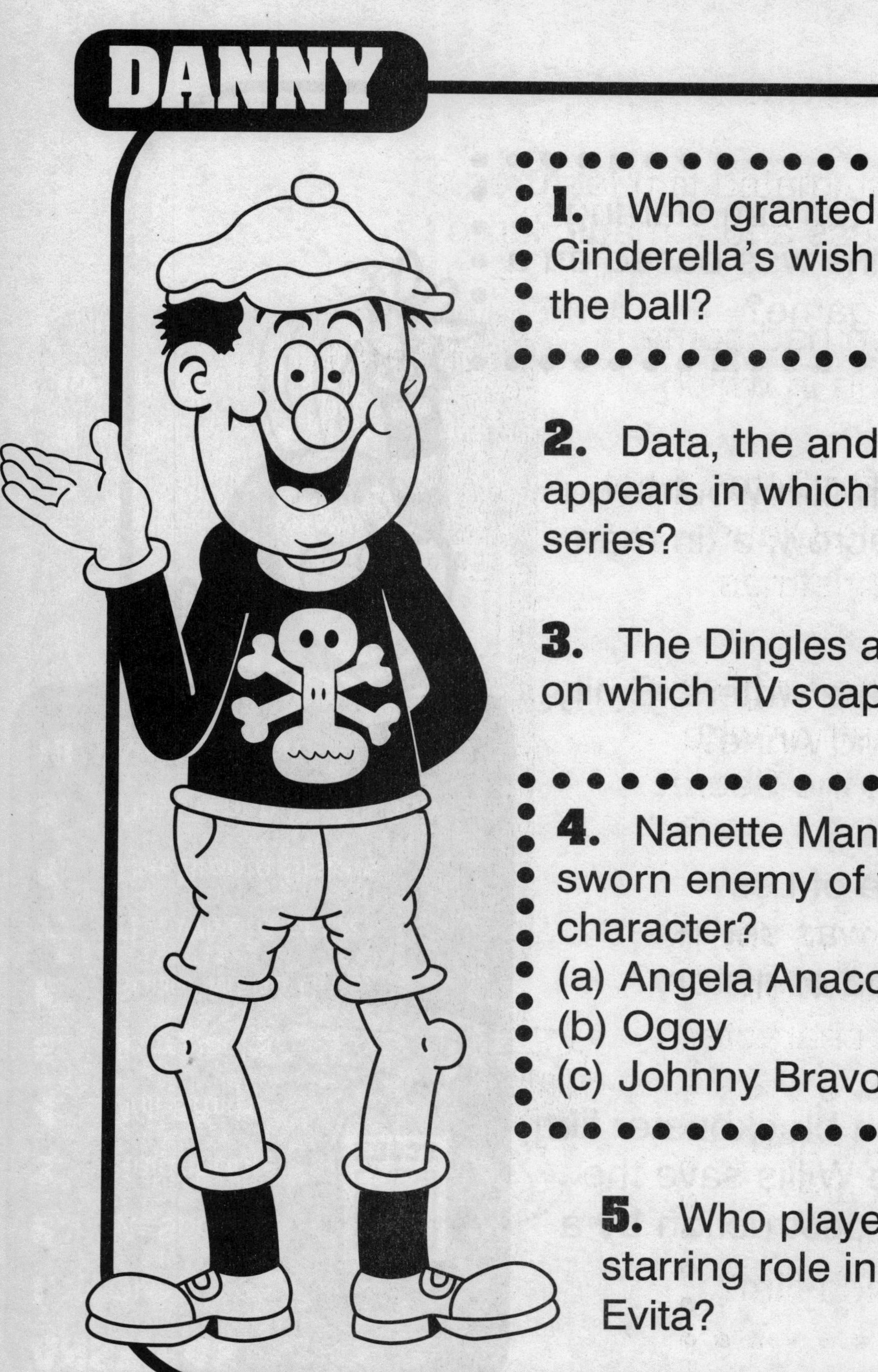

1. Who granted Cinderella's wish to go to the ball?

2. Data, the android, appears in which sci-fi series?

3. The Dingles are regulars on which TV soap?

4. Nanette Manoir is the sworn enemy of which TV character?
(a) Angela Anaconda
(b) Oggy
(c) Johnny Bravo.

5. Who played the starring role in the film Evita?

6. Which animated film featured a genie, princess and a magic lamp?

7. Tim Allen had some Christmas fun in which film?
(a) Miracle On 34th Street
(b) The Santa Clause
(c) White Christmas.

8. Name the English children's author who wrote about the Secret Seven.

9. The Rev. W. Awdry wrote about which well-known character?

10. Timon and Pumbaa are characters from which film?

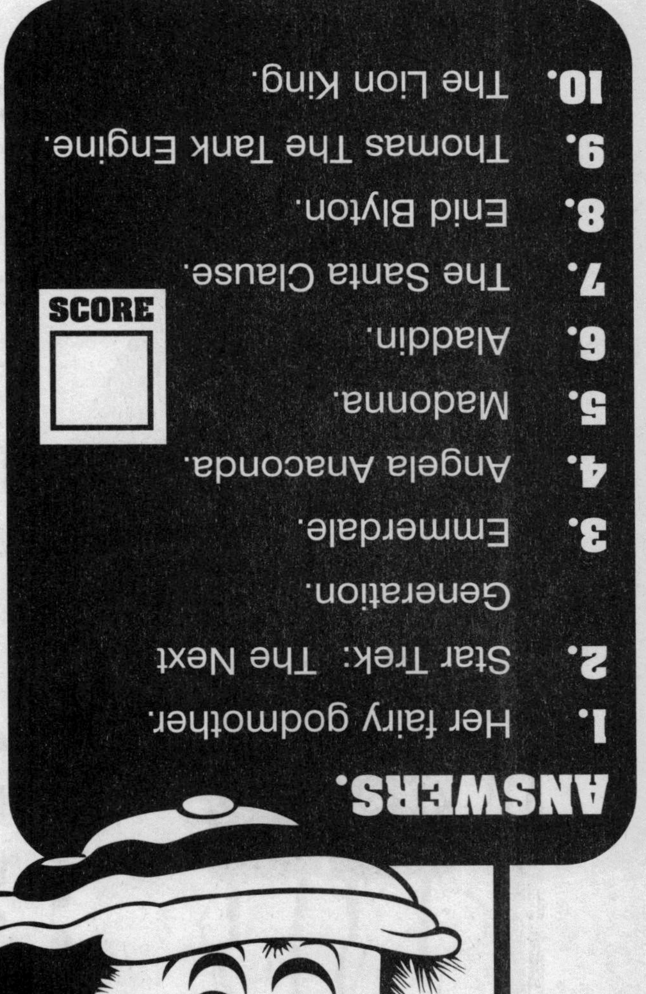

WALTER

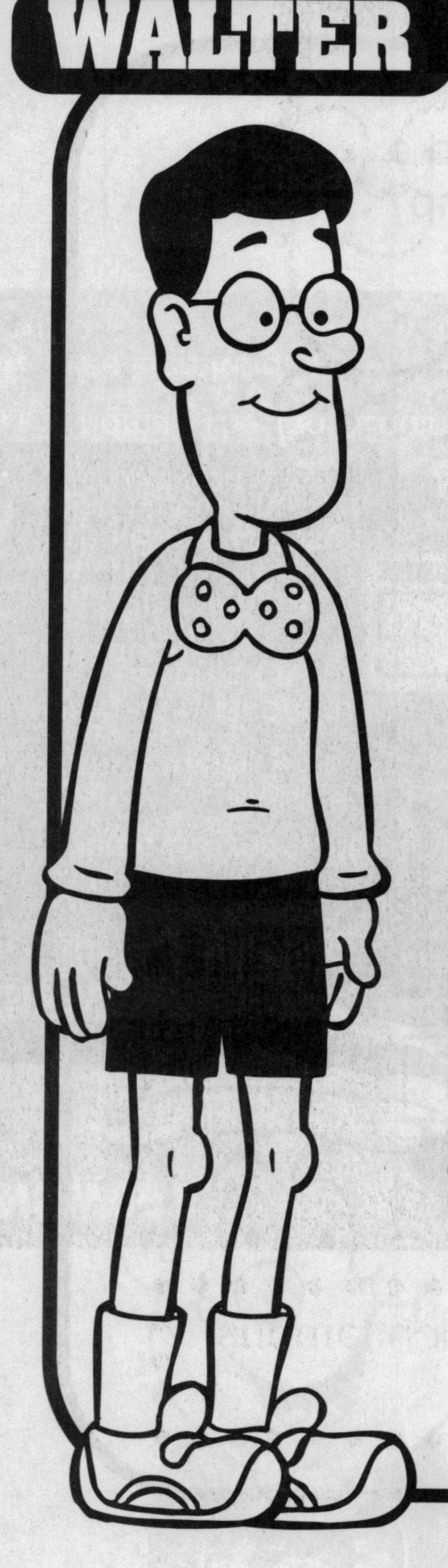

1. Who lived in the cottage discovered by Hansel and Gretel in the woods?

2. Who is Xena in the popular TV series?
(a) a warrior princess
(b) a time traveller
(c) a crime fighter.

3. Which soap has a pub called The Rovers Return?

4. Name the Nutty Professor's crazy family in the films starring Eddie Murphy.

5. Name five actors who have starred in the role of James Bond?

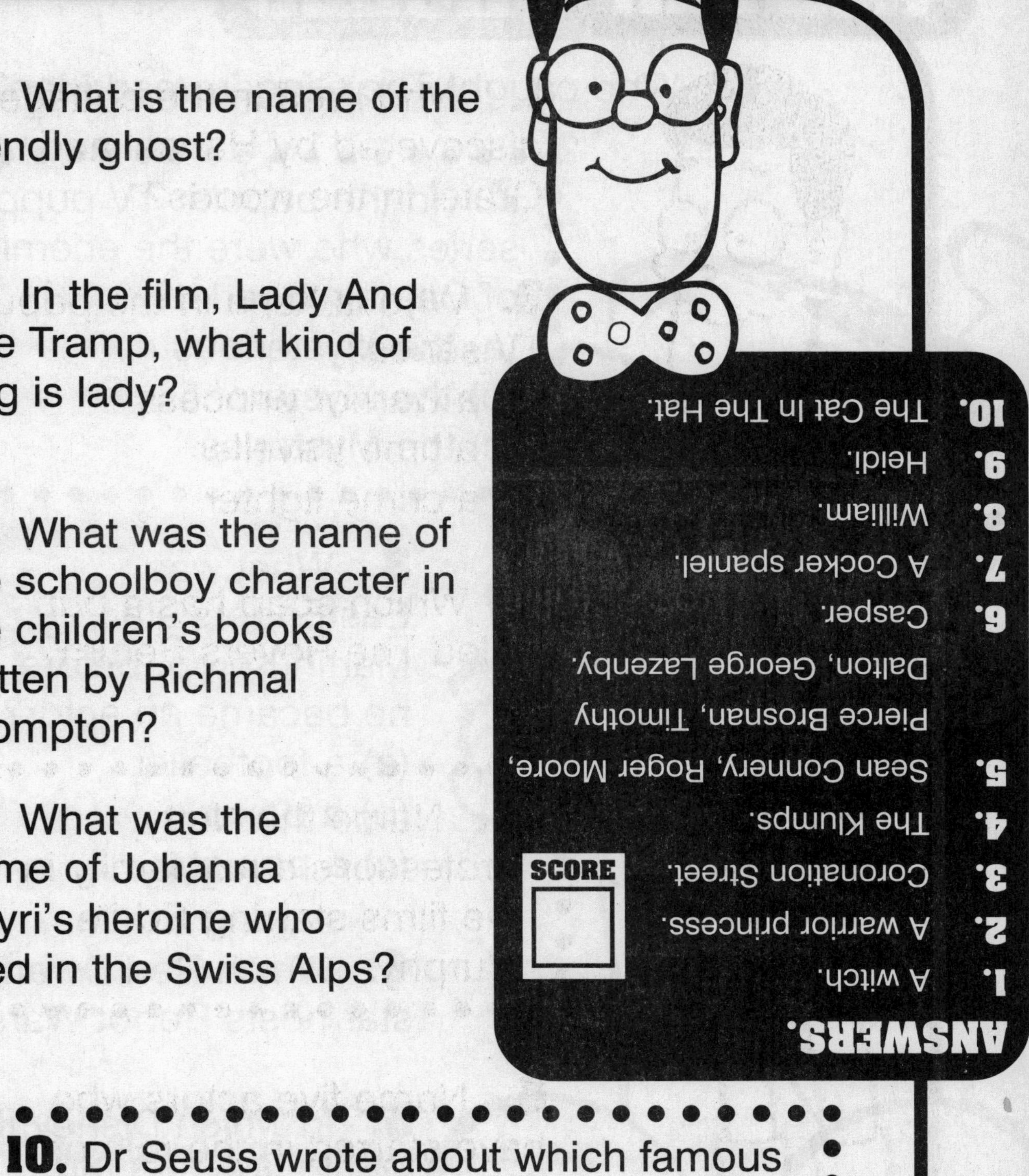

6. What is the name of the friendly ghost?

7. In the film, Lady And The Tramp, what kind of dog is lady?

8. What was the name of the schoolboy character in the children's books written by Richmal Crompton?

9. What was the name of Johanna Spyri's heroine who lived in the Swiss Alps?

10. Dr Seuss wrote about which famous character in 1957?

THE NUMSKULLS

1. Who caught The Gingerbread Man?

2. In the popular TV puppet series who were the enemies of Captain Scarlet?
(a) the Mysterious
(b) the Mysterons
(c) the Mysteries.

3. What was EastEnders star, Martin Kemp, before he became an actor?
(a) a footballer
(b) a boxer
(c) a pop star.

4. Which Red Dwarf star hosts Robot Wars?

5. In which Disney film would you find the characters, Rex and Slinky?

6. Which animated film told the story of a mouse's journey to America?

7. Finish this film title :– Ace Ventura, Pet _ _ _ _ _ _ _ _ _ ?

8. Born Free, written by Joy Adams, is the story of which creature?

9. In the novel, A Tale Of Two Cities, what were the two cities?

10. Who wrote The Horrible Histories and Terrible Tudors?

PLUG

1. What did Jack trade for the magic beans that grew into the beanstalk?

2. Which TV series features a hologram called Rimmer?

3. Jack Ryder plays which popular EastEnders character?

4. Who is the host of the long-running game show, Family Fortunes?

5. What is the name of the fourth Star Wars film to be made?

6. In which film and cartoon does the character Olive Oyl appear?

7. Which of these films did not star Jim Carey... The Truman Show, The Mask, My Favourite Martian?

8. What is the name of the boy hero in the books written and drawn by Herge?

9. Name the book, written by Johann R. Wyss, about a family stranded on a desert island.

10. In the story of Androcles and the lion, how does Androcles befriend the Lion?

ANSWERS.

1. A cow.
2. Red Dwarf.
3. Jamie Mitchell.
4. Les Dennis.
5. Star Wars Episode I: The Phantom Menace.
6. Popeye.
7. My Favourite Martian.
8. Tin Tin.
9. Swiss Family Robinson.
10. Androcles removes a thorn from the lion's paw.

SCORE

CUDDLES AND DIMPLES

1. How did the ugly duckling find out that he was a swan?

2. Which popular cartoon series features a hero who spins webs?

3. What is the surname of Coronation Street regulars, Jack and Vera?

4. Where do The Simpsons live?

5. Which actress played the part of Rose in 'Titanic'?

6. Gotham City is the home of which superhero?

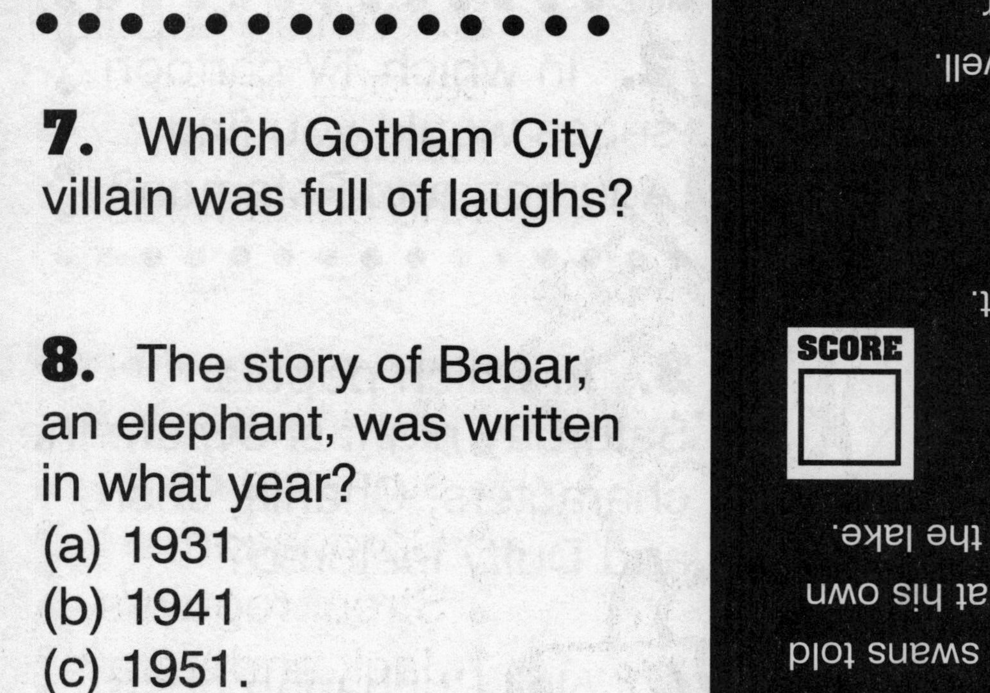

7. Which Gotham City villain was full of laughs?

8. The story of Babar, an elephant, was written in what year?
(a) 1931
(b) 1941
(c) 1951.

9. Who wrote the novel Animal Farm?

10. Which series features a futuristic car called Kitt?

ANSWERS.

1. Some other swans told him to look at his own reflection in the lake.
2. Spiderman.
3. Duckworth.
4. Springfield.
5. Kate Winslet.
6. Batman.
7. The Joker.
8. 1931.
9. George Orwell.
10. Knight Rider.

SCORE

BALL BOY

1. How did the wolf disguise himself from Red Riding Hood?

2. In which TV cartoon series would you find Agumon and Patamon?

3. In which popular Saturday night show are the characters, Charlie, Josh and Duffy featured?

4. Neil Buchanan hosts which popular TV crafts show?

5. What was the name of the toy astronaut in Toy Story?

6. Which Nick Park film is based on the film The Great Escape?

7. Which creatures starred in the film A Bug's Life?

8. Which Scots poet and songwriter is remembered on January 25th each year?

9. Which type of animals are featured in Watership Down?

10. Where is the TV soap Neighbours set?
(a) Erinsborough
(b) Erin Town
(c) Erinvale.

ANSWERS.

1. He dressed in Grandma's clothes and hid in her bed.
2. Digimon.
3. Casualty.
4. Art Attack.
5. Buzz Lightyear.
6. Chicken Run.
7. Ants.
8. Robert Burns.
9. Rabbits.
10. Erinsborough.

SCORE

MOLLY

1. How did the grateful shoemaker thank the two little elves who helped him?
(a) he made them little shoes
(b) he made them new clothes
(c) he made them a cake.

2. In the TV series, Masked Rider, what does the hero ride?
(a) a horse
(b) a bicycle
(c) a motor bike.

3. Which long-running radio soap tells of the lives of country folk?

4. Which TV series features a Mountie called Fraser?

5. Elton John wrote the music for which Disney animated film?

6. Who or what was the star of the film Paulie?

7. Which film told the story of two dogs and a cat trying to find their way home?

8. Narnia is the name of the hidden kingdom discovered by the children in which famous book?

9. Who wrote The Time Machine and War Of The Worlds?

10. Neil Morrissey and Martin Clunes starred in which popular TV comedy?

ANSWERS.

1. He made them new clothes.
2. A motor bike.
3. The Archers.
4. Due South.
5. The Lion King.
6. A parrot.
7. The Incredible Journey.
8. The Lion, The Witch and the Wardrobe.
9. H. G. Wells.
10. Men Behaving Badly.

3 BEARS

1. Who were the musicians of Bremen?

2. In which cartoon TV series do Ash, Brock and Misty appear?

3. Which soap has a pub called The Vic?

4. Which TV comedy features a psychiatrist with his own radio show?

5. Robin Williams was trapped in a board game in which film?

6. Which film starred a killer whale?

7. Which ex Bond star played the voice of the dragon in Dragonheart?
(a) Roger Moore
(b) Timothy Dalton
(c) Sean Connery.

8. When was the book Mary Poppins written?
(a) 1904
(b) 1934
(c) 1984.

9. Who visits Wonderland in the books by Lewis Caroll?

10. Can you name the first ever James Bond film?

ANSWERS.
1. A donkey, a dog, a cockerel and a cat.
2. Pokemon.
3. EastEnders.
4. Frasier.
5. Jumanji.
6. Free Willy.
7. Sean Connery.
8. 1934.
9. Alice.
10. Dr No.

SCORE

TEACHER

1. What was the name of Pinocchio's maker and adopted father?

2. What are Mewtwo, Charizard and Squirtle?

3. Which popular series takes place in and around Sun Hill Police Station?

4. Who is Ross's sister in Friends?

5. In which film did actor John Goodman star with a lot of very tiny people?

6. Which Friends actor starred in Lost In Space?

7. Which film character wanted to phone home?

8. What is the name of the boy hero in Maurice Sendak's, Where The Wild Things Are?

9. What type of creature is Bilbo Baggins in the J. R. R. Tolkien books?

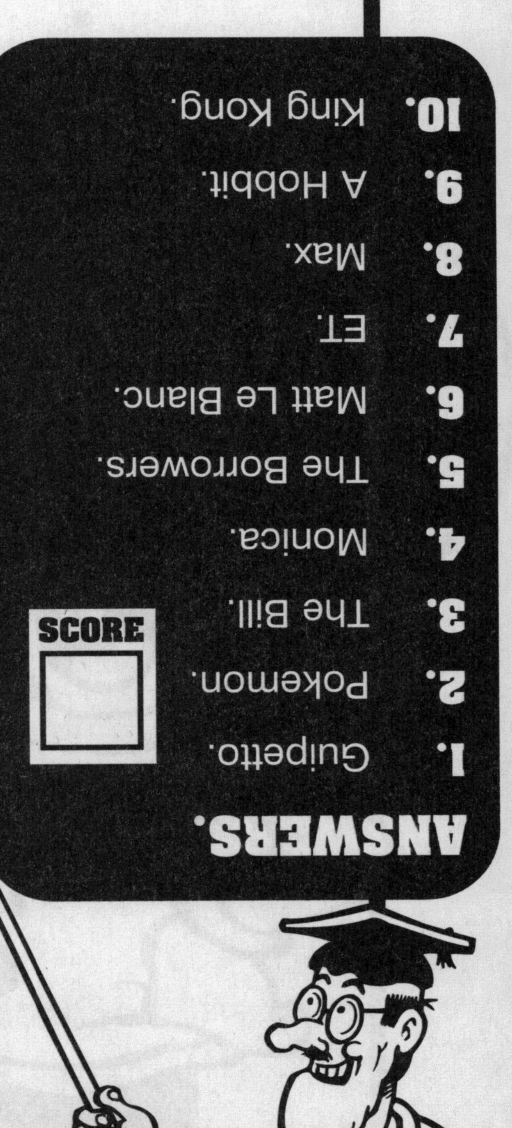

10. Which film creation met its downfall on the Empire State Building?

BRAIN DUANE

1. What did the first little pig build his house with?

2. Complete the title of this TV show:- Third Rock From The _ _ _?

3. Which soap features characters, Gail and Martin Platt?

4. Complete this TV cartoon title:- Oggy And The _ _ _ _ _ _ _ _ _ _ _ _ _?

5. In which city was the film Mary Poppins set?

6. Antonio Banderas was a sword-wielding hero in which film?

7. In their film, which European city do Rugrats, Chuckie and Co. visit?

8. When did Beatrix Potter write about Peter Rabbit?
(a) 1890
(b) 1902
(c) 1922.

9. Which author wrote the books about a fantasy Discworld?

10. Which film features Neera, the Iguanodon?

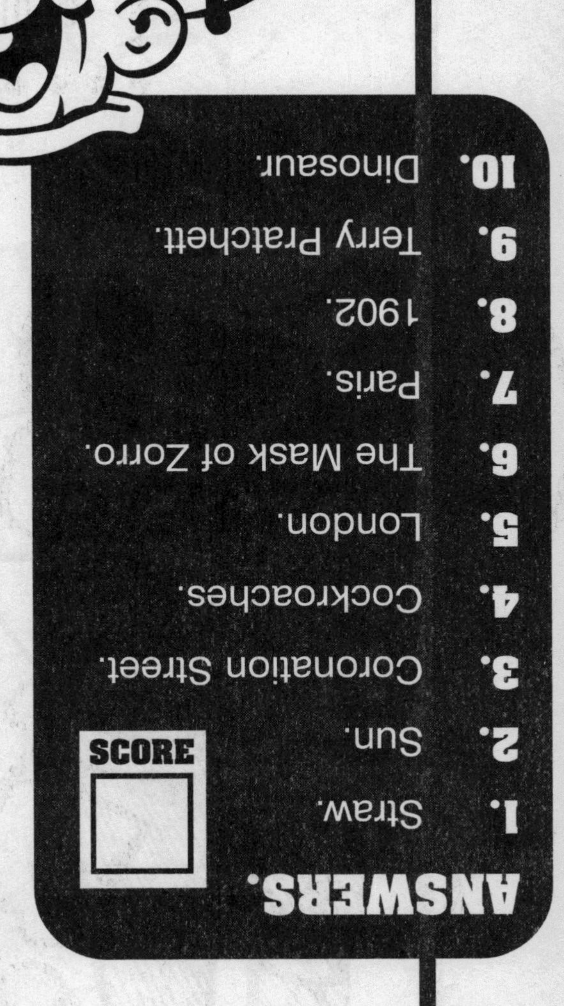

DESPERATE DAN

1. What made The Sleeping Beauty fall asleep?

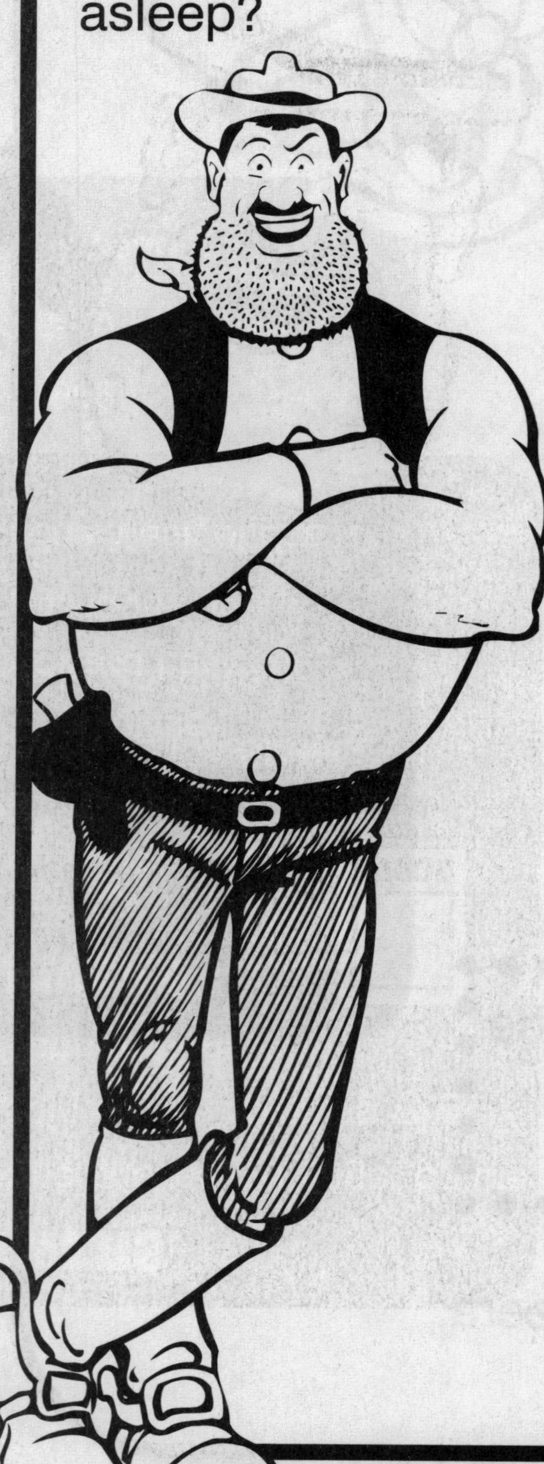

2. Virgil, Gordon and Brains are three of the heroes in which Gerry Anderson puppet series?

3. Which soap features character Jack Sugden?

4. What is the name of the hotel owner in the popular comedy classic, Fawlty Towers?

5. Which of these actors did NOT play Batman:- George Clooney, Keanu Reeves, Michael Keaton, Val Kilmer?

6. Crocodile Dundee starred which Australian actor?

7. Which film character could "Talk to the animals"?

8. Which English writer achieved fame for his nonsense, verse and limericks?

9. Who wrote The Snowman and Father Christmas?

10. Who wrote Little Women?

ANSWERS.

1. She pricked her finger on the spindle of a spinning wheel.
2. Thunderbirds.
3. Emmerdale.
4. Basil.
5. Keanu Reeves.
6. Paul Hogan.
7. Dr Doolittle.
8. Edward Lear.
9. Raymond Briggs.
10. Louisa May Alcott.

SCORE

FATTY

1. Jack stole a hen from the giant's castle at the top of the beanstalk. What could the hen do?

2. What is the name of the teenage witch in the popular TV series?

3. Which TV soap features characters, Harold and Madge?

4. What is the subject of the Top Gear programme?

5. In which Disney film does the song, "A Whole New World" appear?

6. Who was captain of the Millennium Falcon?

7. Which 'monster' film, set in Scotland, starred Ted Danson?

8. Who wrote Huckleberry Finn and Tom Sawyer?

9. In which series of books would you find the character, Obelix?

10. Can you name the Three Musketeers?

ANSWERS.

1. The hen could lay golden eggs.
2. Sabrina.
3. Neighbours.
4. Cars.
5. Aladdin.
6. Han Solo.
7. Loch Ness.
8. Mark Twain.
9. Asterix The Gaul.
10. Athos, Porthos and Aramis.

1. In the fairy tale, who took Gerda's brother, Kay, to live in her ice-palace?

2. David Duchovny plays which popular TV character?

3. Mike Baldwin is a regular character in which TV soap?

4. This popular children's TV show celebrated its twenty-first anniversary in the year 2000. Can you name it?

5. Who was the child star in Home Alone?

6. Who starred in the Indiana Jones films?

7. Which Disney cartoon girl pretended to be a boy?
(a) Ariel
(b) Mulan
(c) Belle.

8. When was The Secret Garden written?
(a) 1871
(b) 1911
(c) 1928.

9. Complete this book title... Swallows And ________.

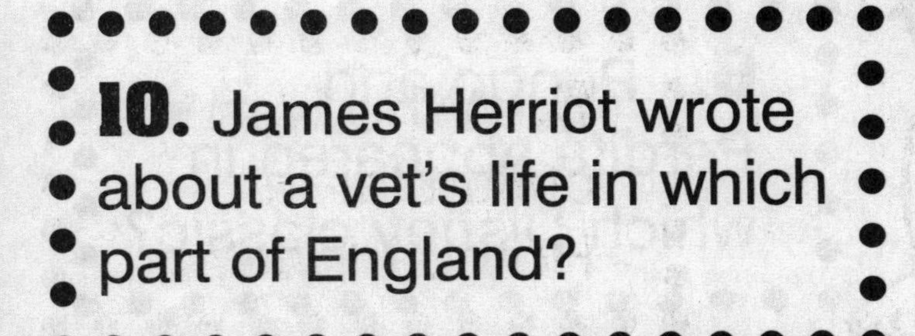

10. James Herriot wrote about a vet's life in which part of England?

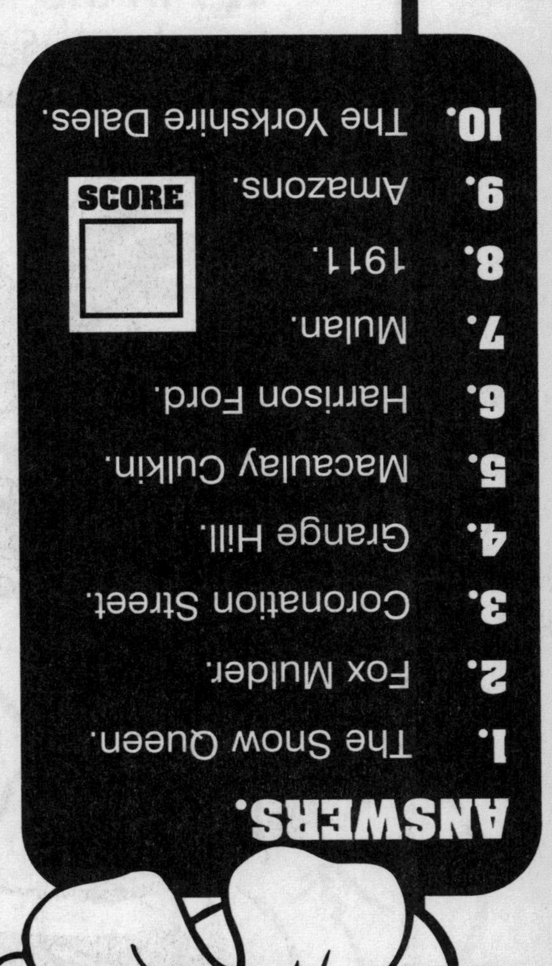

IVY

1. In the fable of the lion and the mouse, the lion spares the mouse's life. How does the mouse thank the lion?

2. Which actress plays the leading role in Buffy the Vampire Slayer?

3. In which TV soap would you find the character Toadfish?

4. Which favourite TV puppet has friends called Sue and Sweep?

5. Pongo and Perdita appeared in which Disney classic?

6. Who co-starred with Will Smith in Men In Black?

7. Which of these films was not made by Disney:- The Land Before Time, Tarzan, The Parent Trap?

8. Which famous story features Wendy and Tinkerbell?

9. In which famous tale would you find the characters, Little John and Will Scarlet?

10. Excalibur is the name of the sword in which famous story?

ANSWERS.

1. The mouse frees the lion from the net in which he has been trapped.
2. Sarah Michelle Gellar.
3. Neighbours.
4. Sooty.
5. 101 Dalmatians.
6. Tommy Lee Jones.
7. The Land Before Time.
8. Peter Pan.
9. Robin Hood.
10. Tales of King Arthur.

1. How many times was the wolf successful when he huffed and puffed to blow the little pigs' houses down?

2. Lara Croft is the heroine of which computer game?

3. Which popular soap features characters Beth and Luke Morgan?

4. Who is the host of TV quiz show Who Wants To Be A Millionaire?

5. In the film, Beethoven, what kind of dog was the star?

6. Which film starred Robin Williams as Peter Pan?

7. Which band performed the theme song of the Bond film, The World Is Not Enough?

8. What is the name of the author of Five Children and It?

9. Sue Townsend is the author of which character's well-known diaries?

10. Where does Rupert The Bear live?

ANSWERS.

1. Twice.
2. Tomb Raider.
3. Hollyoaks.
4. Chris Tarrant.
5. A St Bernard.
6. Hook.
7. Garbage.
8. E. Nesbit.
9. Adrian Mole.
10. Nutwood.

SCORE

BLINKY

1. In Beauty and the Beast what did Beauty ask her father to bring back for her from his travels?

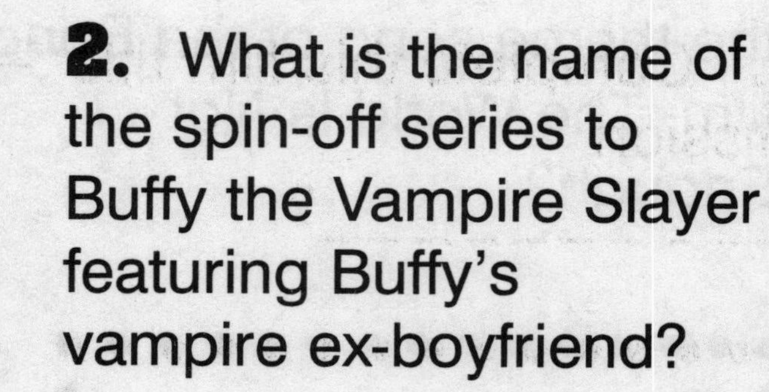

2. What is the name of the spin-off series to Buffy the Vampire Slayer featuring Buffy's vampire ex-boyfriend?

3. Wendy Richards plays which EastEnder character?

4. What is the name of Homer Simpson's boss?

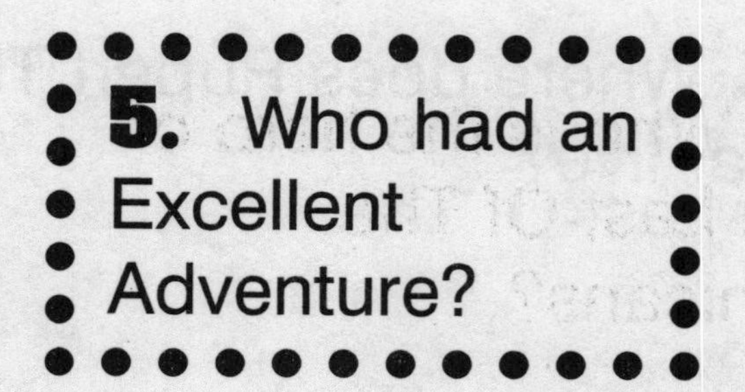

5. Who had an Excellent Adventure?

6. Who or what was Stuart Little in the film of the same name?

7. Complete this film title :– Mission

___________?

8. Who wrote The Big Friendly Giant and Charlie and the Chocolate Factory?

9. What is the name of the lion in the Narnia stories?

10. Who is the hero of The Last Of The Mohicans?

ANSWERS.

1. A rose.
2. Angel.
3. Pauline Fowler.
4. Mr Burns.
5. Bill and Ted.
6. A mouse.
7. Impossible.
8. Roald Dahl.
9. Aslan.
10. Hawkeye.

SCORE

GNASHER

1. What was unusual about the hero of the story Tom Thumb?

2. Which cartoon series features Blossom, Bubbles and Buttercup?

3. In the TV soap EastEnders, the character Frank Butcher was played by which Cockney comedian?

4. What are the Chuckle brothers' names?

5. Who starred as Robin Hood in the film Robin Hood, Prince of Thieves?

6. In which cartoon/film does the character Wolverine feature?

7. Who played Batman in Batman Forever?
(a) Michael Keaton
(b) Val Kilmer
(c) George Clooney.

8. For which kind of writing is the Smarties Prize awarded?

9. Who wrote 20,000 Leagues Under The Sea?
(a) Sir Arthur Conan Doyle
(b) Edgar Allan Poe
(c) Jules Verne.

10. In which cartoon strip would you find the characters Charlie Brown and Woodstock?

ANSWERS.

1. He was very small - the size of a thumb.
2. The Powerpuff Girls.
3. Mike Reid.
4. Barry and Paul.
5. Kevin Costner.
6. The X-Men.
7. Val Kilmer.
8. Children's fiction.
9. Jules Verne.
10. Peanuts.

SCORE

SPORT & MUSIC

DENNIS

1. What kind of races take place on the Isle of Man every year?

2. In which sport do games begin with a bully-off?

3. When were the Olympic Games last held in the UK?

4. In golf what would you find in a bunker?

5. In which sport did Jonathan Edwards win a gold medal at the Sydney Olympics?
(a) long jump
(b) high jump
(c) triple jump.

6. Which instrument is the larger:- a violin or a viola?

7. Which girl band recorded the songs "Jumpin Jumpin" and "Say My Name"?

8. Is contralto the highest or lowest female voice?

9. When did Sir Alex Ferguson become manager of Manchester United?
(a) 1984
(b) 1989
(c) 1992.

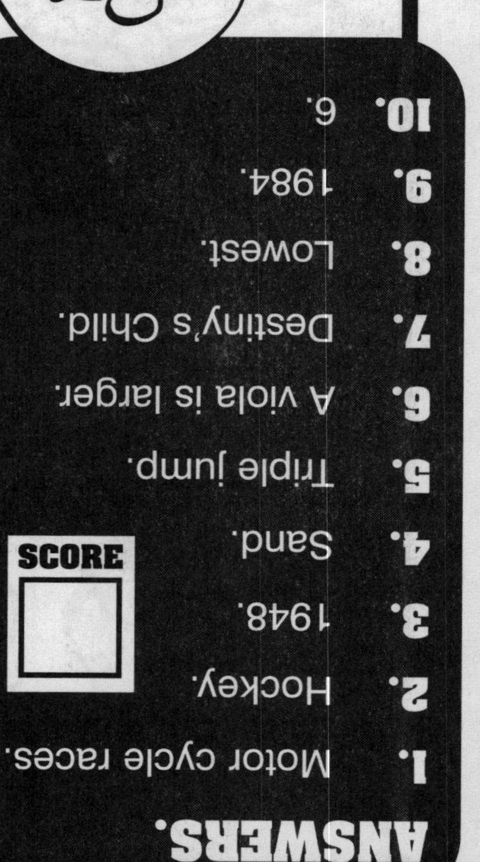

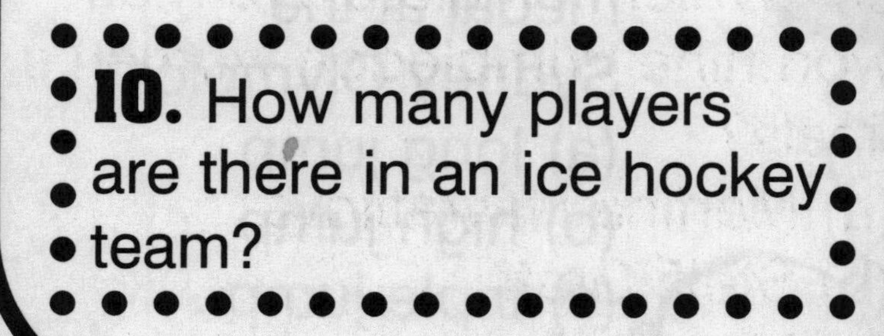

10. How many players are there in an ice hockey team?

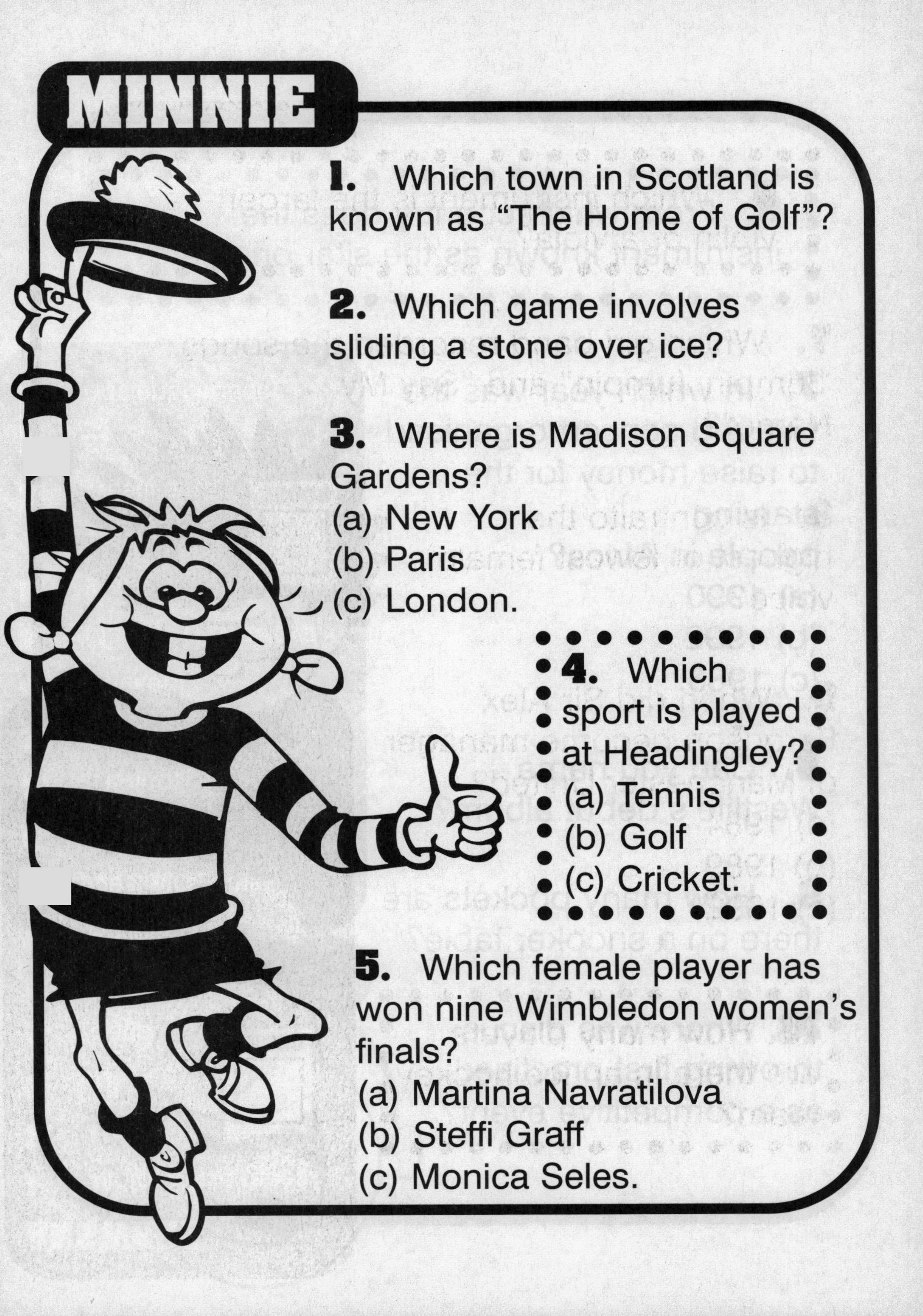
MINNIE
1. Which town in Scotland is known as "The Home of Golf"?
2. Which game involves sliding a stone over ice?
3. Where is Madison Square Gardens?
(a) New York
(b) Paris
(c) London.
4. Which sport is played at Headingley?
(a) Tennis
(b) Golf
(c) Cricket.
5. Which female player has won nine Wimbledon women's finals?
(a) Martina Navratilova
(b) Steffi Graff
(c) Monica Seles.

6. From which country does the instrument known as the sitar originate?

7. In which year was the Live Aid concert organised to raise money for the starving
people in Africa?
(a) 1990
(b) 1992
(c) 1985.

8. Can you name Westlife's debut album?

9. How many pockets are there on a snooker table?

10. Where was discus-throwing first practised as a competitive event?

BILLY WHIZZ

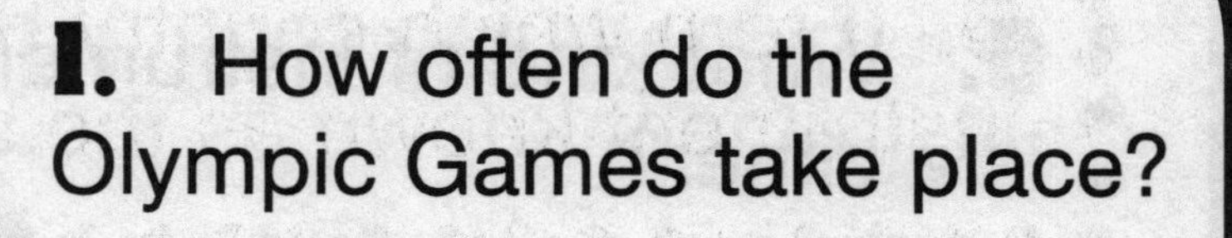

1. How often do the Olympic Games take place?

2. What is a spinnaker?
(a) a sail
(b) an oar
(c) a canoe.

3. In which sport did Steve Backley win a silver medal at the 2000 Olympics?

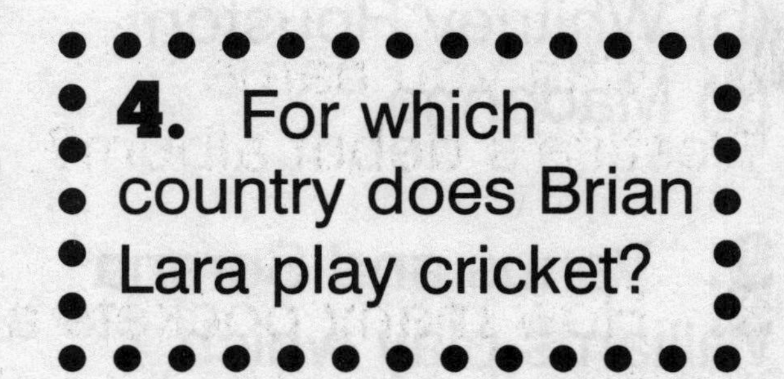

4. For which country does Brian Lara play cricket?

5. Which golfer won the 2000 Open Championship in St Andrews?

6. What kind of instrument is a zither?

7. Paul McCartney was a member of which world famous band?

8. Who is the most successful female artist of all time?
(a) Tina Turner
(b) Whitney Houston
(c) Madonna.

9. Venus and Serena Williams play which sport?

10. Which Scottish football team plays at Ibrox?

ANSWERS.

1. Every four years.
2. A sail.
3. Throwing the javelin.
4. West Indies.
5. Tiger Woods.
6. A stringed instrument.
7. The Beatles.
8. Madonna.
9. Tennis.
10. Rangers.

SCORE

BANANAMAN

1. When were skateboards invented?
(a) 1936
(b) 1958
(c) 1982.

2. In which sport did Muhammad Ali excel?

3. White Hart Lane is the home to which football club?
(a) Tottenham Hotspur
(b) Chelsea
(c) Everton.

4. A prancing horse is the symbol for which motor racing team?

5. When did the first ever crossword puzzle appear?
(a) 1933 (b) 1923 (c) 1913.

6. Is a cornet a brass or woodwind instrument?

7. Which instrument was played by Frederic Chopin?
(a) guitar
(b) piano
(c) violin.

8. Which male singer had a big hit with "Livin' La Vida Loca"?

9. Which type of sport takes place at Monaco and Brands Hatch?

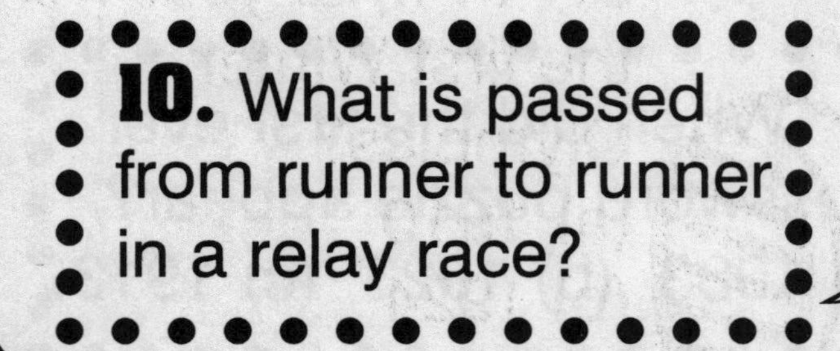

10. What is passed from runner to runner in a relay race?

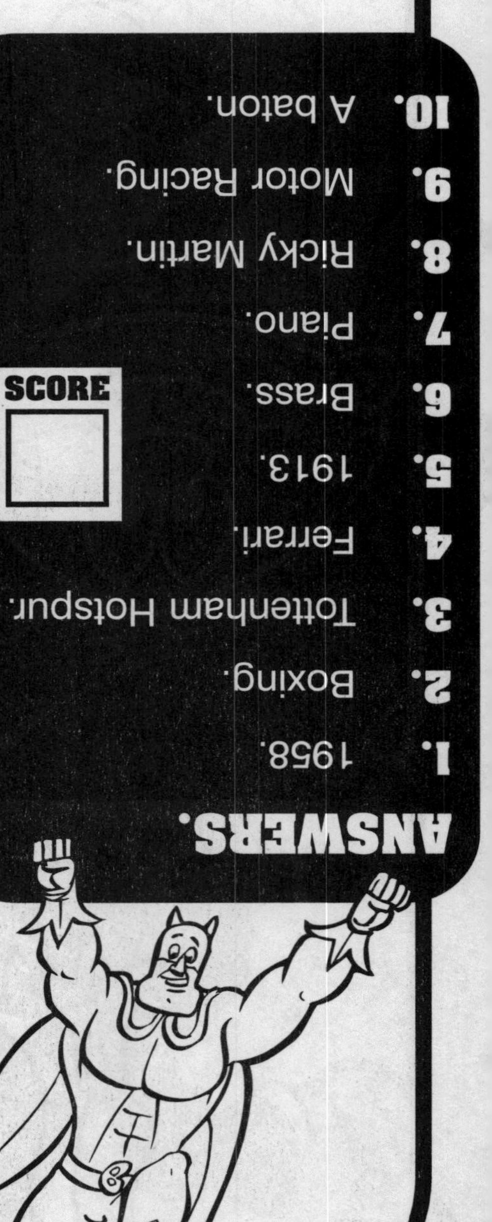

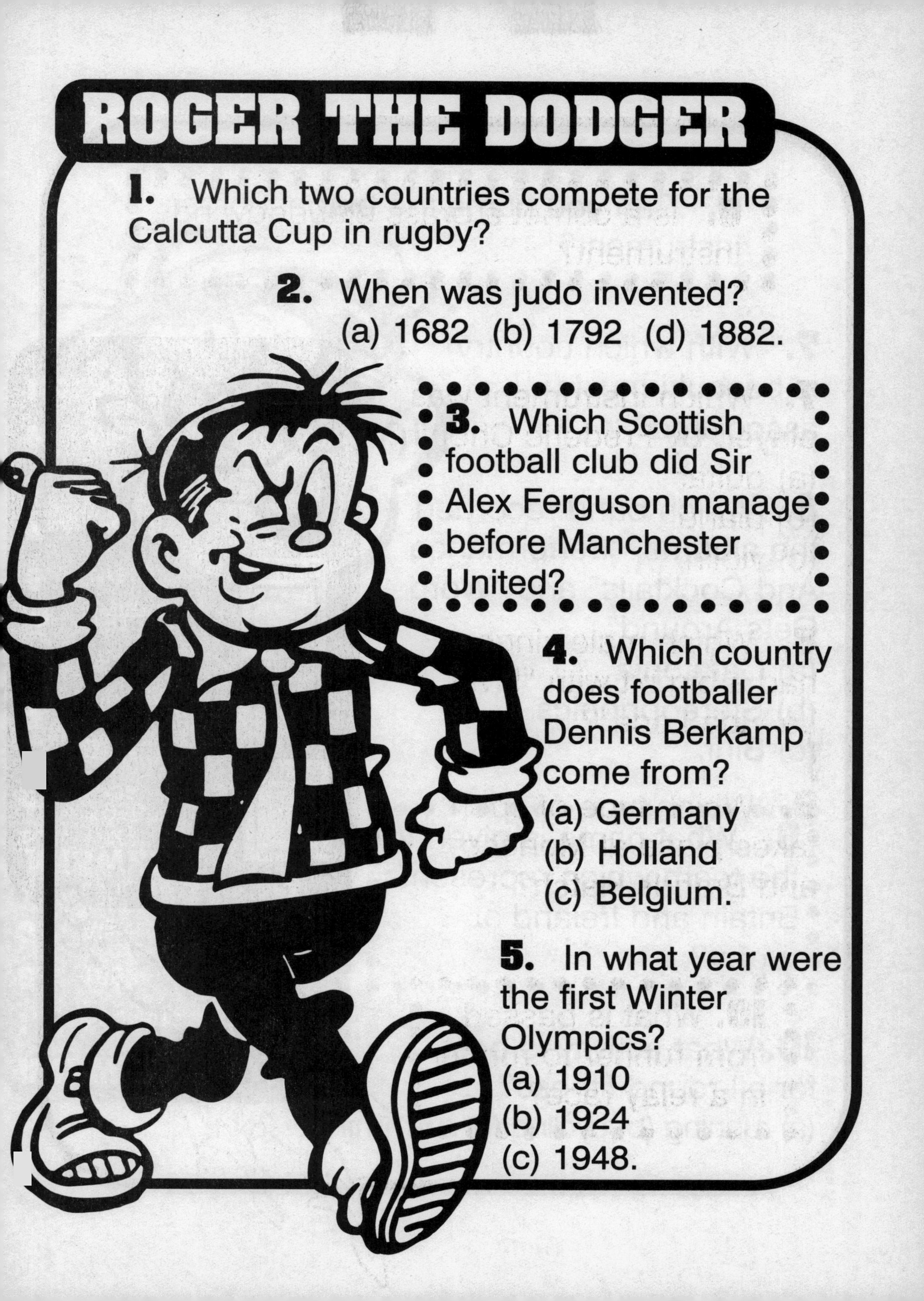

ROGER THE DODGER

1. Which two countries compete for the Calcutta Cup in rugby?

2. When was judo invented?
(a) 1682 (b) 1792 (d) 1882.

3. Which Scottish football club did Sir Alex Ferguson manage before Manchester United?

4. Which country does footballer Dennis Berkamp come from?
(a) Germany
(b) Holland
(c) Belgium.

5. In what year were the first Winter Olympics?
(a) 1910
(b) 1924
(c) 1948.

6. Can you name the biggest brass instrument?
7. With which country is bazouki music associated?
8. Which band recorded the albums, "Performance And Cocktails" and "Word Gets Around".
(a) Catatonia
(b) Stereophonics
(c) Blur.
9. What name is given to the team which represents Britain and Ireland at rugby?
10. What activity is best for all-round fitness?
(a) running (b) cycling (c) swimming.
ANSWERS.
1. Scotland and England.
2. 1882.
3. Aberdeen.
4. Holland.
5. 1924.
6. Tuba.
7. Greece.
8. Stereophonics.
9. The Lions.
10. Swimming.
SCORE

BERYL THE PERIL

1. Which two countries compete for the Ashes, and at what sport?

2. In which sport would you use crampons?

3. Which nation's rugby team is known as "The Springboks"?

4. With which sport do you associate Eddie Irvine and Mika Hakkinen?

5. When did the game of Monopoly go on sale for the first time?
(a) 1935
(b) 1955
(c) 1965.

6. How would you play a euphonium?
(a) strike it (b) blow it (c) strum it.

7. When were CDs developed?
(a) 1965
(b) 1969
(c) 1972.

8. Who recorded "No Scrubs" and "Unpretty"?
(a) TLC
(b) All Saints
(c) Spice Girls.

9. Name the instrument played by Elton John?

10. With which native Australian musical instrument is the entertainer Rolf Harris associated?

ANSWERS.

1. England and Australia, cricket.
2. Winter climbing.
3. South Africa.
4. Formula One racing.
5. 1935.
6. Blow it (it is a bass tuba).
7. 1972.
8. TLC.
9. Piano.
10. Didgeridoo.

SCORE

DANNY

1. How many players are there in a Rugby League team?
(a) 9 (b) 11 (c) 13.

2. Where is Aintree racecourse?
(a) London
(b) Manchester
(c) Liverpool.

3. Which British rower has won a record five Olympic gold medals?

4. Trot and canter are terms in which activity?

5. In which year was the first women's Rugby World Cup held?
(a) 1961 (b)1981 (c)1991.

6. How many strings does a cello have? (a) 3 (b) 6 (c) 4.

7. Name the composer of 'Swan Lake' and 'The Nutcracker Suite'.
(a) Tchaikovsky
(b) Mozart
(c) Stravinsky.

8. Which popular female artist recorded "Born To Make You Happy" and "Oops!....I Did It Again"?
(a) Madonna
(b) Celine Dion
(d) Britney Spears.

9. What kind of musical instrument is a Hammond?

10. In which Italian city is La Scala opera house?
(a) Milan (b) Rome (c) Venice

ANSWERS.

1. 13.
2. Liverpool.
3. Steve Redgrave.
4. Horse riding.
5. 1991.
6. Four.
7. Tchaikovsky.
8. Britney Spears.
9. Electric Organ.
10. Milan.

SCORE

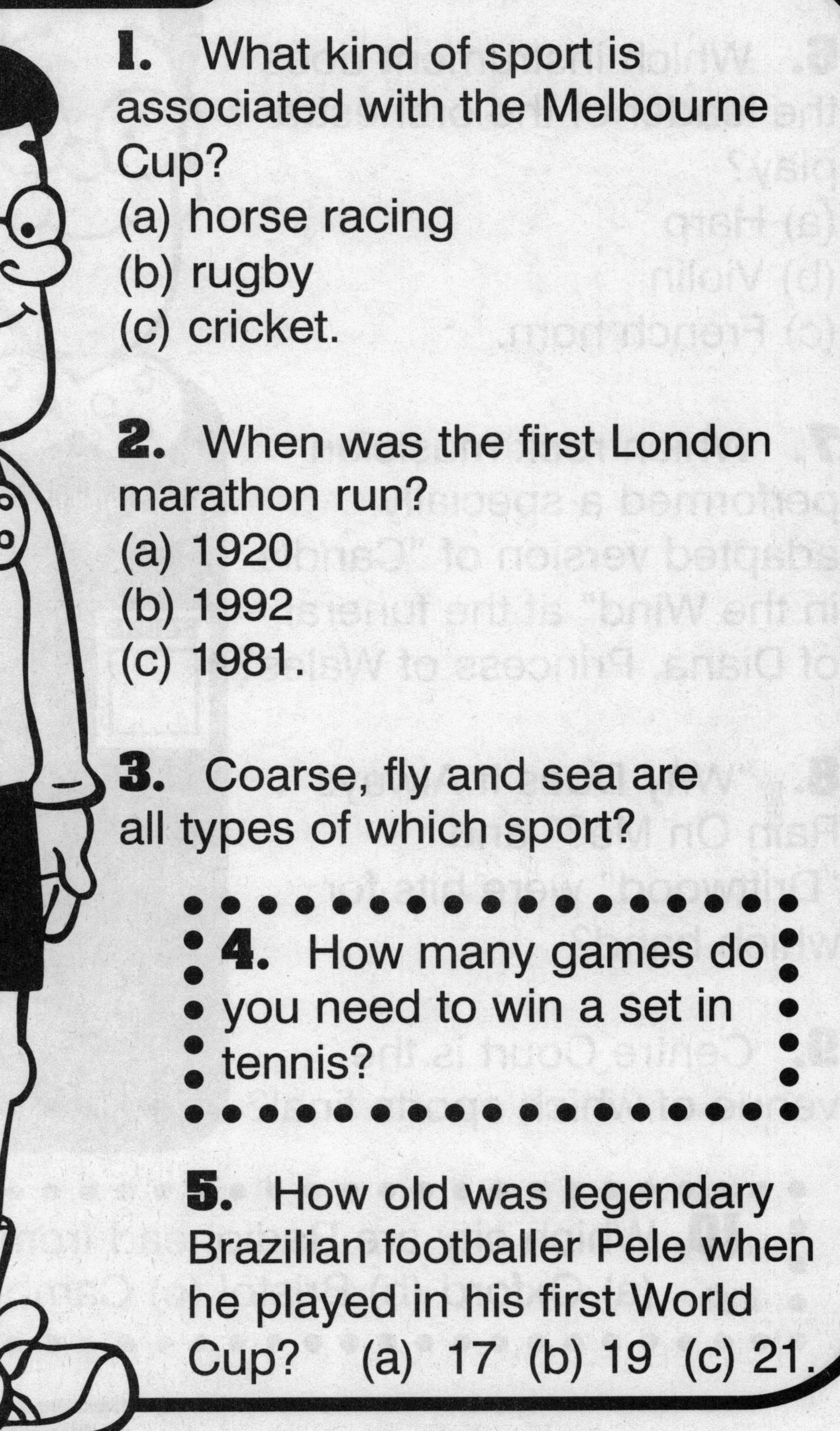

WALTER

1. What kind of sport is associated with the Melbourne Cup?
(a) horse racing
(b) rugby
(c) cricket.

2. When was the first London marathon run?
(a) 1920
(b) 1992
(c) 1981.

3. Coarse, fly and sea are all types of which sport?

4. How many games do you need to win a set in tennis?

5. How old was legendary Brazilian footballer Pele when he played in his first World Cup? (a) 17 (b) 19 (c) 21.

6. Which instrument does the leader of the orchestra play?
(a) Harp
(b) Violin
(c) French horn.

7. Which rock musician performed a specially adapted version of "Candle in the Wind" at the funeral of Diana, Princess of Wales?

8. "Why Does It Always Rain On Me?" and "Driftwood" were hits for which band?

9. Centre Court is the venue of which sports final?

10. Which city are Radiohead from?
(a) Oxford (b) Bristol (c) Cambridge.

ANSWERS.

1. Horse racing.
2. 1981.
3. Fishing.
4. 6.
5. 17.
6. Violin.
7. Elton John.
8. Travis.
9. Wimbledon Tennis Final.
10. Oxford.

SCORE

THE NUMSKULLS

1. Where did the largest ever soccer crowd watch the final of the World Cup in 1950?

2. In which game do the players take part in line-outs?

3. Which British female athlete won the heptathlon gold medal at the Sydney Olympics?

4. Which is the odd one out:- discus, pole-vault, hammer, javelin?

5. In which sport might you hear the term a "googly"?

6. How many pedals are there on a grand piano?
(a) 2 (b) 3 (c) 6.

7. Which city in Austria is home to a world famous boys' choir?

8. Steptacular was a hit album for which band?
(a) Steps
(b) TLC
(c) Oasis.

9. Which sport is played at the Superbowl?

10. How many players are there in a hockey team?
(a) 9
(b) 15
(c) 11.

ANSWERS.

1. Brazil.
2. Rugby.
3. Denise Lewis.
4. Pole. The others are throwing events.
5. Cricket.
6. Three.
7. Vienna.
8. Steps.
9. American football.
10. 11.

SCORE

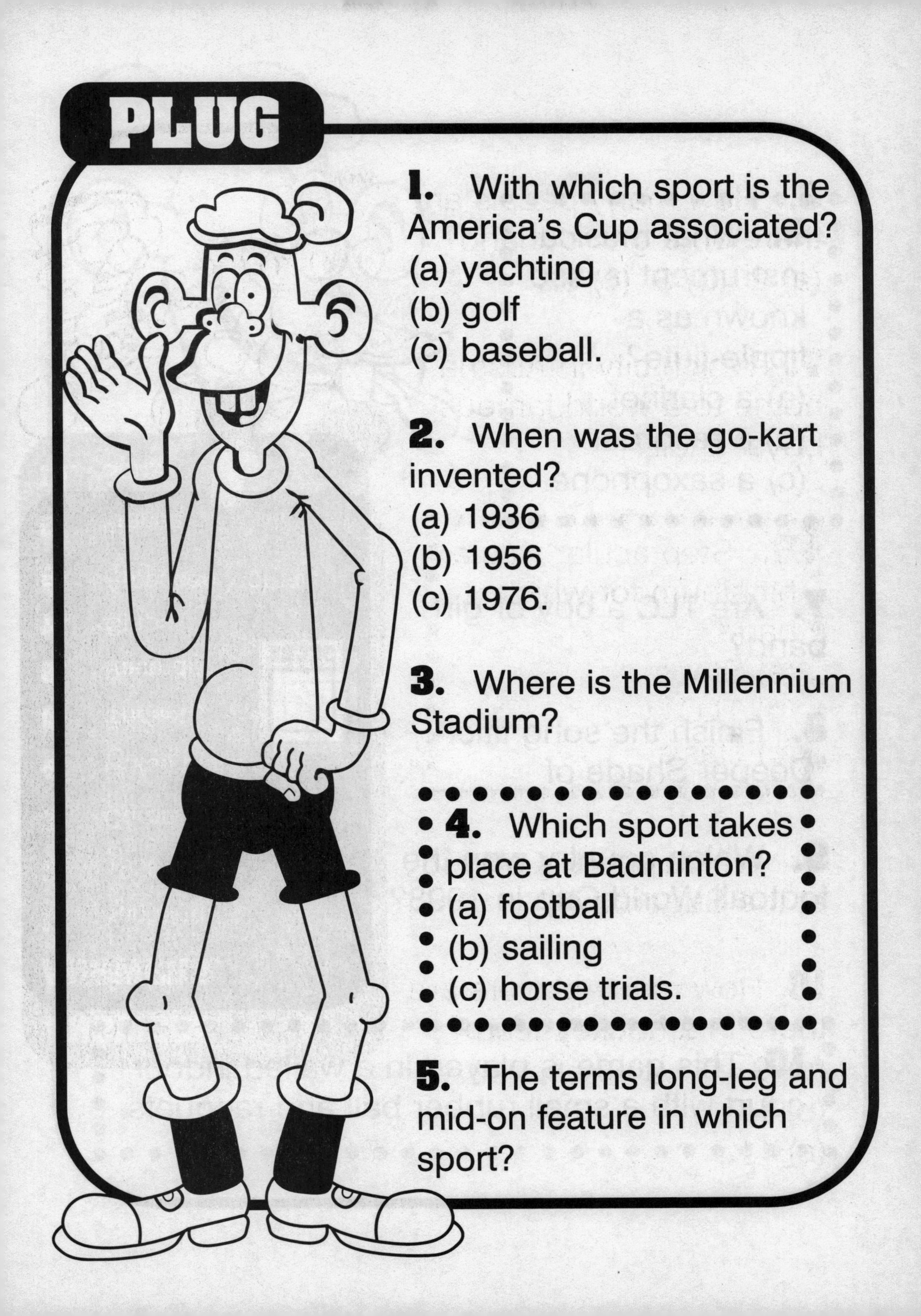
PLUG
1. With which sport is the America's Cup associated?
(a) yachting
(b) golf
(c) baseball.
2. When was the go-kart invented?
(a) 1936
(b) 1956
(c) 1976.
3. Where is the Millennium Stadium?
4. Which sport takes place at Badminton?
(a) football
(b) sailing
(c) horse trials.
5. The terms long-leg and mid-on feature in which sport?

6. What musical instrument is also known as a fipple-flute?
(a) a clarinet
(b) a recorder
(c) a saxophone.

7. Are TLC a boy or girl band?

8. Finish the song title:- "Deeper Shade of _ _ _ _ ".

9. Which country won the football World Cup in 1998?

10. This game is played in a walled indoor court with a small rubber ball and racquets.

ANSWERS.

1. Yachting.
2. 1956.
3. Cardiff.
4. Horse trials.
5. Cricket.
6. Recorder.
7. Girl.
8. "Blue".
9. France.
10. Squash.

SCORE

CUDDLES AND DIMPLES

1. Where were the first modern Olympics held? (a) Paris (b) Lisbon (c) Athens.

2. Which sport would you associate with the World Series?

3. In which game would you find fast or spin bowlers?

4. In which sport are the terms axel, salchow and toe loop used?

5. In which sport are the terms albatross, bogey and slice likely to be used?

6. Which is lower:- bass or treble?

7. From which part of the United States does Cajun music originate?

8. The album, Schizophonic, was recorded by which ex Spice Girl?

9. In which sport would the asymmetric bars be used?

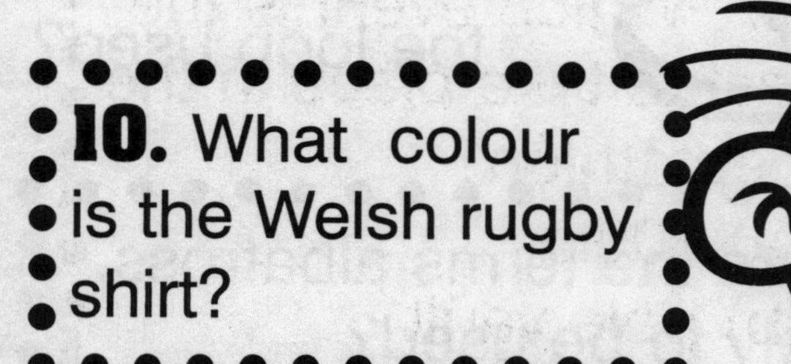

10. What colour is the Welsh rugby shirt?

ANSWERS.

1. Athens.
2. Baseball.
3. Cricket.
4. Figure skating.
5. Golf.
6. Bass.
7. The southern states (in particular Louisiana).
8. Geri Halliwell.
9. Gymnastics.
10. Red.

SCORE

BALL BOY

1. For what purpose is a velodrome used?
(a) ice skating (b) athletics (c) cycle racing.

2. In which year was the first football World Cup held?
(a) 1910
(b) 1920
(c) 1930.

3. Which football team plays at The Stadium Of Light?
(a) Manchester United
(b) Sunderland
(c) Arsenal.

4. Which event is the last to take place in the heptathlon?
(a) 800m
(b) pole vault
(c) steeple chase.

5. Can you name the game, played with a ball, that was once played by North American Indians?
(a) badminton
(b) lacrosse
(c) hockey.

6. Which musical instrument has a bag and drones?

7. Before she became Victoria Beckham, what was Posh Spice's surname?

8. The album, Brand New Day, was recorded by which top British male artist?

9. The first printed music appeared in Europe in - (a) 1480 (b) 1596 (c) 1602?

10. Which sport features the crawl and the butterfly?

ANSWERS.
1. Cycle racing.
2. 1930.
3. Sunderland.
4. 800m.
5. Lacrosse.
6. Bagpipes.
7. Adams.
8. Sting.
9. 1480.
10. Swimming.

SCORE

MOLLY

1. How many gold medals did Great Britain win in the 2000 Olympics? (a) 6 (b) 11 (c) 13.

2. How many riders are there in a polo team? (a) 4 (b) 8 (c) 10.

3. Which sport does David Ginola play?

4. Which sport is performed using ribbons, balls and hoops?
(a) rhythmic gymnastics
(b) water polo
(c) horse riding.

5. If you were doing a "snow plough" what sport would you be taking part in?
(a) skating
(b) snow boarding
(c) skiing.

6. Woodwind is a name for one section of an orchestra. Can you name two more?

7. Can you name the famous Minogue sisters?

8. The song "Against All Odds" was recorded by Westlife and which top female artist?
(a) Celine Dion
(b) Cher
(c) Mariah Carey.

9. In which sport would you use an épée?
(a) archery
(b) fencing
(c) sailing.

10. In which sport might a lure be used?
(a) fishing (b) archery (c) shooting.

ANSWERS.

1. 11.
2. 4.
3. Football.
4. Rhythmic gymnastics.
5. Skiing.
6. String, brass or percussion.
7. Kylie and Dannii.
8. Mariah Carey.
9. Fencing.
10. Fishing.

SCORE

3 BEARS

1. In which sport is a period of play called a chukka?

2. For which sport were the Marquess of Queensberry rules drawn up?

3. Where would you find greens and bunkers?

4. Which sport has steeplechase and flat racing?

5. What sport does Ryan Giggs play?

6. Name the largest stringed instrument plucked by hand.

7. Finish the song lyric... "There ain't no party like..."

8. The hits "Sha La La La La" and "Cheeka Bow Wow" (That Computer Song) were recorded by which band?

9. Aikido and Kendo are types of what?

10. Which rugby team plays at The Stoop?
(a) Saracens
(b) Barbarians
(c) Harlequins.

TEACHER

1. In "Alice in Wonderland", the Queen of Hearts played this game using flamingos as mallets. What game was it?

2. In 1908, the first All Alaskan Sweepstake took place. What was it?
(a) a cross-country ski race
(b) a sled dog race
(c) a horse race.

3. In which sport can you do the Fosbury Flop?

4. How long are each of the periods in an ice-hockey match?
(a) 20 mins.
(b) 30 mins.
(c) 40 mins.

5. If you were using an aqualung, mask and mouth-piece, what activity would you be taking part in?

6. How many strings does a guitar usually have?

7. When were the first portable cassette players on sale?
(a) 1969
(b) 1979
(c) 1989.

8. Which female artist recorded the album, Walk Of Life?

9. What is the centre of an archery target called?
(a) The bull's-eye
(b) The circle
(c) The gold.

10. How many strings does a ukulele have?
(a) 3 (b) 8 (c) 4.

ANSWERS.
1. Croquet.
2. A sled dog race.
3. High jump.
4. 20 minutes.
5. Scuba diving
6. 6.
7. 1979.
8. Billie Piper.
9. The gold.
10. 4.

SCORE

BRAIN DUANE

1. In which country was the first game of squash played?
(a) India
(b) Egypt
(c) UK.

2. Who was the youngest ever men's Wimbledon Singles Champion?

3. In which race does the leader wear the Yellow Jersey?

4. What is the final event in the decathlon?
(a) high jump
(b) 110m hurdles
(c) 1,500m race.

5. Which sport awards the Lonsdale Belt?

6. What is the other name for a mouth organ?

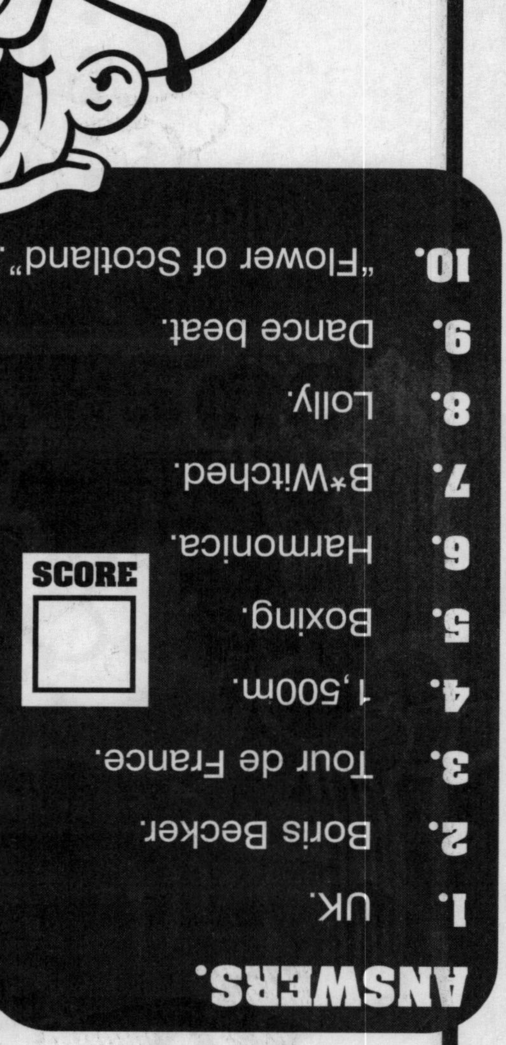

7. Which girl band includes Keavy and Sinead?

8. The song "Vive La Radio" was a hit for which artist?

9. Techno, house and jungle are types of what?

10. What is the name of the song now sung as an anthem before Scottish international rugby matches?

DESPERATE DAN

1. How many players are there in an American football team?
(a) 11
(b) 15
(c) 13.

2. How many events are there in the decathlon?

3. What game would you be playing if you were "out for a duck"?

4. How many rings are there in the Olympic symbol?

5. Which sportsmen use rods and reels?

6. What would you do with a plectrum?

7. From what items are the instruments in a steel band traditionally made?

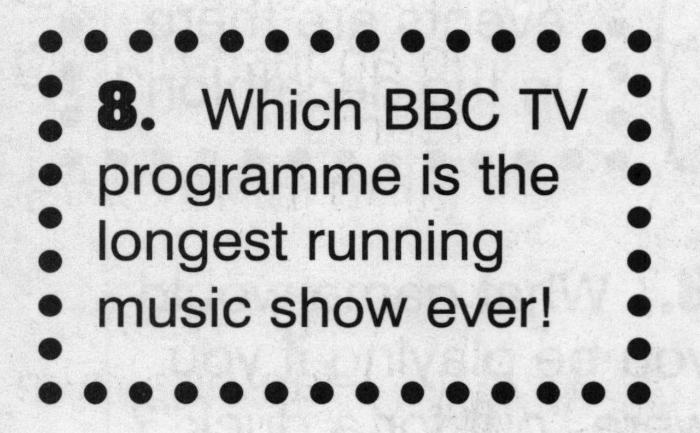

8. Which BBC TV programme is the longest running music show ever!

9. In which sport would you use a puck?

10. Which boy band sang "Picture Of You" for Bean : The Movie?

ANSWERS.

1. 11.
2. 10.
3. Cricket.
4. 5.
5. Fishermen.
6. Pluck the strings of a musical instrument.
7. Oil drums.
8. Top of The Pops.
9. Ice hockey.
10. Boyzone.

SCORE

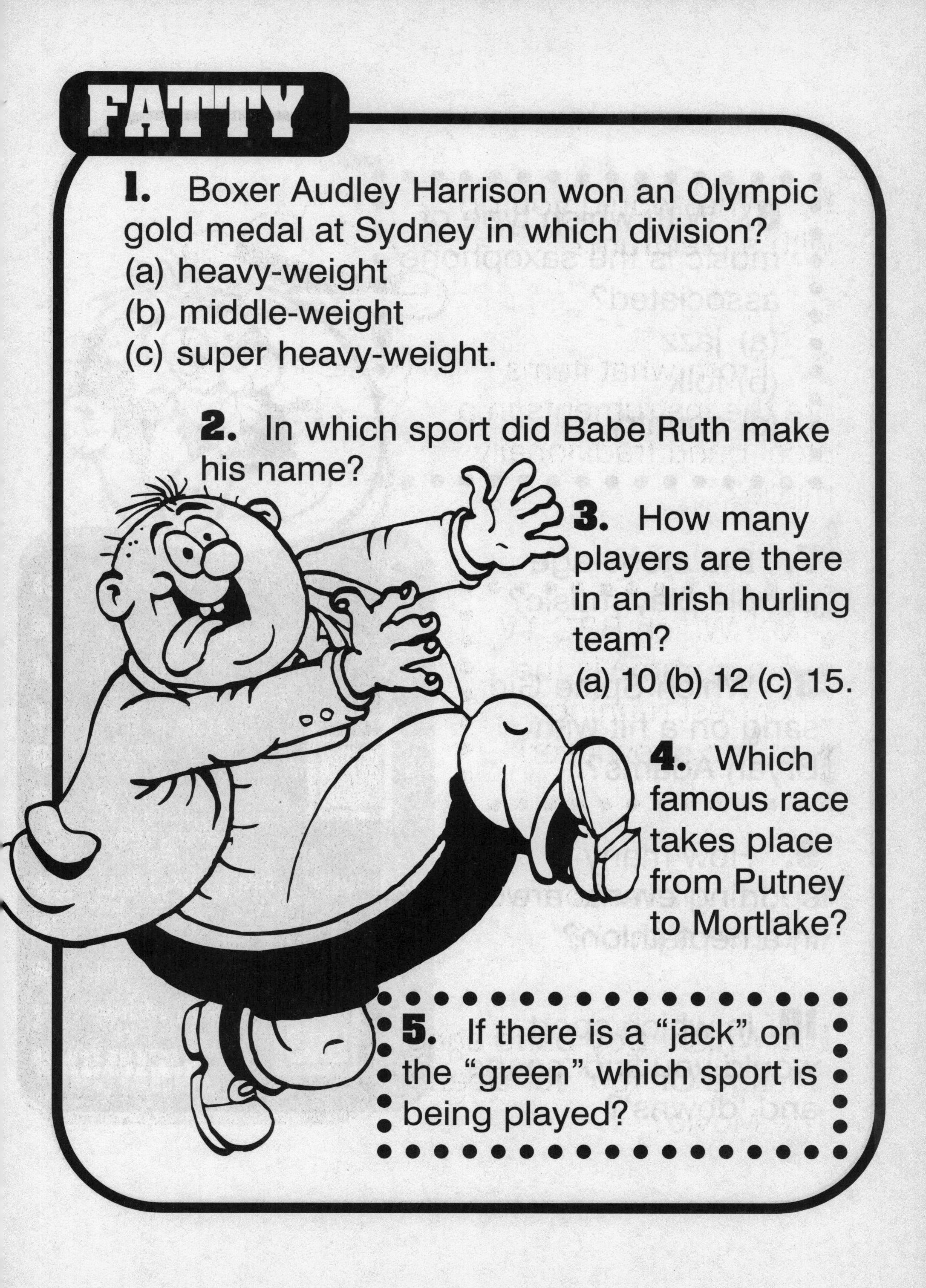

FATTY

1. Boxer Audley Harrison won an Olympic gold medal at Sydney in which division?
(a) heavy-weight
(b) middle-weight
(c) super heavy-weight.

2. In which sport did Babe Ruth make his name?

3. How many players are there in an Irish hurling team?
(a) 10 (b) 12 (c) 15.

4. Which famous race takes place from Putney to Mortlake?

5. If there is a "jack" on the "green" which sport is being played?

6. With which type of music is the saxophone associated?
(a) jazz
(b) folk
(c) country.

7. Did stone-age people play music?

8. Which Spice Girl sang on a hit with Bryan Adams?

9. How many sporting events are in a heptathlon?

10. In which sport would you find 'snaps' and 'downs'?

ANSWERS.

1. Super heavy-weight.
2. Baseball.
3. 15.
4. The Oxford and Cambridge Boat Race.
5. Bowls.
6. Jazz.
7. Yes.
8. Mel C.
9. 7.
10. American Football.

SCORE

BEA

1. With which sport are Jayne Torvill and Christopher Dean associated?

2. How many players are on a court in a basketball team?

3. In which sport does a cox control the team?

4. Can you name the world's most popular indoor sport?
(a) basketball
(b) squash
(c) table tennis.

5. Traditionally, what is a cricket bat made of?
(a) sycamore
(b) ash
(c) willow

6. With which musical instrument are the names Steinway and Bechstein most commonly associated?

(a) bagpipes
(b) violin
(c) piano.

7. With what device would you play a violin?

8. What is the highest female voice?

9. Which three sports make up the gruelling triathlon?

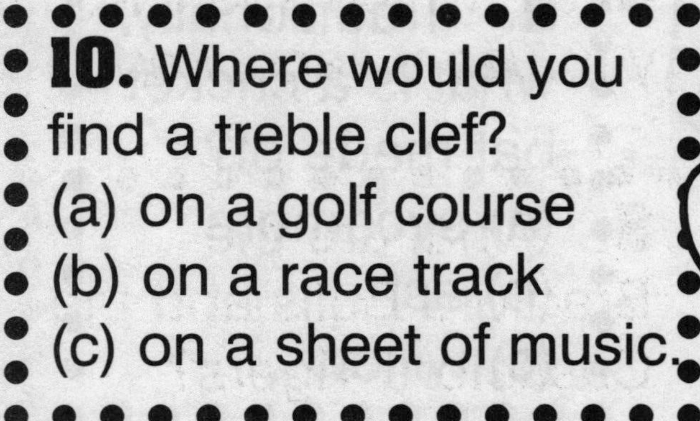

10. Where would you find a treble clef?
(a) on a golf course
(b) on a race track
(c) on a sheet of music.

ANSWERS.

1. Ice skating.
2. Five.
3. Rowing.
4. Basketball.
5. Willow.
6. Piano.
7. A bow.
8. Soprano.
9. Swimming, cycling and running.
10. On a sheet of music.

SCORE

IVY

1. When was the first game of rugby played?
(a) 1784 (b) 1823 (c) 1886.

2. Name the game, similar to basketball, where the players are not allowed to bounce-dribble the ball.

3. The Noucamp Stadium is home to which football team?
(a) Real Madrid
(b) Barcelona
(c) Valencia.

4. In which sport would you use a sand wedge?

5. What are the Bradford Bulls and the Castleford Tigers?

6. With which country is the balalaika associated?
(a) Turkey (b) Greece (c) Russia.

7. Is the strathspey, Scottish dance music or military music?

8. In which year did cult band ABBA win the Eurovision Song contest?
(a) 1964 (b) 1974 (c) 1984.

9. Robbie Williams was a member of which band before going solo?

10. How high above the water is the board in a high diving contest?
(a) 10 m (b) 15m (c) 12 m.

ANSWERS.

1. 1823.
2. Netball.
3. Barcelona.
4. Golf.
5. Rugby League teams.
6. Russia.
7. Scottish dance music.
8. 1974.
9. Take That.
10. 10 m.

SCORE

SMIFFY

1. In which country was the sport of curling invented?

2. What is a Skidoo?

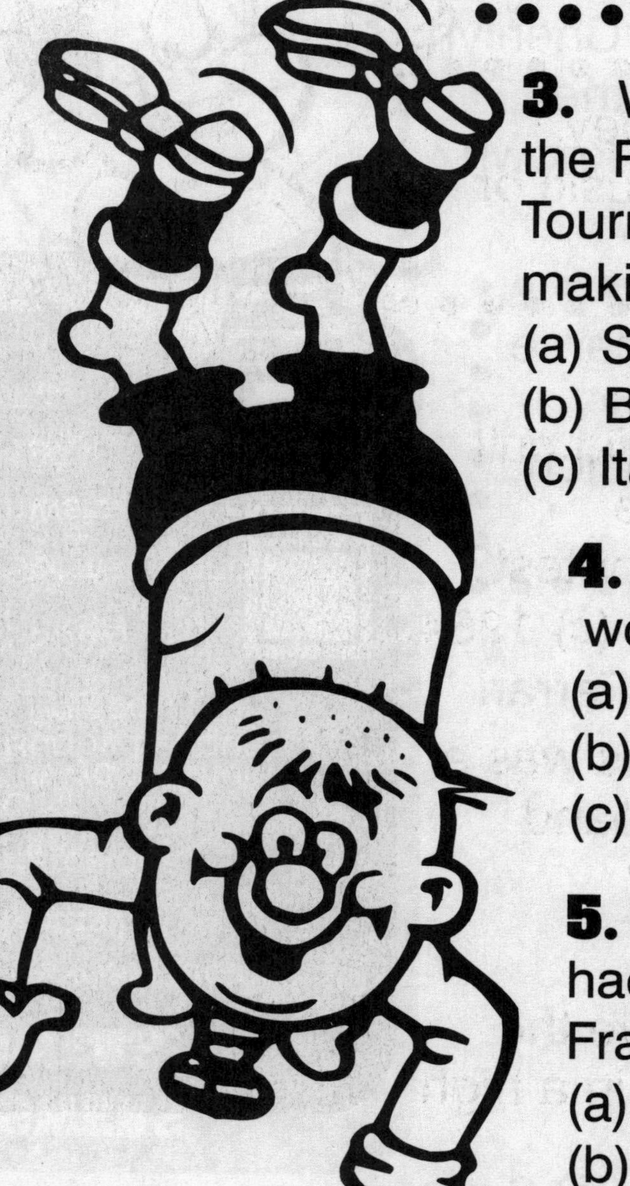

3. Which country joined the Five Nations Rugby Tournament in 2000, making it the Six Nations?
(a) Spain
(b) Belgium
(c) Italy.

4. Which sportsman would use a barbell?
(a) a hammer thrower
(b) a weightlifter
(c) a cyclist.

5. Which country has had the most Tour De France wins?
(a) Luxembourg
(b) Denmark
(c) France.

6. Flamenco music comes from which country?

7. Her real name is Cherilyn, but by what name is the famous singer better known?

8. What was the name of the song sung by ABBA in the Eurovision Song Contest?

9. What colour are Ferrari motor racing cars?
(a) yellow
(b) blue
(c) red.

10. How wide is a gymnastic beam?
(a) 14 cm (b) 10 cm (c) 8 cm.

ANSWERS.

1. Scotland.
2. A snow motor scooter.
3. Italy.
4. A weightlifter.
5. France.
6. Spain.
7. Cher.
8. Waterloo.
9. Red.
10. 10 cm.

SCORE

BLINKY

1. How many red balls are there on a snooker table at the start of a game?
(a) 10 (b) 12 (c) 15.

2. When did the world's first balloon race take place?
(a) 1886 (b) 1890 (c) 1906.

3. Where would you find Chance and Community Chest cards?

4. Which sport takes place in a Dojo?
(a) wrestling
(b) boxing
(c) judo.

5. With which sport do you associate Michael and Ralf Schumacher?

6. What is the name for the device which can imitate the sounds of different instruments?

7. What is the name of the rock group with which the late Freddie Mercury was lead singer?

8. In what year was the first electric guitar made?
(a) 1962 (b) 1942 (c) 1932.

9. The terms snatch, clean and jerk appear in what sport? (a) weightlifting
(b) wrestling
(c) gymnastics.

10. What nationality are the bands the Stereophonics and Catatonia?
(a) Welsh
(b) Irish
(c) American

ANSWERS.

1. 15.
2. 1906.
3. On a Monopoly Board.
4. Judo.
5. Formula One racing.
6. Synthesiser.
7. Queen.
8. 1932.
9. Weightlifting.
10. Welsh.

SCORE

GNASHER

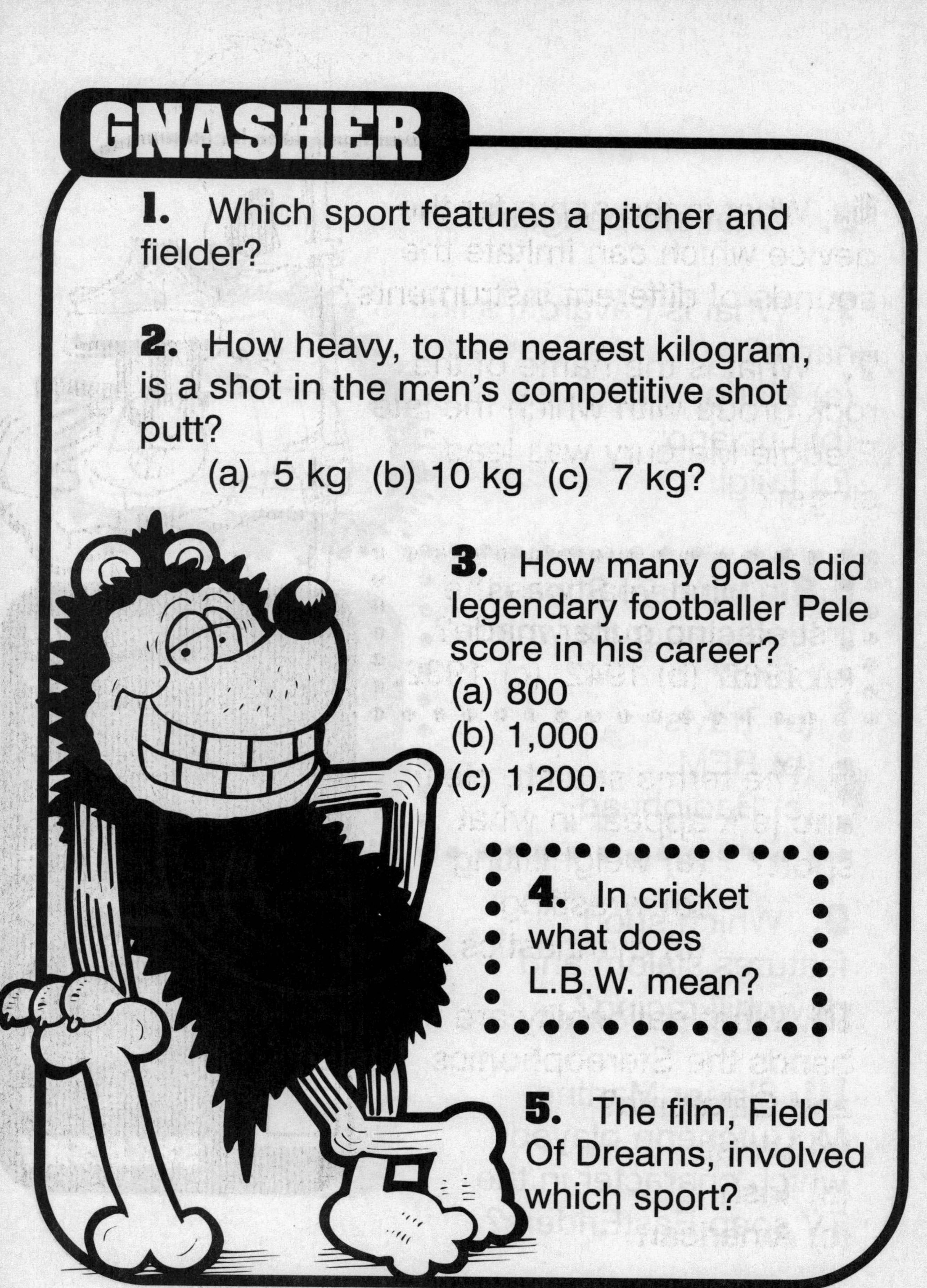

1. Which sport features a pitcher and fielder?

2. How heavy, to the nearest kilogram, is a shot in the men's competitive shot putt?
(a) 5 kg (b) 10 kg (c) 7 kg?

3. How many goals did legendary footballer Pele score in his career?
(a) 800
(b) 1,000
(c) 1,200.

4. In cricket what does L.B.W. mean?

5. The film, Field Of Dreams, involved which sport?

6. What are bongos?

7. What is Pavarotti's first name?
(a) Mario
(b) Luciano
(c) Luigi.

8. Michael Stipe is lead singer for which band?
(a) Travis
(b) REM
(c) Radiohead.

9. Which sport features slalom and downhill racing?

10. Singer Martine McCutcheon played which character in the TV soap EastEnders?

ANSWERS.
1. Baseball.
2. 7 kg.
3. 1,200.
4. Leg Before Wicket.
5. Baseball.
6. Drums played by hand.
7. Luciano.
8. REM.
9. Skiing.
10. Tiffany.

SCORE

NATURAL WORLD

DENNIS

1. How many bones are there in the human body?

(a) 175 (b) 206 (c) 260.

2. What are Basmati and Patna forms of?

3. Where in the insect world would you find soldiers and workers?

4. If someone had jaundice what colour would their skin be?

(a) grey
(b) red
(c) yellow.

5. What is the name given to a fox's tail?

6. How many muscles are in the human body? Over -
(a) 600
(b) 500
(c) 400.

7. What is the name given to a group of stars?

8. Which country does saki come from?

9. Can a flying squirrel really fly?

10. How many species of plants are there? Over...
(a) 400,000
(b) 200,000
(c) 100,000.

ANSWERS.

1. 206.
2. Rice.
3. In an ants' nest.
4. Yellow.
5. A brush.
6. 600.
7. A constellation.
8. Japan.
9. No - it can only glide.
10. 400,000.

SCORE

MINNIE

1. What is the name of a beaver's house?

2. How long is a giant ant-eater's tongue?
(a) 30 cm
(b) 60 cm
(c) 10 cm.

3. What is a Beluga?

4. What is a limequat?

5. What does an omnivore eat?
(a) fish
(b) animals and plants
(c) plants.

6. Where would you find taste buds?

7. How far is the earth from the sun?
(a) 63 million miles
(b) 93 million miles
(c) 103 million miles.

8. What is the main ingredient in risotto?

9. What is the largest rodent in the world?
(a) the coypu
(b) the capybara
(c) the woodchuck.

10. What is a Banyan?
(a) a fruit
(b) a vegetable
(c) a tree.

ANSWERS.
1. A lodge.
2. 60 cm.
3. A type of whale.
4. A cross between a lime and a kumquat.
5. Animals and plants.
6. In your mouth.
7. 93 million miles.
8. Rice.
9. The capybara.
10. A tree.

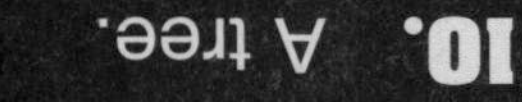

BILLY WHIZZ

1. How many eyelids does a crocodile have?
(a) 3 (b) 2 (c) 1.

2. Where would you find the iris and the cornea?

3. If you count the rings on the inside of a tree trunk, what will it tell you?

4. What are shallots?
(a) onions
(b) potatoes
(c) peppers.

5. What is a Tasmanian Devil?
(a) an animal
(b) a tornado
(c) a tidal wave.

6. What is the name for the hard substance which covers the teeth?

7. What do we call it when a new moon passes between the sun and the earth?

8. What is feta cheese made from?

9. Is a koala really a bear?

10. Which tree produces acorns?

ANSWERS.

1. 3.
2. The eye.
3. How old the tree is.
4. Onions.
5. An animal.
6. Enamel.
7. A solar eclipse.
8. Goats' milk (or sometimes ewes' milk).
9. No - it is a marsupial.
10. Oak.

SCORE

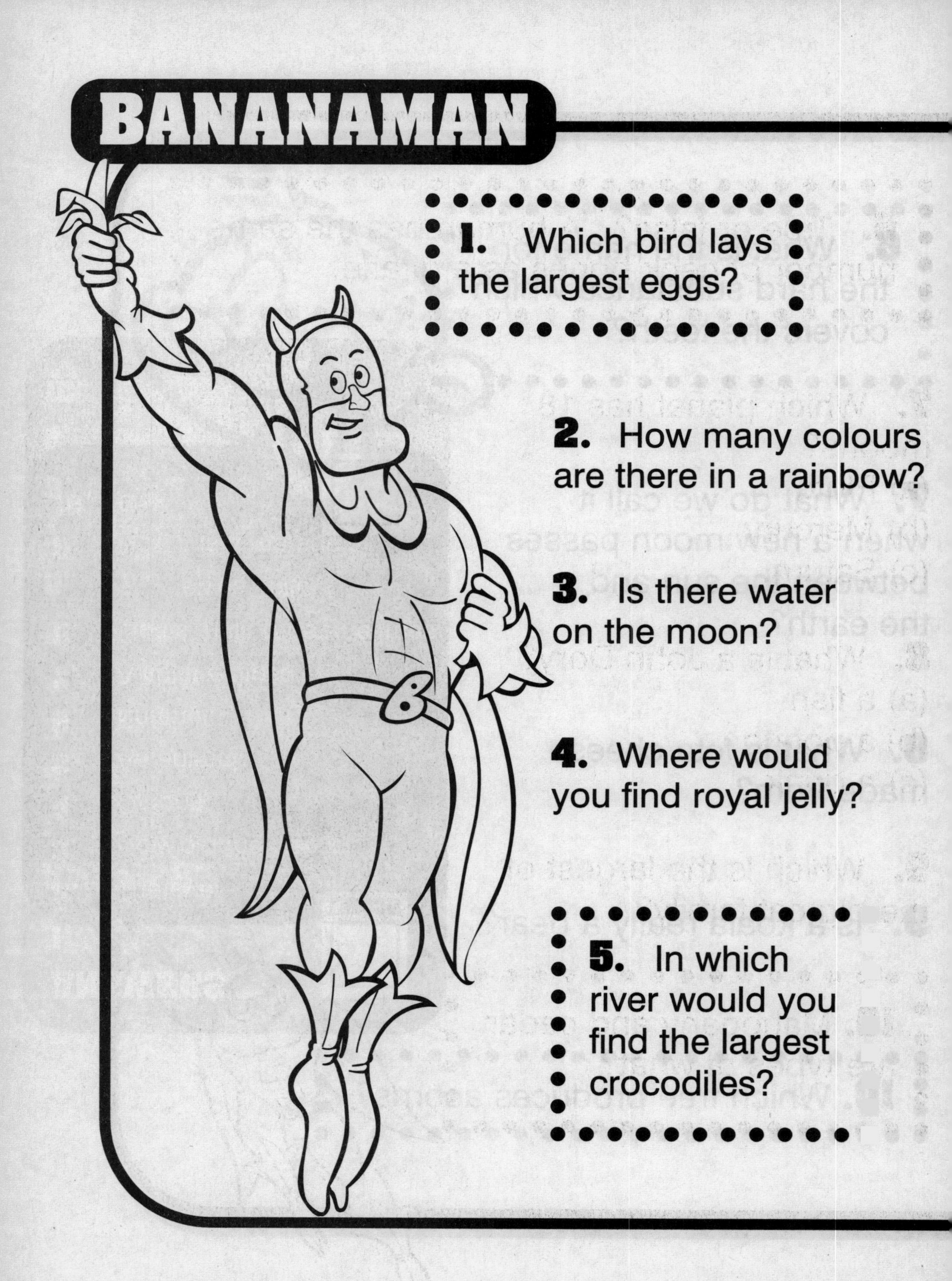

BANANAMAN

1. Which bird lays the largest eggs?

2. How many colours are there in a rainbow?

3. Is there water on the moon?

4. Where would you find royal jelly?

5. In which river would you find the largest crocodiles?

6. True or false? A human has the same number of neck bones as a giraffe.

7. Which planet has 18 moons?
(a) Pluto
(b) Mercury
(c) Saturn.

8. What is a John Dory?
(a) a fish
(b) a potato
(c) a drink.

9. Which is the largest of the big cat family?

10. Mahogany and cedar are types of what?

ROGER THE DODGER

1. Where might natural pearls be found?

2. If something is nocturnal when will it most likely be seen?

3. What is a Rhea?

4. True or false? Plastic can be made from coal?

5. What is a narwhal's spike made of?

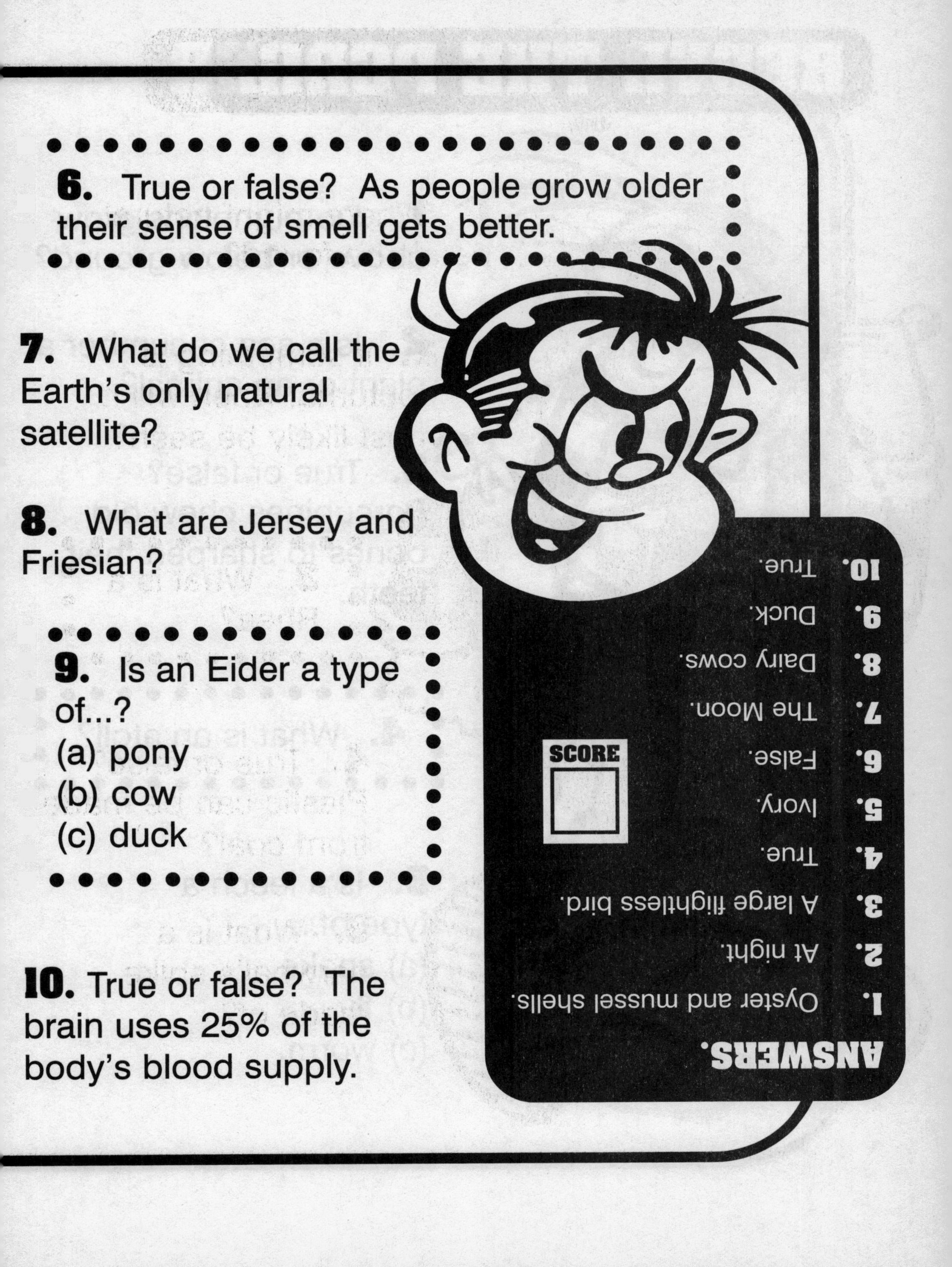

6. True or false? As people grow older their sense of smell gets better.

7. What do we call the Earth's only natural satellite?

8. What are Jersey and Friesian?

9. Is an Eider a type of...?
(a) pony
(b) cow
(c) duck

10. True or false? The brain uses 25% of the body's blood supply.

ANSWERS.

1. Oyster and mussel shells.
2. At night.
3. A large flightless bird.
4. True.
5. Ivory.
6. False.
7. The Moon.
8. Dairy cows.
9. Duck.
10. True.

SCORE

BERYL THE PERIL

1. Do pumpkins grow above or below ground?

2. Is a sea cucumber a plant or an animal?

3. True or false? Porcupines chew old bones to sharpen their teeth.

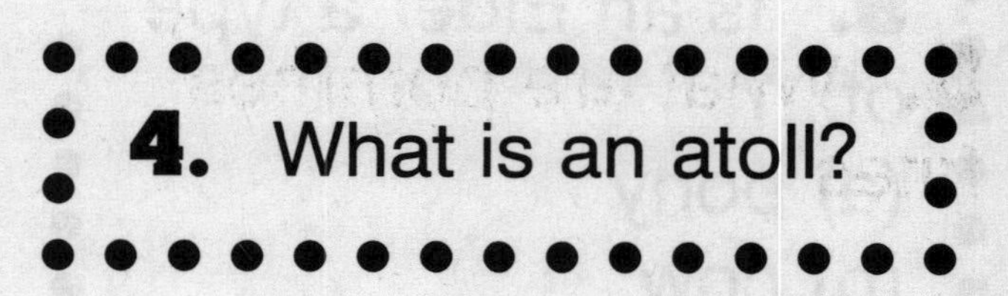

5. Is a leech a type of...
(a) snake
(b) fly
(c) worm.

6. Where is the cerebrum?
(a) the lungs
(b) the heart
(c) the brain.

7. What is the name of the brightest star in the night sky?
(a) Sirius
(b) Canopus
(c) Antares.

8. What are pommes frites?

9. Which is bigger - the African or the Indian elephant?

10. What is the explosive end to a star called?

ANSWERS.

1. Above.
2. Animal.
3. True.
4. A ring of coral islands.
5. Worm.
6. The brain.
7. Sirius.
8. Chips (French fries).
9. African elephants are larger than Indian elephants and have larger ears.
10. A supernova.

SCORE

DANNY

1. Havana and Burmese are types of what?

2. What are measured in hands?

3. Is coffee made from the roasted fruit or leaves of the coffee tree?

4. What do koalas eat?

5. Which animal lives the longest?

6. What are the large blood vessels which carry blood AWAY from the heart called?

7. What do we call a new star?

8. What is the main ingredient when making an omelette?

9. Why are zebra skins like fingerprints?

10. If a dish is served flambé, what does this mean?

ANSWERS.

SCORE

1. Cat.
2. Horses.
3. Fruit.
4. Eucalyptus leaves.
5. The giant tortoise.
6. Arteries.
7. A nova.
8. Eggs.
9. No two zebra skins are ever the same. Each zebra has its own individual pattern of black and white markings, just as each person has his or her own particular fingerprints pattern.
10. It is set alight before it is served.

WALTER

1. How many wings does a bee have?

2. Where will you find polar bears? The Arctic or the Antarctic?

3. Alpacas are native to which part of the world?

4. Which of these foods contains calcium:- apples, chicken, lettuce or cheese?

5. What kind of animal is a Suffolk Punch?
(a) a pig
(b) a sheep
(c) a horse.

6. True or false? When hearing, humans can detect 1,500 tones.

7. What is the brightest planet in our solar system?

8. What country do we associate with tortillas?

9. What kind of creature is a dugong?

10. True or false? Anteaters have no teeth.

THE NUMSKULLS

1. What do giant pandas eat?

2. What kind of creatures are Swallowtail and Peacock?

3. What is Gaspacho?
(a) soup
(b) a dance
(c) a game.

4. Why does an owl have such large eyes?

5. What food is known as "the staff of life"?
(a) bread
(b) fish
(c) meat.

6. Where are the ulna and radius bones?
(a) the feet
(b) the knee
(c) the forearm.

7. What is the star nearest to Earth?

8. What are meringues made from?

9. What is the name given to a badger's nest?

10. Where would you find the oldest living trees on earth?

ANSWERS.

1. Bamboo shoots.
2. Butterflies.
3. Soup.
4. To help it see in the dark.
5. Bread.
6. The forearm.
7. The sun.
8. Egg whites and sugar.
9. A sett.
10. Arizona, U.S.A.

SCORE

PLUG

1. Do stalactites grow up or down?

2. How long do honey bees live?
(a) 1 month
(b) 6 months
(c) 1 year.

3. True or false? There are over 100 muscles in the human face?

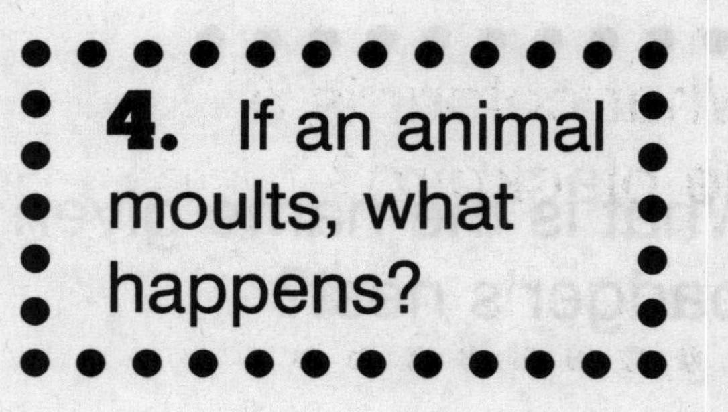
4. If an animal moults, what happens?

5. What would you see in a Botanic Garden?

6. What gas do we breathe out?

7. What is the name for our galaxy?

8. What kind of meat is traditionally used in moussaka?

9. What colour is a female blackbird?

10. What substance makes bread rise?

ANSWERS.

1. Down.
2. A month.
3. True.
4. It sheds, hair, feathers or skin.
5. Plants.
6. Carbon dioxide.
7. The Milky Way.
8. Lamb.
9. A female blackbird is brown.
10. Yeast.

1. In a normal life span, how much skin does the human body shed?

(a) 10 kg
(b) 18 kg
(c) 28 kg.

2. Which of these is not a primate:- chimpanzee, pangolin, gorilla?

3. Which material is stronger:- brass, copper or zinc?

4. Which of these is the common name for an iron oxide? (a) salt (b) rust (c) steel.

5. What colour is vermilion?

6. True or false? Most people blink about 50 times a minute.

7. What is the other name for the constellation known as The Hunter?

8. What are zucchini otherwise known as?

9. What is the name for frogs' eggs?

10. Is a sea gooseberry a fruit or an animal?

ANSWERS.

1. 18 kg
2. Pangolin.
3. Brass.
4. Rust.
5. Red.
6. False.
7. Orion.
8. Courgettes.
9. Frogspawn.
10. An animal.

SCORE

BALL BOY

1. What are Samoyeds, Salukis and Schipperkes?

2. What might you eat on Shrove Tuesday?

3. What is an alloy?

4. Which of these materials is synthetic:- sand, wool, plastic or straw?

5. What are zircon, cornelian and jasper?

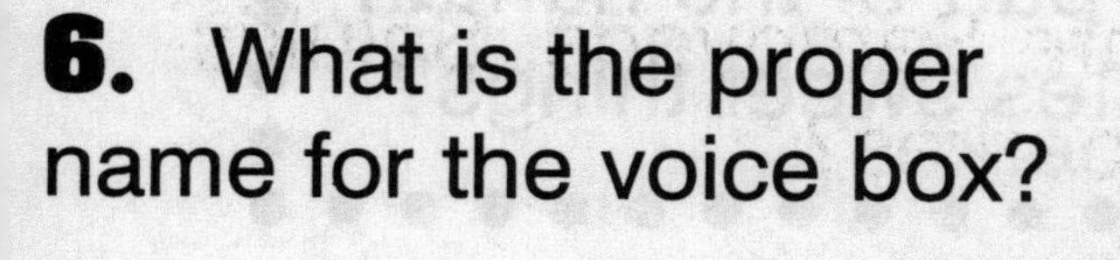

6. What is the proper name for the voice box?

7. How many planets are there in our solar system?

8. What is the main ingredient in dahl?

9. Where is a rattlesnake's 'rattle'?

10. What popular snack fits this description:- roasted puffed-up maize?

ANSWERS.

1. Breeds of dogs.
2. Pancakes.
3. A mixture of metals.
4. Plastic.
5. Precious stones.
6. The larynx.
7. Nine.
8. Lentils.
9. In its tail.
10. Pop corn.

SCORE

MOLLY

1. Which part of the human tongue tastes sweet things?

2. What are linguine, penne and rigatoni?
(a) pasta
(b) shellfish
(c) vegetables.

3. If all the primary colours were mixed together what colour would be made?

4. What does synthetic mean?

5. Which creature starts life as a tadpole?

6. True or false? The lungs contain 2,400 km of airways.

7. A young kangaroo is called a billy, a jimmy or a joey?

8. An orange tree can produce around how many oranges a year?
(a) 500
(b) 750
(c) 1000.

9. Is a crocodile a mammal or a reptile?

10. To the nearest degree Celsius, what is normal body temperature?

ANSWERS.

SCORE

1. The tip.
2. Pasta.
3. White.
4. Something that is man made.
5. A frog.
6. True.
7. Joey
8. 1,000
9. A reptile.
10. Thirty-seven degrees.

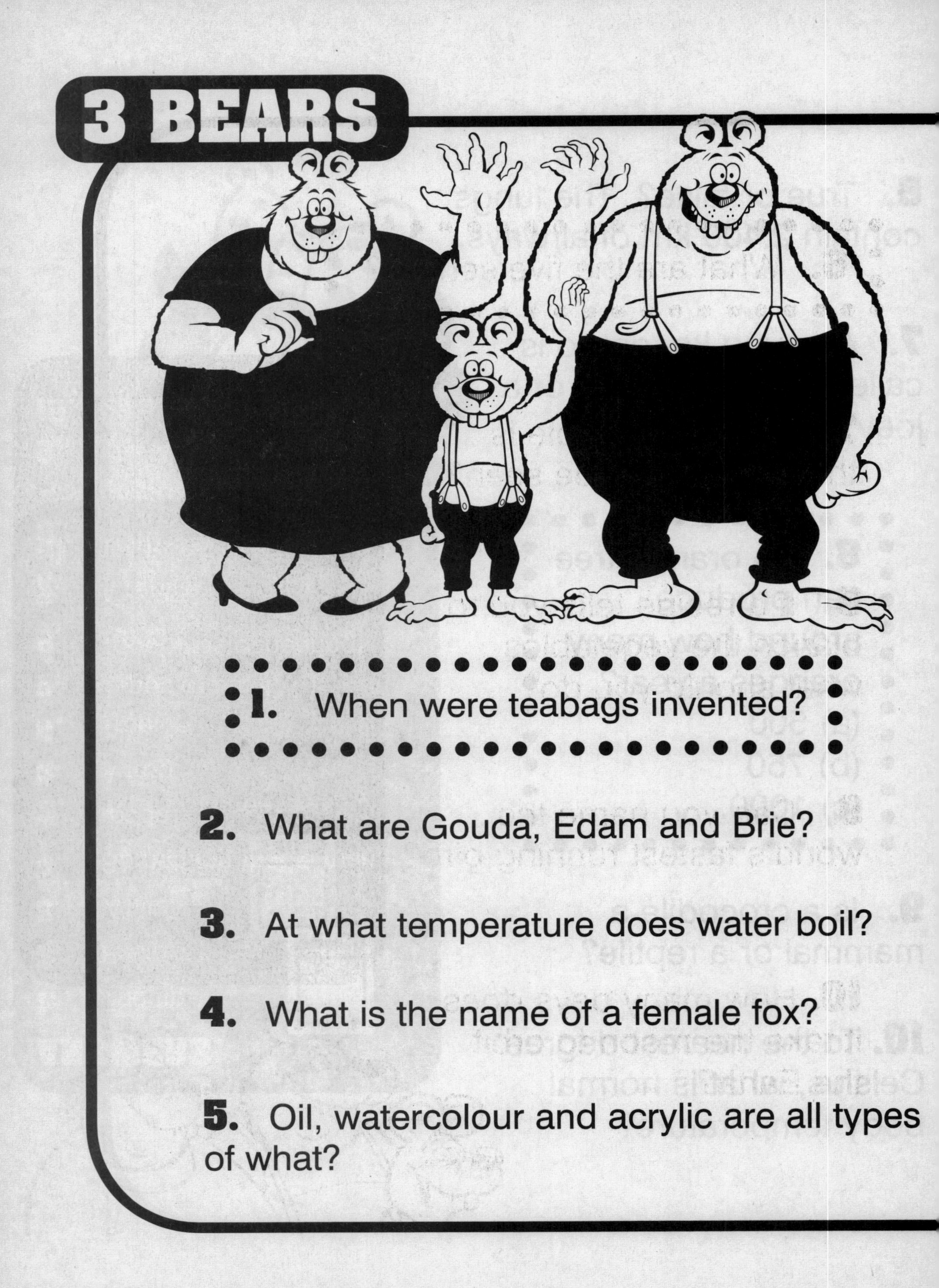

1. When were teabags invented?

2. What are Gouda, Edam and Brie?

3. At what temperature does water boil?

4. What is the name of a female fox?

5. Oil, watercolour and acrylic are all types of what?

6. What are the five senses?

7. Over which pole is the Pole Star to be seen?

8. If a recipe tells you to blanch the vegetables, what should you do?

9. Can you name the world's fastest running bird?

10. How many days does it take the moon to orbit the Earth?

ANSWERS.

1. 1920.
2. Types of cheeses.
3. 100C.
4. A vixen.
5. Types of paint.
6. Touch, taste, hearing, sight and smell.
7. The North.
8. Immerse them briefly in boiling water.
9. The African ostrich.
10. 28 days.

TEACHER

1. Which vegetable is nicknamed 'ladies' fingers?
(a) okra
(b) French beans
(c) chillies.

2. What are Demerara and Muscovada?

3. What are cappuccino and expresso?

4. Do fish have eyelids?

5. Which bird is the national emblem of New Zealand?

6. In which parts of the body would you find ball and socket joints?

7. What is a meteorite?

8. Which is the odd one out:- potato, carrot, pea or turnip?

9. What is the largest bee in a bees' nest called?

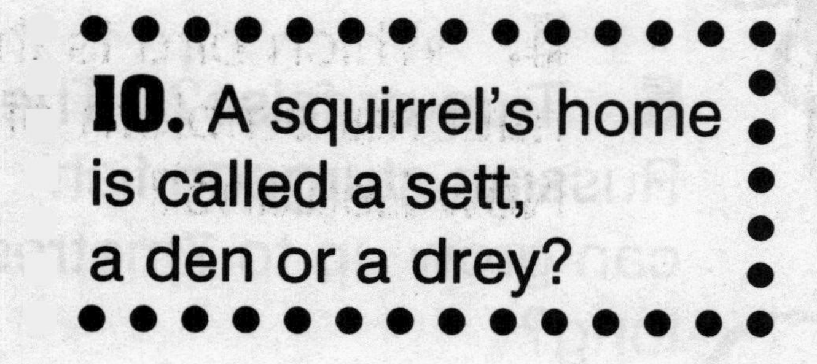

10. A squirrel's home is called a sett, a den or a drey?

BRAIN DUANE

1. Where does maple syrup come from?

2. Which fruit when dried produces sultanas, raisins and currants?

3. What is a Hibiscus?
(a) a flowering plant
(b) a sailing ship
(c) a bird of paradise.

4. What would a saline solution contain?
(a) salt
(b) alcohol
(c) sugar.

5. True or false? The Russian sturgeon fish can grow up to 7metres long?

6. Where would you find dentine?
(a) the nails
(b) the hair
(c) the teeth.

7. What do we call the study of heavenly bodies?

8. Which animal does venison come from?

9. Are bats really blind?

10. Is the two-toed sloth a vegetarian?

DESPERATE DAN

1. Approximately, how much milk does it take to make 1 kilo of butter?

(a) 22 litres
(b) 10 litres
(c) 20 litres.

2. How big was the largest octopus ever found? Over...
(a) 7 metres wide
(b) 9 metres
(c) 12 metres.

3. True or false? The first dogs were tamed over 30,000 years ago?

4. Where do natural ultraviolet rays come from?

5. What is caviar?

6. In which part of the body are the biceps to be found and what are they?

7. How many star constellations are there?
(a) 33
(b) 66
(c) 88.

8. What is the main ingredient of guacamole?

9. What is the name of the animal that has teeth that can gnaw through tree trunks, a tail like a paddle and great dam-building skills?

10. Are sponges plants or animals?

ANSWERS.
1. 22 litres.
2. 9 metres.
3. False.
4. The sun.
5. Fish eggs.
6. In the arm. Biceps are muscles.
7. 88.
8. Avocado.
9. A beaver.
10. Animals.

SCORE

FATTY

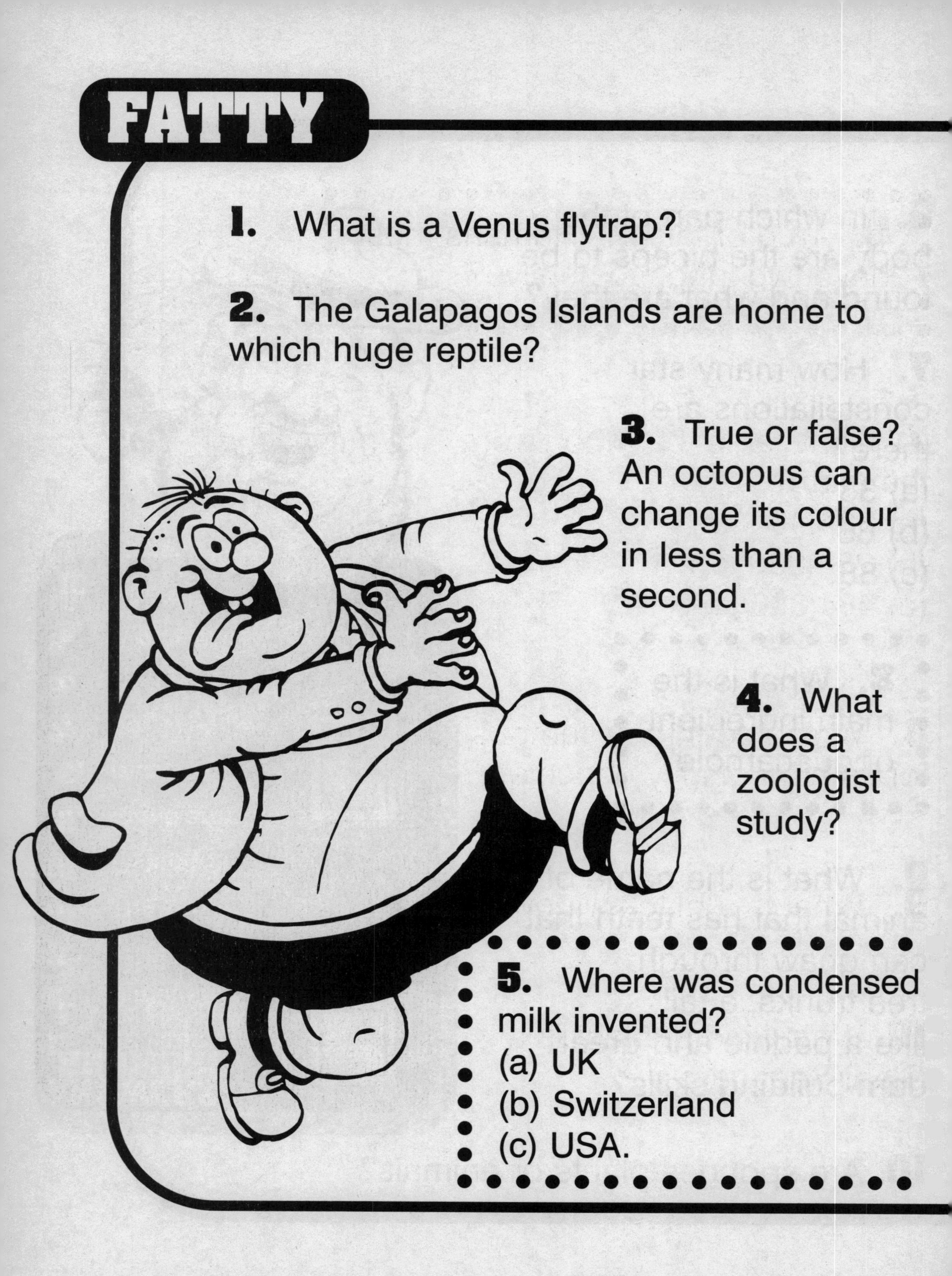

1. What is a Venus flytrap?

2. The Galapagos Islands are home to which huge reptile?

3. True or false? An octopus can change its colour in less than a second.

4. What does a zoologist study?

5. Where was condensed milk invented?
(a) UK
(b) Switzerland
(c) USA.

6. True or false? Humans must have two lungs to survive?

7. How far is the moon from the earth?
(a) 384,400 km
(b) 284,200 km
(c) 484,300 km.

8. Which country is famous for its high quality chocolate?

9. What is a black widow?

10. What kind of plant is a Giant Sagauaro?

ANSWERS.

1. A carnivorous plant.
2. The giant tortoise.
3. True.
4. Animals.
5. Switzerland.
6. False.
7. 384,400 km
8. Belgium.
9. A poisonous spider.
10. A cactus.

SCORE

BEA

1. In which continent would you find humming birds?

2. Can you name Britain's largest bird?

3. Which country is the world's leading coffee grower?

4. How would you prepare dehydrated food?

5. What are, Postman, Nero, and Birdwing types of?

6. How many kidneys does the human body have?

7. What does the Big Bang theory explain?

8. Which country does Gruyere cheese come from?

9. What is the largest kind of shark called?

10. What are wasps' nests made of?

ANSWERS.

1. South America.
2. Golden eagle.
3. Brazil.
4. By adding water to it.
5. Butterfly.
6. Two.
7. The origins of the Universe.
8. Switzerland.
9. The whale shark.
10. Chewed wood.

SCORE

IVY

1. Which animals are used to hunt for truffles?

(a) dogs (b) hawks (c) pigs.

2. What is a truffle?

3. What are glaciers?

4. What are the runners of a plant?

(a) leaves
(b) roots
(c) petals.

5. Which country supplies more than half the world's cork?

(a) Portugal
(b) Italy
(c) Spain.

6. The heart and lungs are protected by a cage of bones. What are these bones called?

7. Which is the largest planet in our solar system?

8. What is the hottest part of a chilli pepper?

9. True or false? Australia and Antarctica are the only parts of the world with no native cat species.

10. True or false? Giant clams can live for over 300 years.

ANSWERS.

1. Pigs.
2. A mushroom like fungus.
3. Frozen rivers of ice.
4. Roots.
5. Portugal.
6. The ribs.
7. Jupiter.
8. The seeds.
9. True.
10. False, but they can live over 200 years.

SCORE

1. Where would you find a jaguar?

2. How heavy is an adult elephant tooth?
(a) 4.5 kg
(b) 3.5 kg
(c) 1.5 kg.

3. What do ospreys eat?

4. How would you identify a proboscis monkey?

5. What food would you find on a Swedish smörgasbörd?
(a) cakes
(b) chocolates
(c) sandwiches.

6. Where is the septum:- the nose or the mouth?

7. The oldest existing observatory was built in AD72. Where is it?
(a) Mexico
(b) Italy
(c) South Korea.

8. What is tofu made from?
(a) soya bean curd
(b) flour
(c) vegetables.

9. What is a young hare called?

10. Can you name the world's largest carnivorous land animal?

ANSWERS.

1. South America.
2. 4.5 kg.
3. Fish.
4. By its long nose.
5. Sandwiches.
6. The nose.
7. South Korea.
8. Soya bean curd.
9. A leveret.
10. Alaskan brown bear.

SCORE

BLINKY

1. How many feathers does a swan have?
(a) 30,000 (b) 25,000 (c) 15,000.

2. True or false? Humans can identify around 3,000 smells?

3. What types of creature are Harp, Grey, Fur and Elephant?

4. What is the name for the microscopic sea-creatures eaten by other creatures?
(a) protons
(b) pistons
(c) plankton.

5. Is the condor the swiftest or heaviest bird of prey?

6. True or false? The skin is the body's largest organ.

7. Which planet is also known as 'The Red Planet'?

8. What is a vegan?

9. Which bird lays its eggs in the nests of other birds?

10. What types of creature are cobra, python and cottonmouth?

ANSWERS.

1. 30,000.
2. True.
3. Seal.
4. Plankton.
5. The heaviest.
6. True.
7. Mars.
8. A person who does not eat or use any animal products whatsoever.
9. The cuckoo.
10. Snakes.

GNASHER

1. Where would you find cardiac muscles?
(a) the shoulder
(b) the heart
(c) the back.

2. What species of plant is rice?

3. How many nerve cells are there in the human brain?
(a) 1 million
(b) 15 million
(c) 15 billion.

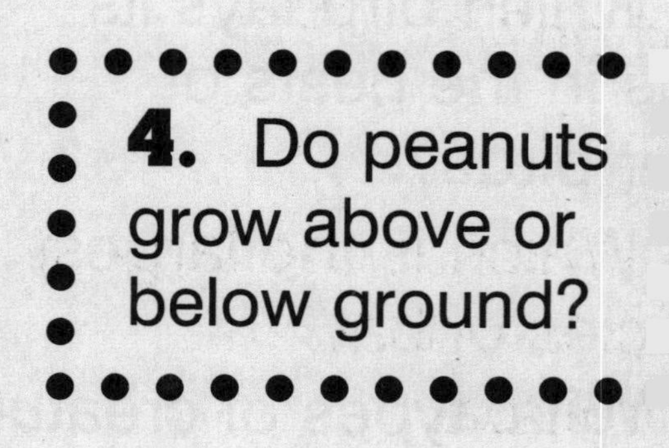

4. Do peanuts grow above or below ground?

5. What colour is saffron?

6. Where would you find red and white cells?

7. Which force causes one heavenly body to orbit another?

8. What colour is the flesh of a kiwi fruit?

9. What do ticks feed on?

10. Which is the largest species of bat?
(a) fruit bat
(b) vampire bat
(c) long-eared bat.

ANSWERS.

1. The heart.
2. Grass.
3. 15 billion.
4. Above.
5. Yellow.
6. In blood.
7. Gravity.
8. Green.
9. Animal or human blood.
10. Fruit bat.

SCORE

HISTORY

DENNIS

1. In a Norman castle, a portcullis was...?
   (a) a bridge (b) a tower (c) an iron gate.

2. Which Cape did Vasco da Gama sail round in 1497?

3. Who fought York in the War of the Roses?
   (a) Surrey
   (b) Lancaster
   (c) Kent.

4. Which came first?
   (a) Bronze Age
   (b) Iron Age
   (c) Stone Age.

5. If Gnasher's great, great grandfather had been a mascot in the Boer War, in which country would he have been?

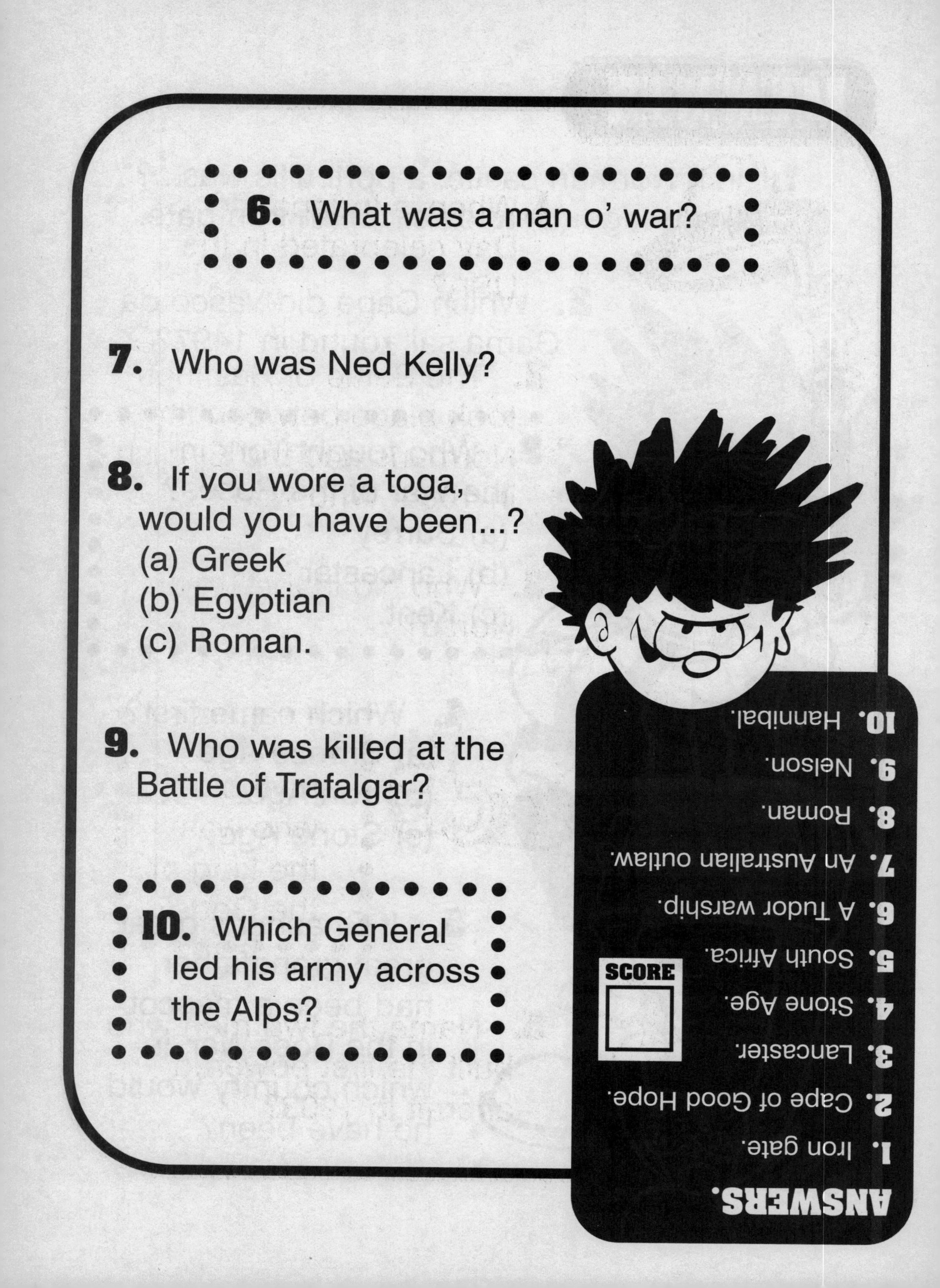

6. What was a man o' war?

7. Who was Ned Kelly?

8. If you wore a toga, would you have been...?
(a) Greek
(b) Egyptian
(c) Roman.

9. Who was killed at the Battle of Trafalgar?

10. Which General led his army across the Alps?

ANSWERS.

1. Iron gate.
2. Cape of Good Hope.
3. Lancaster.
4. Stone Age.
5. South Africa.
6. A Tudor warship.
7. An Australian outlaw.
8. Roman.
9. Nelson.
10. Hannibal.

SCORE

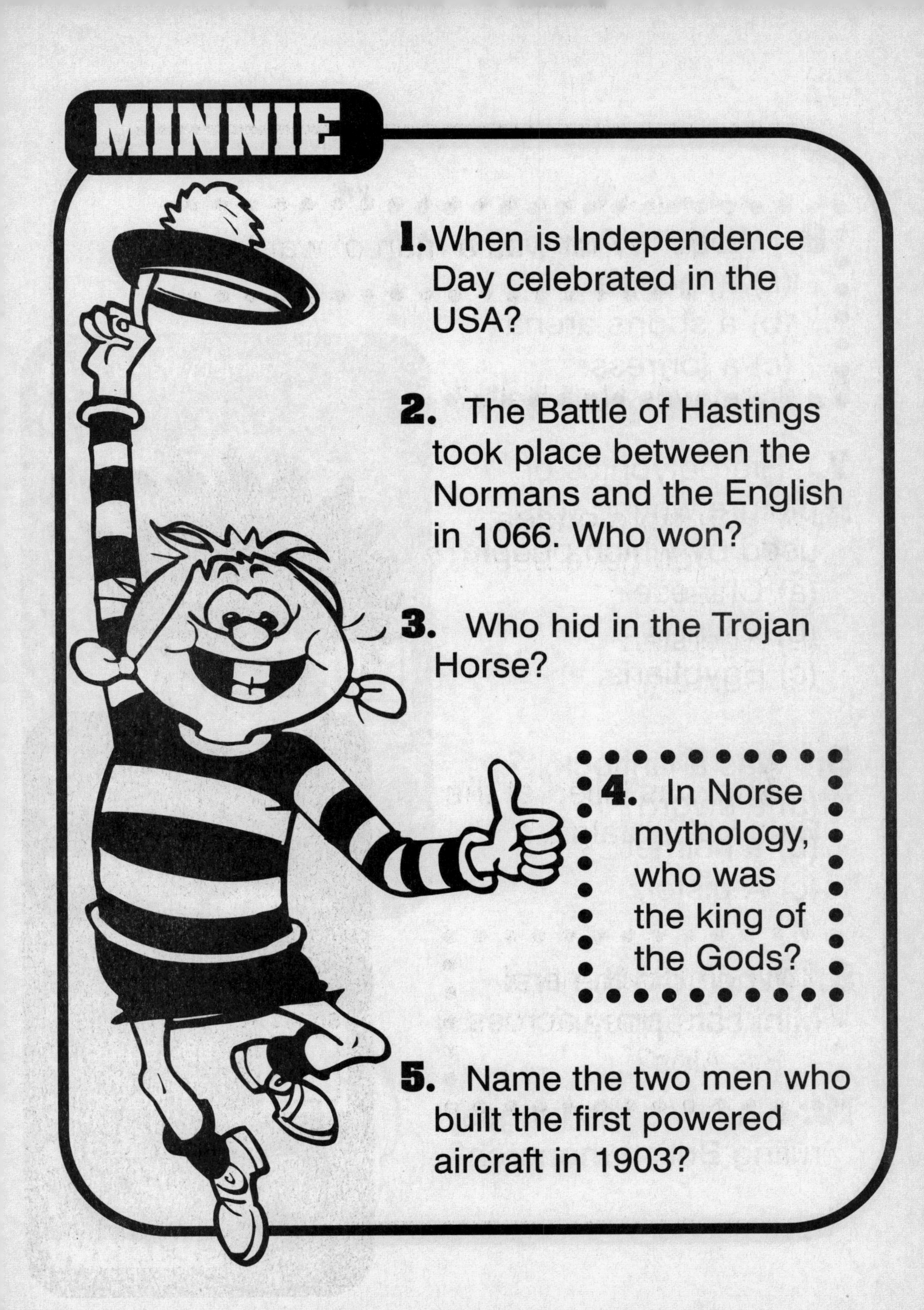
MINNIE
1. When is Independence Day celebrated in the USA?
2. The Battle of Hastings took place between the Normans and the English in 1066. Who won?
3. Who hid in the Trojan Horse?
4. In Norse mythology, who was the king of the Gods?
5. Name the two men who built the first powered aircraft in 1903?

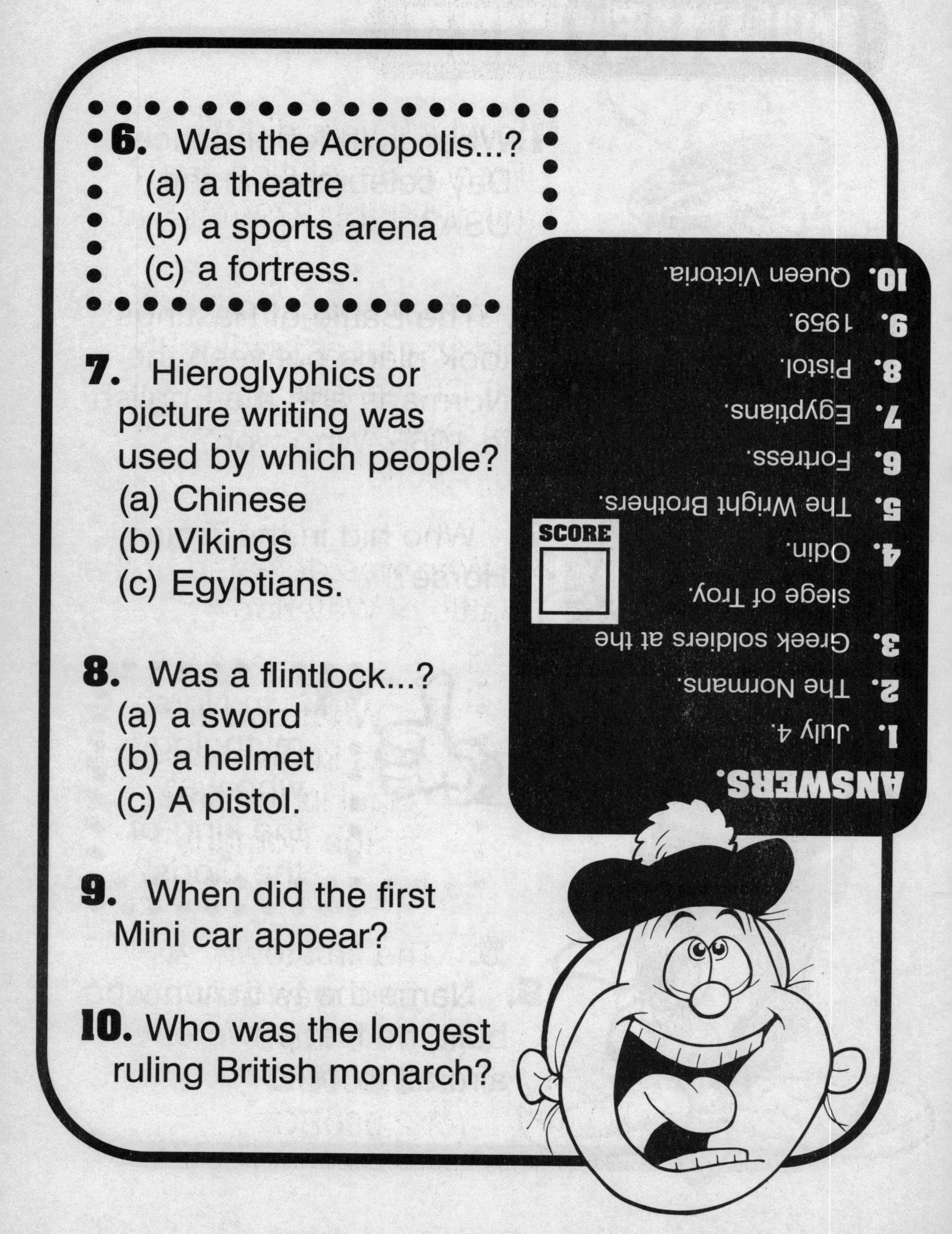

6. Was the Acropolis...?
(a) a theatre
(b) a sports arena
(c) a fortress.

7. Hieroglyphics or picture writing was used by which people?
(a) Chinese
(b) Vikings
(c) Egyptians.

8. Was a flintlock...?
(a) a sword
(b) a helmet
(c) A pistol.

9. When did the first Mini car appear?

10. Who was the longest ruling British monarch?

ANSWERS.

1. July 4.
2. The Normans.
3. Greek soldiers at the siege of Troy.
4. Odin.
5. The Wright Brothers.
6. Fortress.
7. Egyptians.
8. Pistol.
9. 1959.
10. Queen Victoria.

SCORE

BILLY WHIZZ

1. In which year did the French Revolution start?
(a) 1789 (b)1879 (c)1690.

2. Which space rocket made the first lunar landing?
(a) Challenger
(b) Soyuz
(c) Apollo.

3. Who was defeated at the Battle of Waterloo?

4. What country was known as Gaul in the time of the Romans?

5. The first town, at Jericho was built in...?
(a) 10,000BC
(b) 8,000BC
(c) 2,000BC.

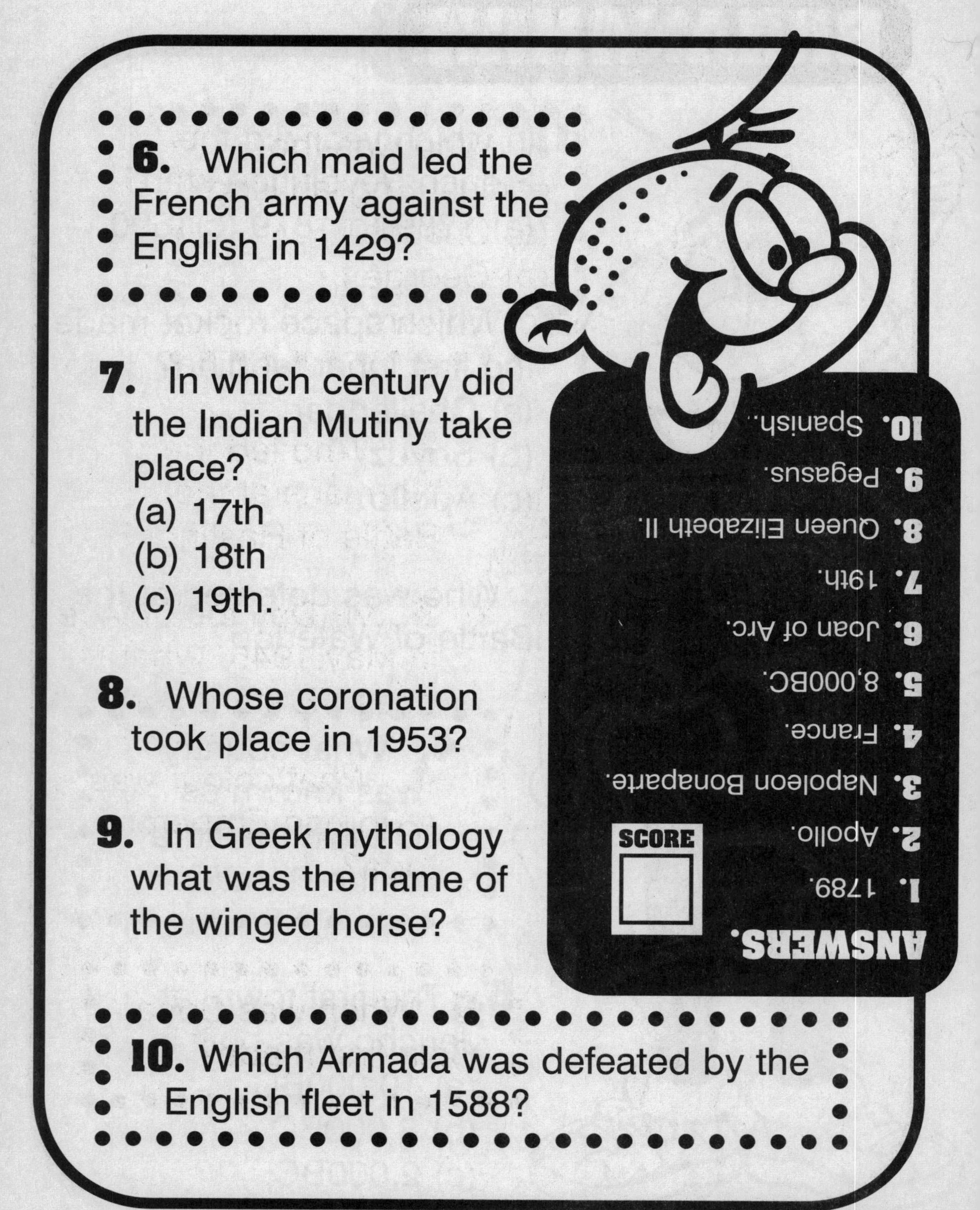

6. Which maid led the French army against the English in 1429?

7. In which century did the Indian Mutiny take place?
(a) 17th
(b) 18th
(c) 19th.

8. Whose coronation took place in 1953?

9. In Greek mythology what was the name of the winged horse?

10. Which Armada was defeated by the English fleet in 1588?

ANSWERS.

1. 1789.
2. Apollo.
3. Napoleon Bonaparte.
4. France.
5. 8,000BC.
6. Joan of Arc.
7. 19th.
8. Queen Elizabeth II.
9. Pegasus.
10. Spanish..

SCORE

BANANAMAN

1. Who was the earliest English king?
(a) Charles I
(b) George I
(c) Edward I.

2. Who led the Normans at the Battle of Hastings?

3. VE Day took place in May 1945. What does VE stand for?

4. What colour was a Roman Emperor's toga?

5. When was Coca-Cola first made?

6. Which passenger ship sunk on its maiden voyage in 1912?

7. Which American president was assassinated in 1865?
(a) Washington
(b) Lincoln
(c) Kennedy.

8. Which explorer discovered the New World in 1492?

9. Which two seas does the Suez Canal connect?

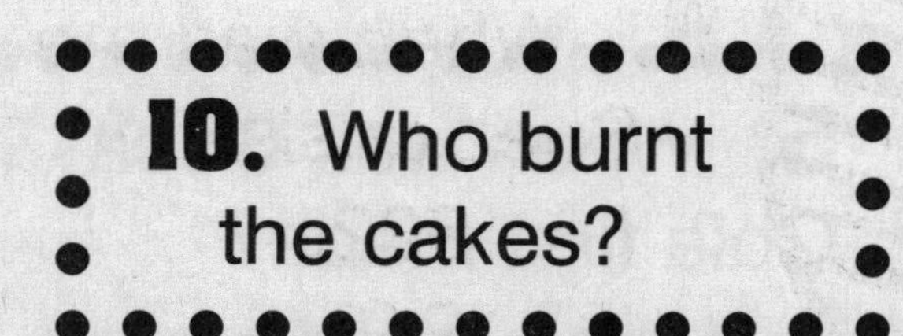

ROGER THE DODGER

1. Who was the last English king to have his head chopped off?

2. Who was the Norse god of thunder?

3. Which legendary creature in Greek mythology only had one eye?

4. Where was the court of King Arthur?

5. When was the Suez crisis?
(a) 1922
(b) 1948
(c) 1956.

6. The first successfully cloned animal was Dolly. What kind of animal was she?
7. What was a pirate flag called?
8. In 1995 what kind of disaster struck the Japanese city of Kobe?
(a) earthquake
(b) tidal wave
(c) hurricane.
9. Which ocean are the Falkland Islands in?
10. From which French port were British troops evacuated during World War II?
(a) Calais (b) Dieppe (c) Dunkirk.
ANSWERS.
1. Charles I.
2. Thor.
3. The Cyclops.
4. Camelot.
5. 1956.
6. Sheep.
7. Jolly Roger.
8. Earthquake.
9. Atlantic.
10. Dunkirk.
SCORE

1. What did Guy Fawkes try to blow up?

2. What was a ballista?
   (a) a castle
   (b) a large catapult
   (c) an armoured warship.

3. What number does the Roman numeral V stand for?

4. Who were the Bow Street Runners?

5. Was Durham Cathedral built by...?
   (a) Romans
   (b) Normans
   (c) Vikings.

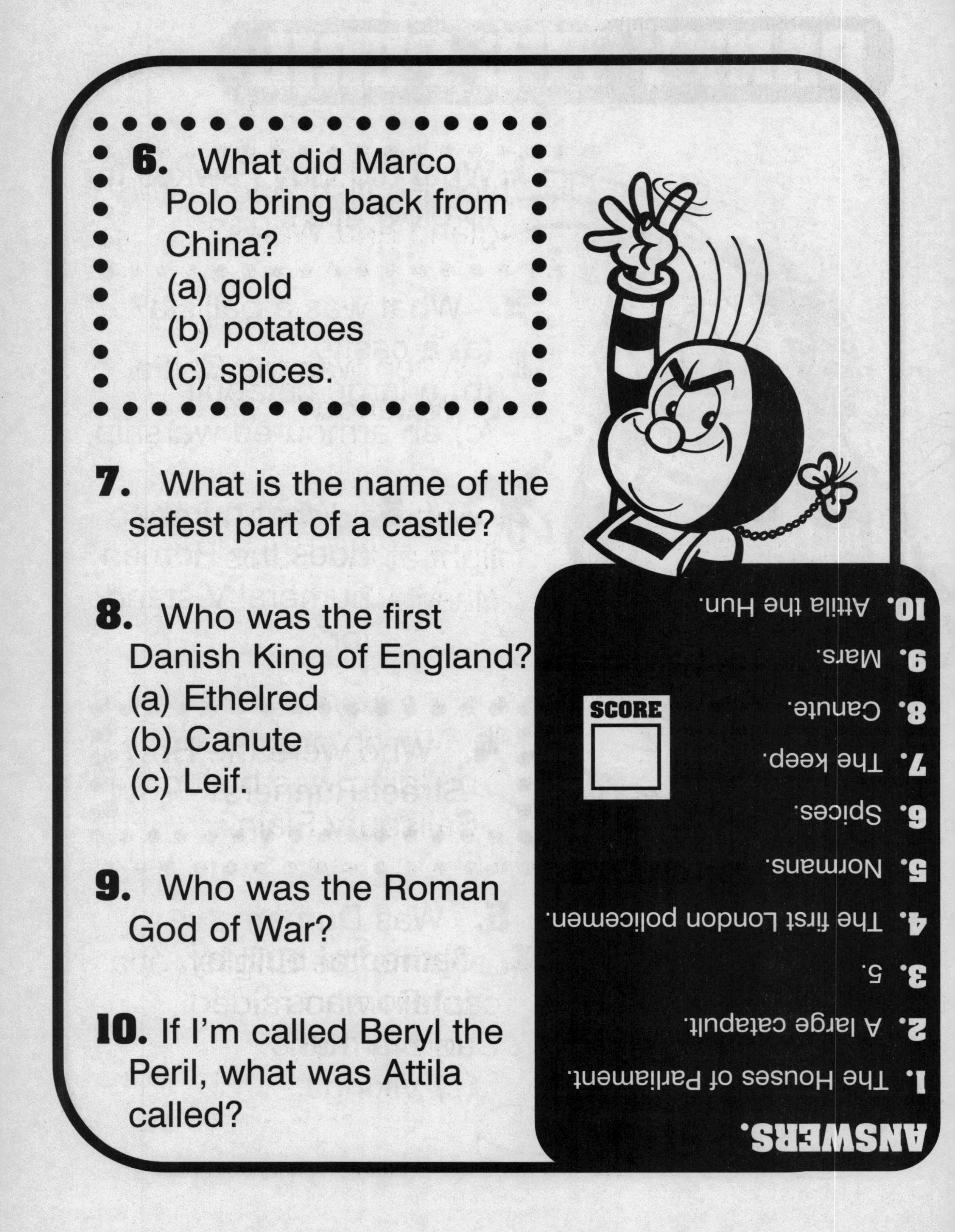

6. What did Marco Polo bring back from China?
(a) gold
(b) potatoes
(c) spices.

7. What is the name of the safest part of a castle?

8. Who was the first Danish King of England?
(a) Ethelred
(b) Canute
(c) Leif.

9. Who was the Roman God of War?

10. If I'm called Beryl the Peril, what was Attila called?

ANSWERS.

1. The Houses of Parliament.
2. A large catapult.
3. 5.
4. The first London policemen.
5. Normans.
6. Spices.
7. The keep.
8. Canute.
9. Mars.
10. Attila the Hun.

SCORE

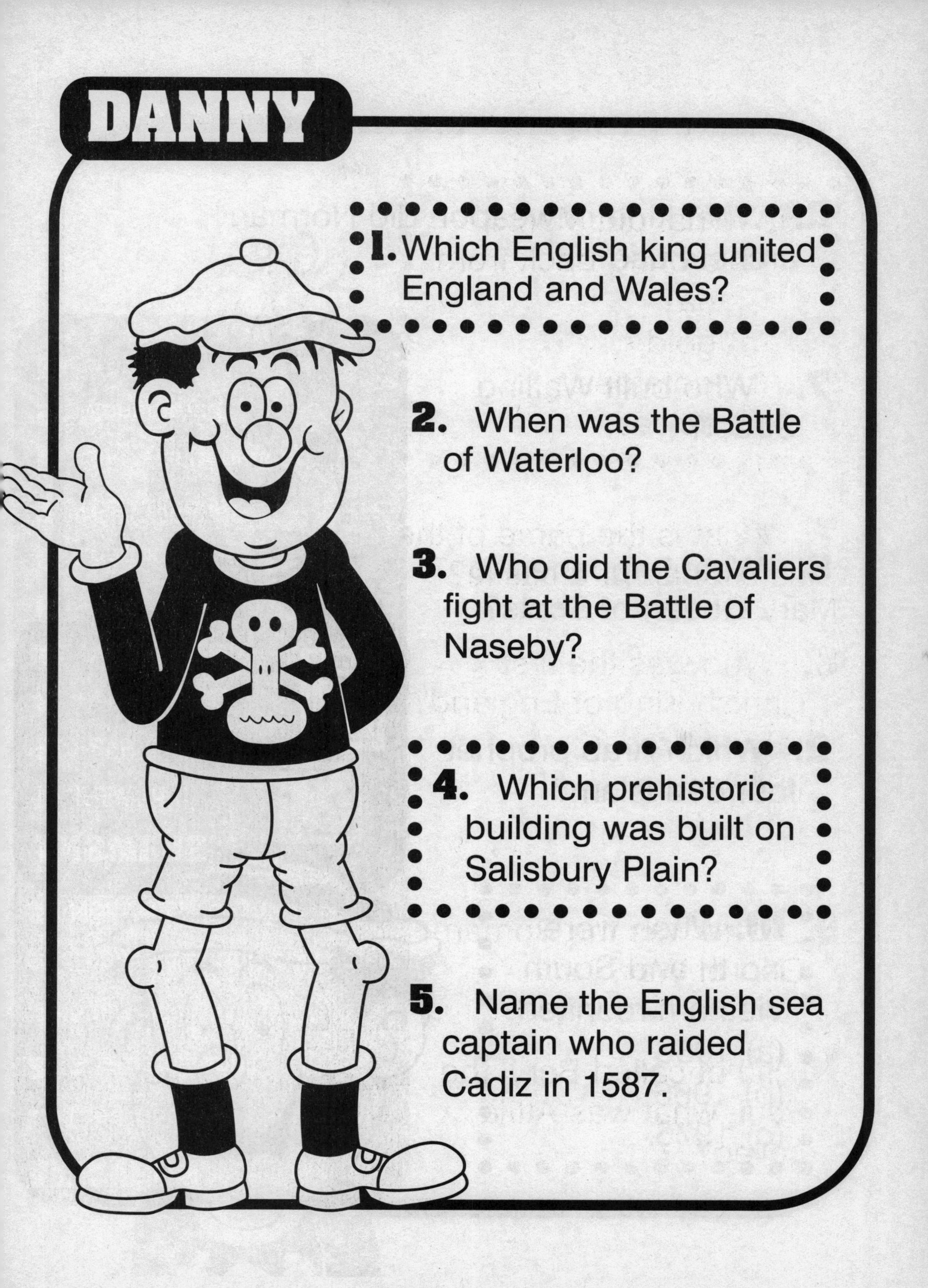
DANNY
1. Which English king united England and Wales?
2. When was the Battle of Waterloo?
3. Who did the Cavaliers fight at the Battle of Naseby?
4. Which prehistoric building was built on Salisbury Plain?
5. Name the English sea captain who raided Cadiz in 1587.

6. What kind of weapon did Norman archers use?

7. Who built Watling Street?

8. What happened to Mary Queen of Scots?

9. Which Arab prophet founded Islam?

10. When were North and South Vietnam reunited?
(a) 1956
(b) 1966
(c) 1976.

ANSWERS.

1. Edward I.
2. 1815.
3. Roundheads.
4. Stonehenge.
5. Sir Francis Drake.
6. Longbows.
7. The Romans.
8. She was beheaded.
9. Mohammed.
10. 1976.

SCORE

1. Which king was known as the Lionheart?

2. Which country has the rose as its emblem?

3. Who signed the Magna Carta?

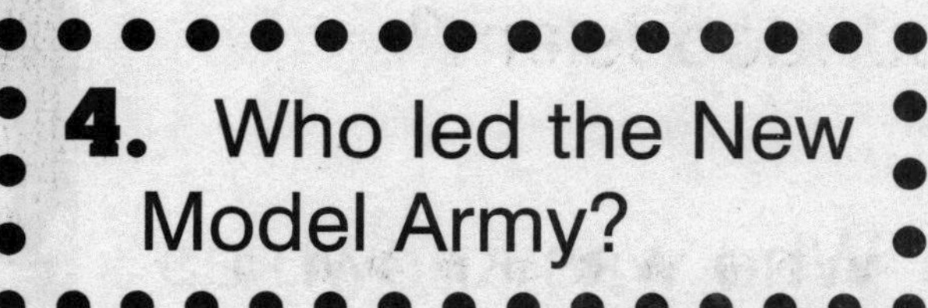

4. Who led the New Model Army?

5. What was a blunderbuss?

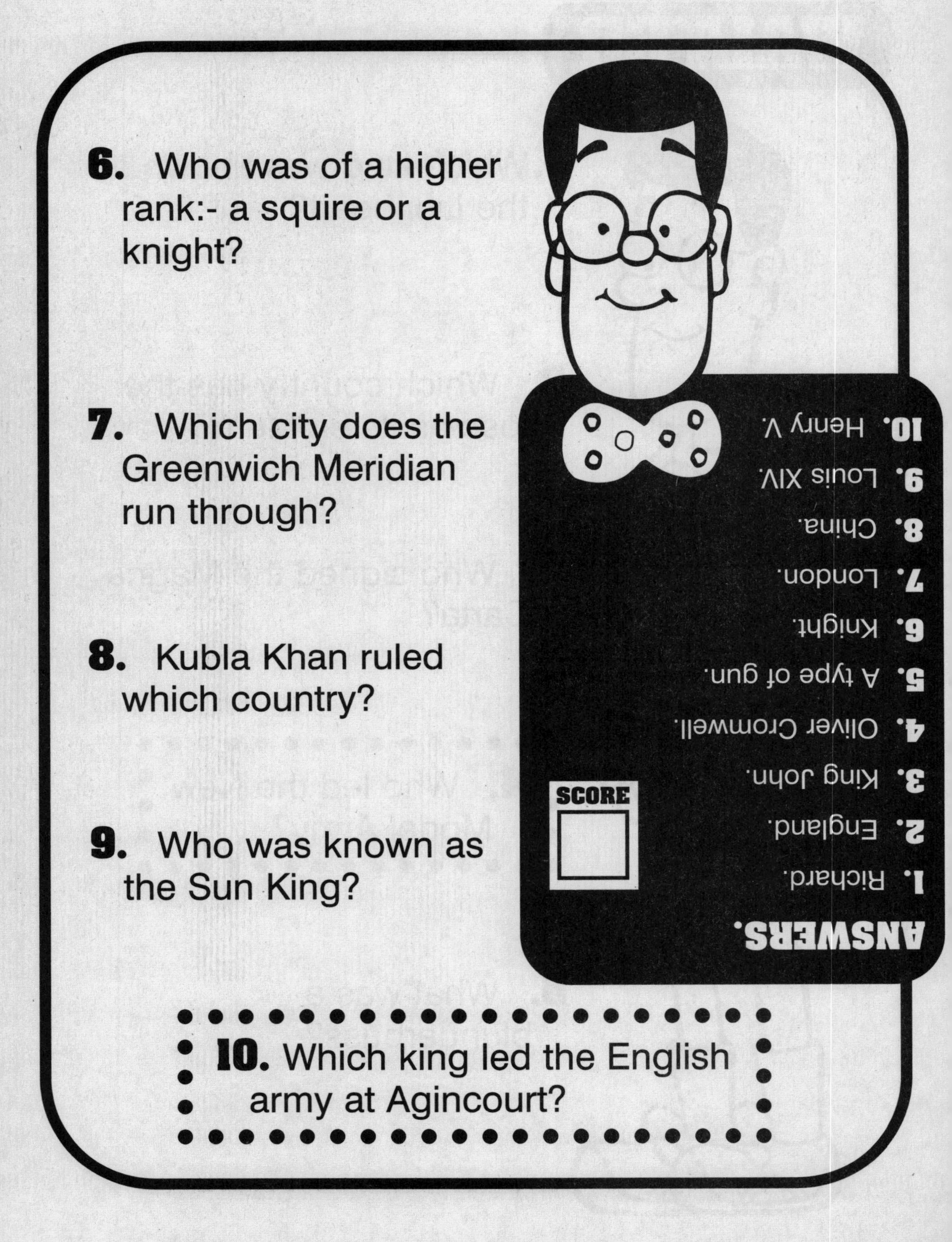

6. Who was of a higher rank:- a squire or a knight?

7. Which city does the Greenwich Meridian run through?

8. Kubla Khan ruled which country?

9. Who was known as the Sun King?

10. Which king led the English army at Agincourt?

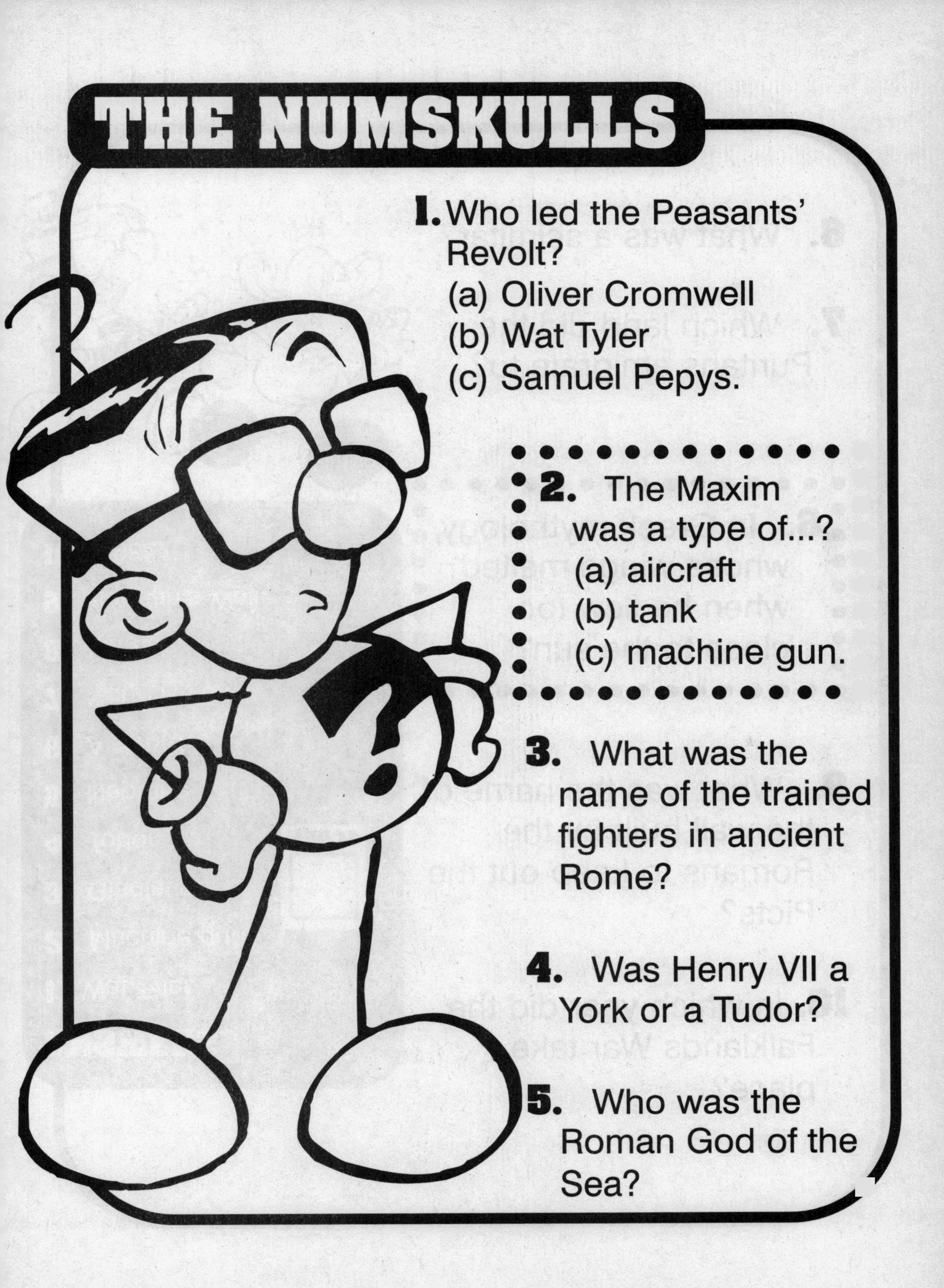

THE NUMSKULLS

1. Who led the Peasants' Revolt?
   (a) Oliver Cromwell
   (b) Wat Tyler
   (c) Samuel Pepys.

2. The Maxim was a type of...?
   (a) aircraft
   (b) tank
   (c) machine gun.

3. What was the name of the trained fighters in ancient Rome?

4. Was Henry VII a York or a Tudor?

5. Who was the Roman God of the Sea?

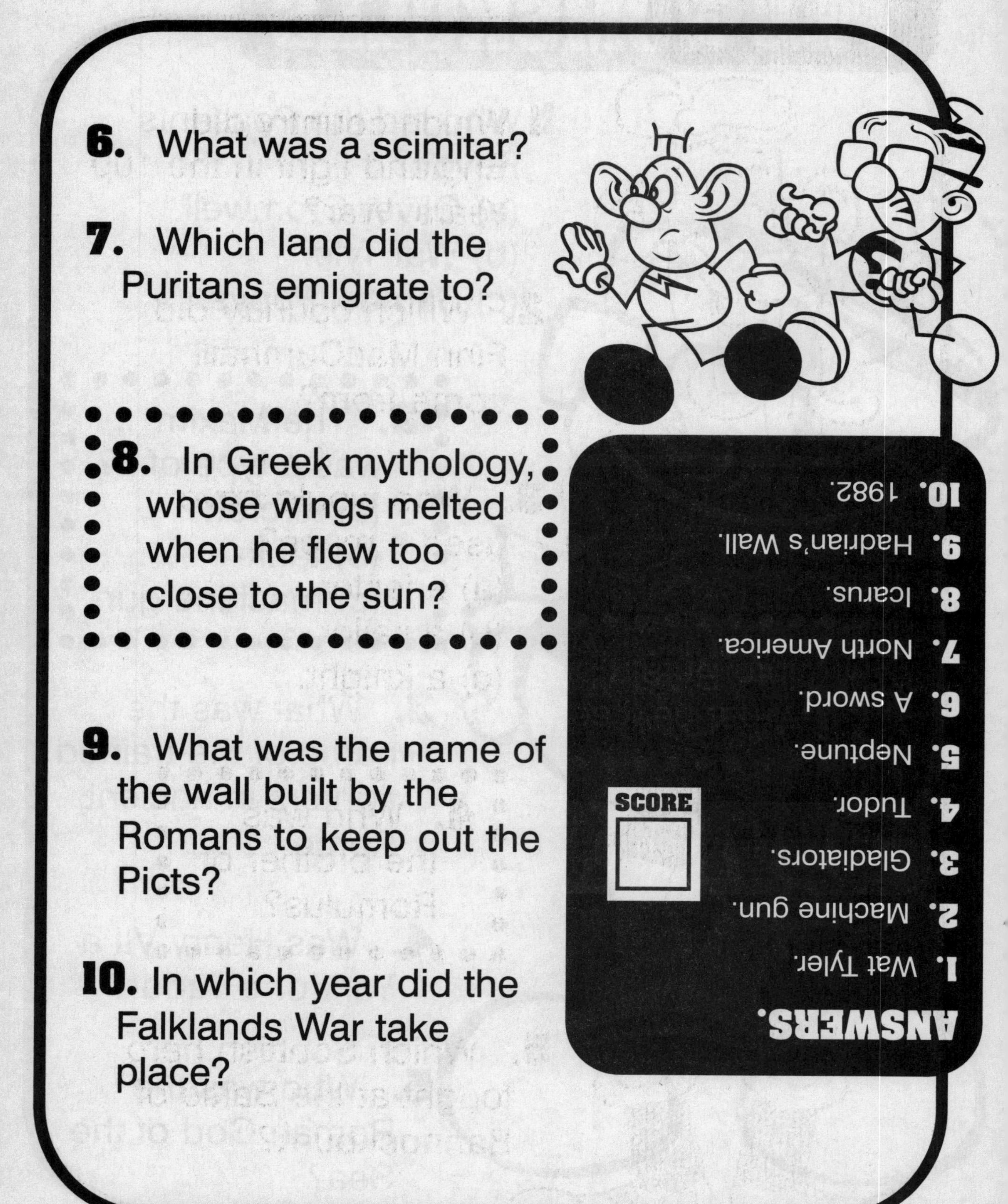

6. What was a scimitar?

7. Which land did the Puritans emigrate to?

8. In Greek mythology, whose wings melted when he flew too close to the sun?

9. What was the name of the wall built by the Romans to keep out the Picts?

10. In which year did the Falklands War take place?

ANSWERS.

1. Wat Tyler.
2. Machine gun.
3. Gladiators.
4. Tudor.
5. Neptune.
6. A sword.
7. North America.
8. Icarus.
9. Hadrian's Wall.
10. 1982.

SCORE

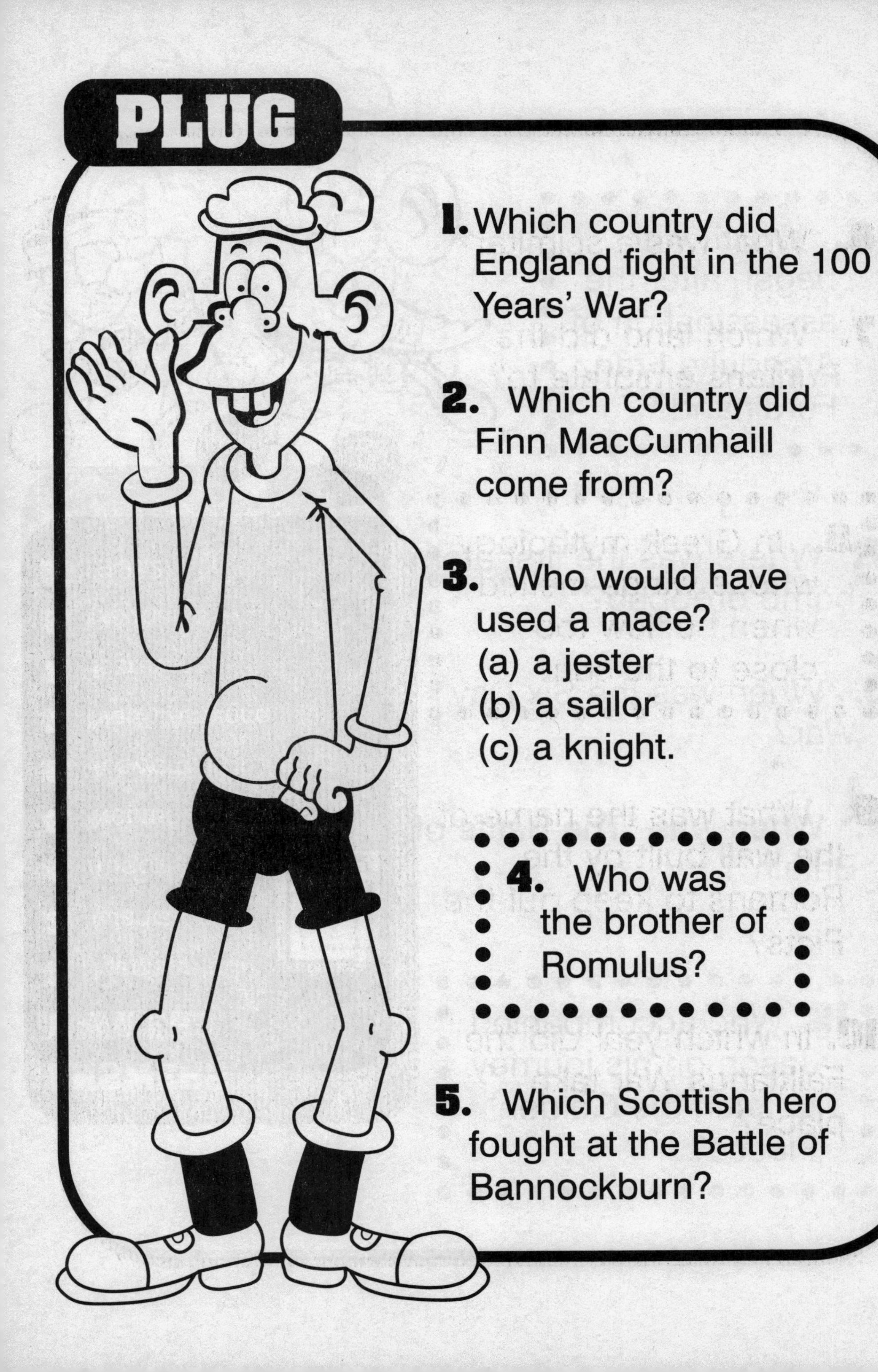

PLUG

1. Which country did England fight in the 100 Years' War?

2. Which country did Finn MacCumhaill come from?

3. Who would have used a mace?
(a) a jester
(b) a sailor
(c) a knight.

4. Who was the brother of Romulus?

5. Which Scottish hero fought at the Battle of Bannockburn?

6. Which war began after the assassination of Archduke Franz Ferdinand?

7. Where was the first atom bomb dropped?

8. When was the Six Day War?

9. When was “The Battle of Britain”?

10. Who accompanied Jason on his journey to fetch the Golden Fleece?

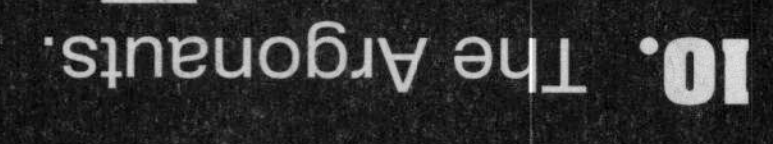

ANSWERS.

1. France.
2. Ireland.
3. A knight.
4. Remus.
5. Robert the Bruce.
6. The First World War.
7. Hiroshima.
8. 1967.
9. 1940.
10. The Argonauts.

SCORE

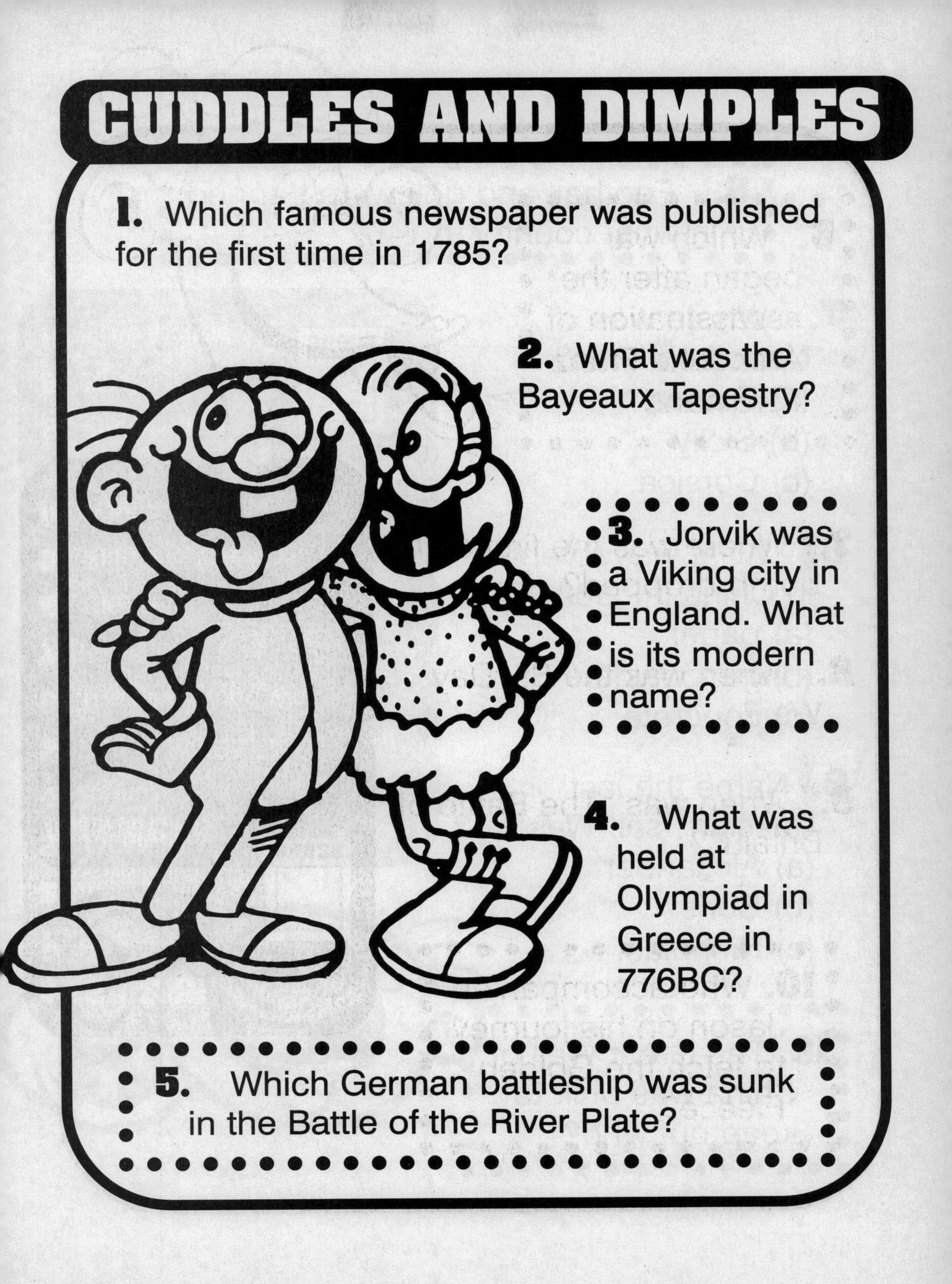
CUDDLES AND DIMPLES
1. Which famous newspaper was published for the first time in 1785?
2. What was the Bayeaux Tapestry?
3. Jorvik was a Viking city in England. What is its modern name?
4. What was held at Olympiad in Greece in 776BC?
5. Which German battleship was sunk in the Battle of the River Plate?

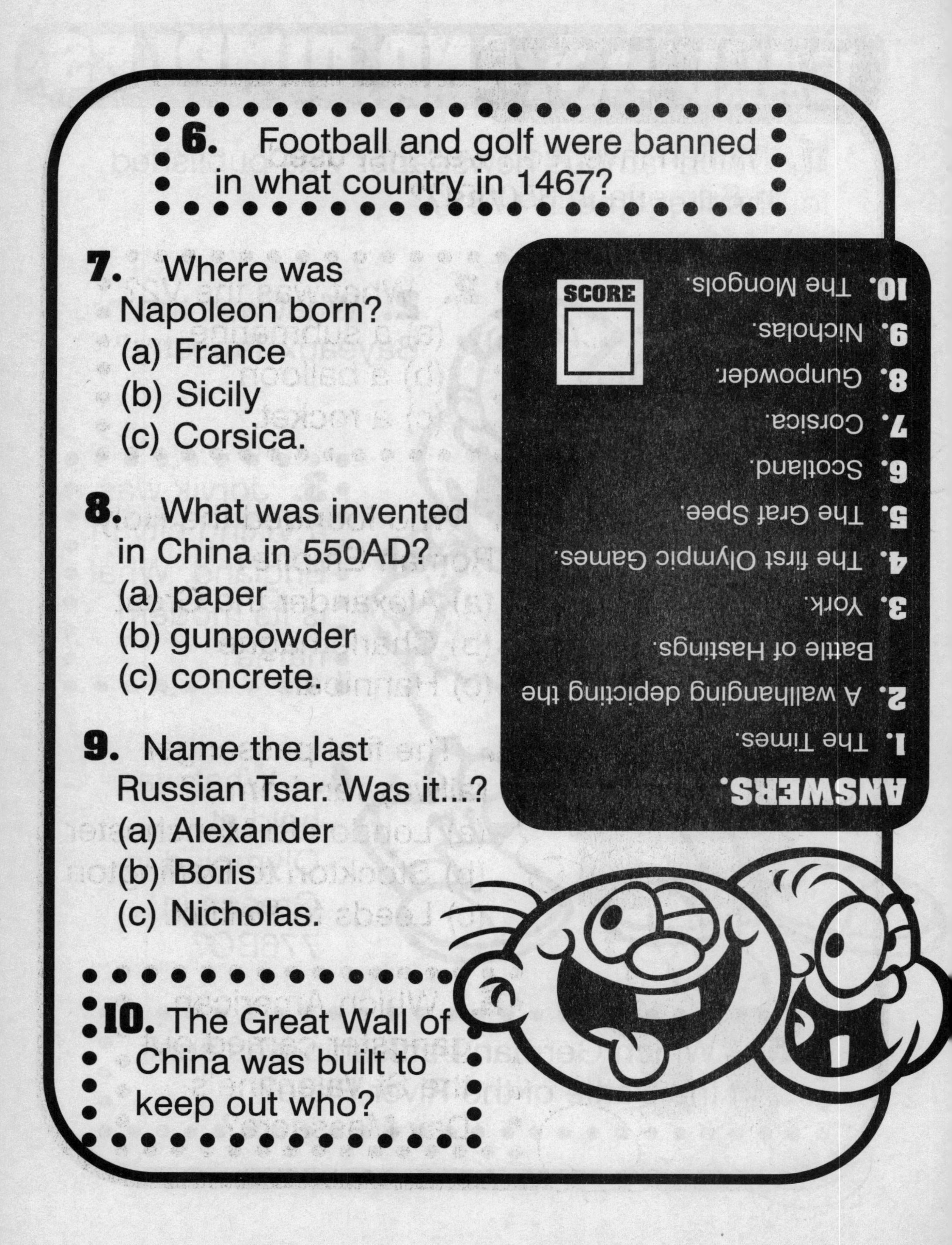

6. Football and golf were banned in what country in 1467?

7. Where was Napoleon born?
(a) France
(b) Sicily
(c) Corsica.

8. What was invented in China in 550AD?
(a) paper
(b) gunpowder
(c) concrete.

9. Name the last Russian Tsar. Was it...?
(a) Alexander
(b) Boris
(c) Nicholas.

10. The Great Wall of China was built to keep out who?

ANSWERS.
1. The Times.
2. A wallhanging depicting the Battle of Hastings.
3. York.
4. The first Olympic Games.
5. The Graf Spee.
6. Scotland.
7. Corsica.
8. Gunpowder.
9. Nicholas.
10. The Mongols.

SCORE

BALL BOY

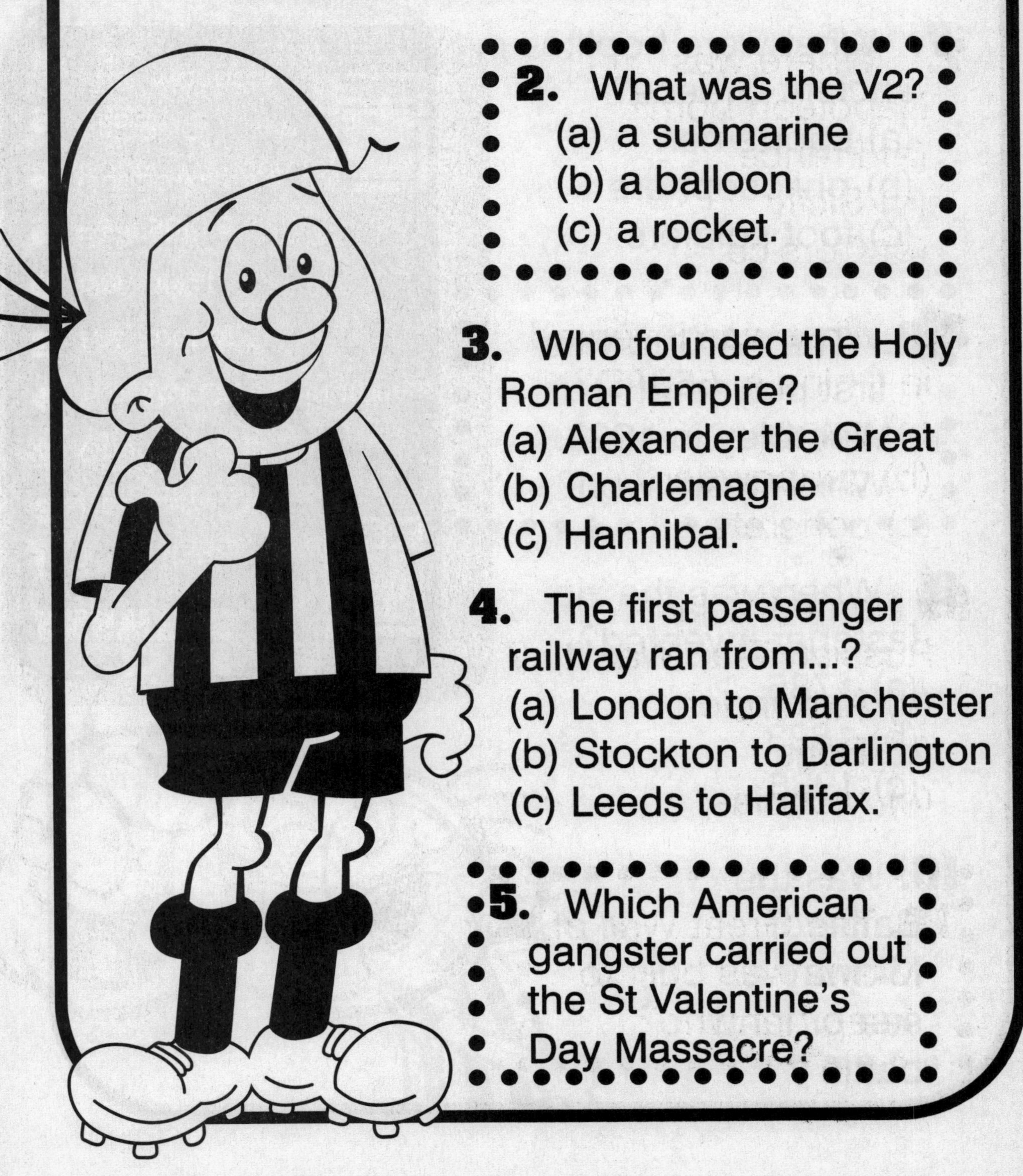

1. Which invention was first used in Sumeria in 3500BC?

2. What was the V2?
(a) a submarine
(b) a balloon
(c) a rocket.

3. Who founded the Holy Roman Empire?
(a) Alexander the Great
(b) Charlemagne
(c) Hannibal.

4. The first passenger railway ran from...?
(a) London to Manchester
(b) Stockton to Darlington
(c) Leeds to Halifax.

5. Which American gangster carried out the St Valentine's Day Massacre?

6. Was President Clinton a Republican or a Democrat?

7. What were hoplites in ancient Greece?
(a) sportsmen
(b) philosophers
(c) foot soldiers.

8. The FA Cup was first played at Wembley in 1923. Which team won?

9. When was the zip fastener invented?
(a) 1785
(b) 1893
(c) 1938.

10. Was the Battle of Midway a sea or land battle ?

ANSWERS.

1. The wheel.
2. Rocket.
3. Charlemagne.
4. Stockton to Darlington.
5. Al Capone.
6. Democrat.
7. Foot soldiers.
8. Bolton Wanderers.
9. 1893.
10. Sea.

SCORE

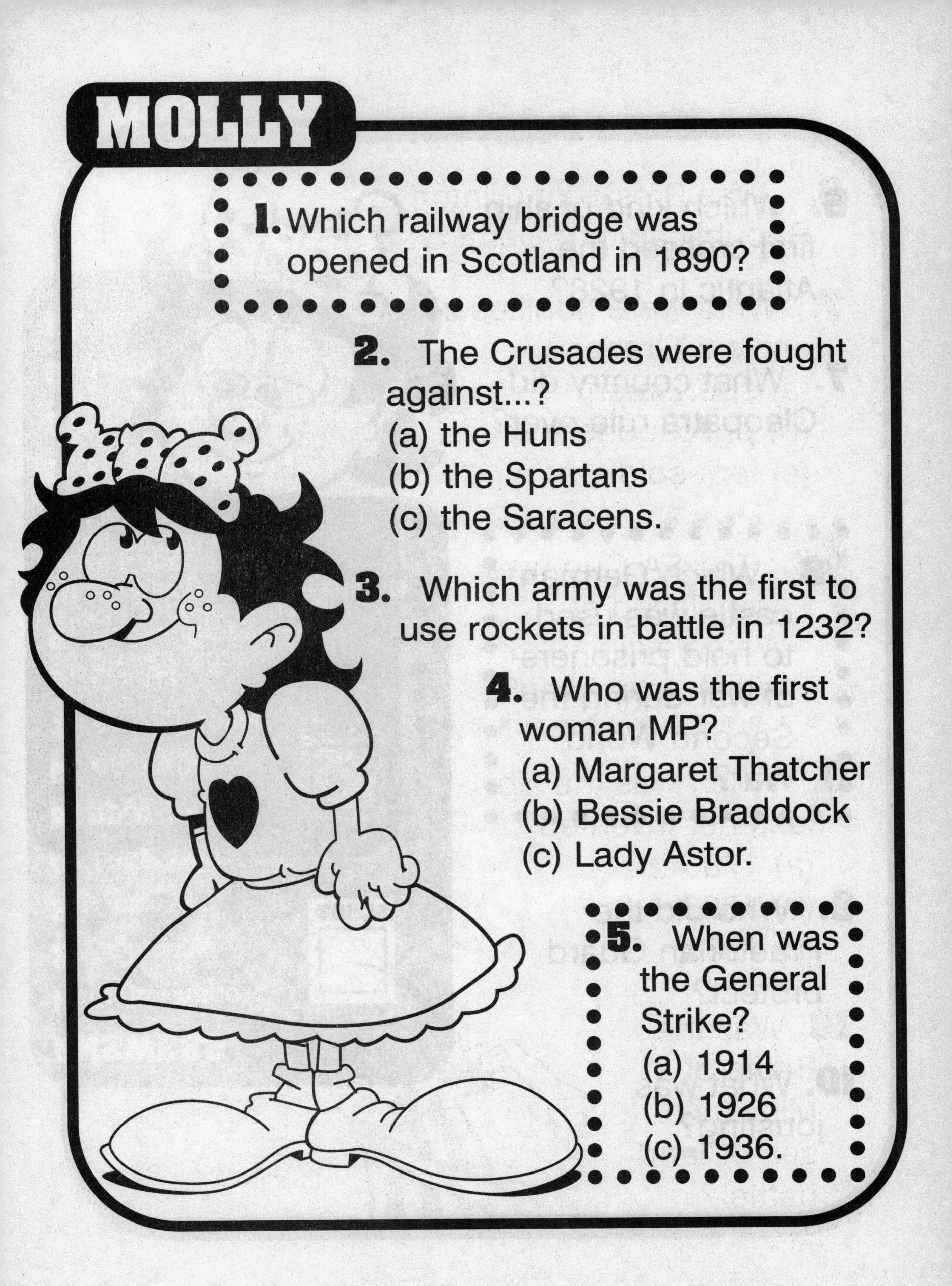
MOLLY
1. Which railway bridge was opened in Scotland in 1890?
2. The Crusades were fought against...?
(a) the Huns
(b) the Spartans
(c) the Saracens.
3. Which army was the first to use rockets in battle in 1232?
4. Who was the first woman MP?
(a) Margaret Thatcher
(b) Bessie Braddock
(c) Lady Astor.
5. When was the General Strike?
(a) 1914
(b) 1926
(c) 1936.

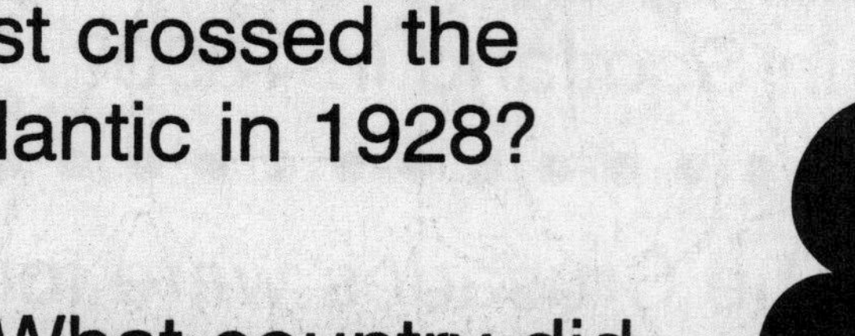

6. Which kind of ship first crossed the Atlantic in 1928?

7. What country did Cleopatra rule over?

8. Which German castle was used to hold prisoners of war during the Second World War?

9. Who did the Praetorian Guard protect?

10. What was jousting?

ANSWERS.

1. Forth Bridge.
2. Saracens.
3. Chinese.
4. Lady Astor.
5. 1926.
6. An airship.
7. Ancient Egypt.
8. Colditz.
9. Roman Emperors.
10. Fighting between knights on horseback.

3 BEARS
1. Who was the Red Baron?
2. When were driving tests first introduced in Britain? (a) 1925 (b) 1934 (c) 1951.
3. Which country was once ruled by Shoguns?
4. HMS Victory was the flagship of which English sailor?
(a) Francis Drake
(b) Walter Raleigh
(c) Horatio Nelson.

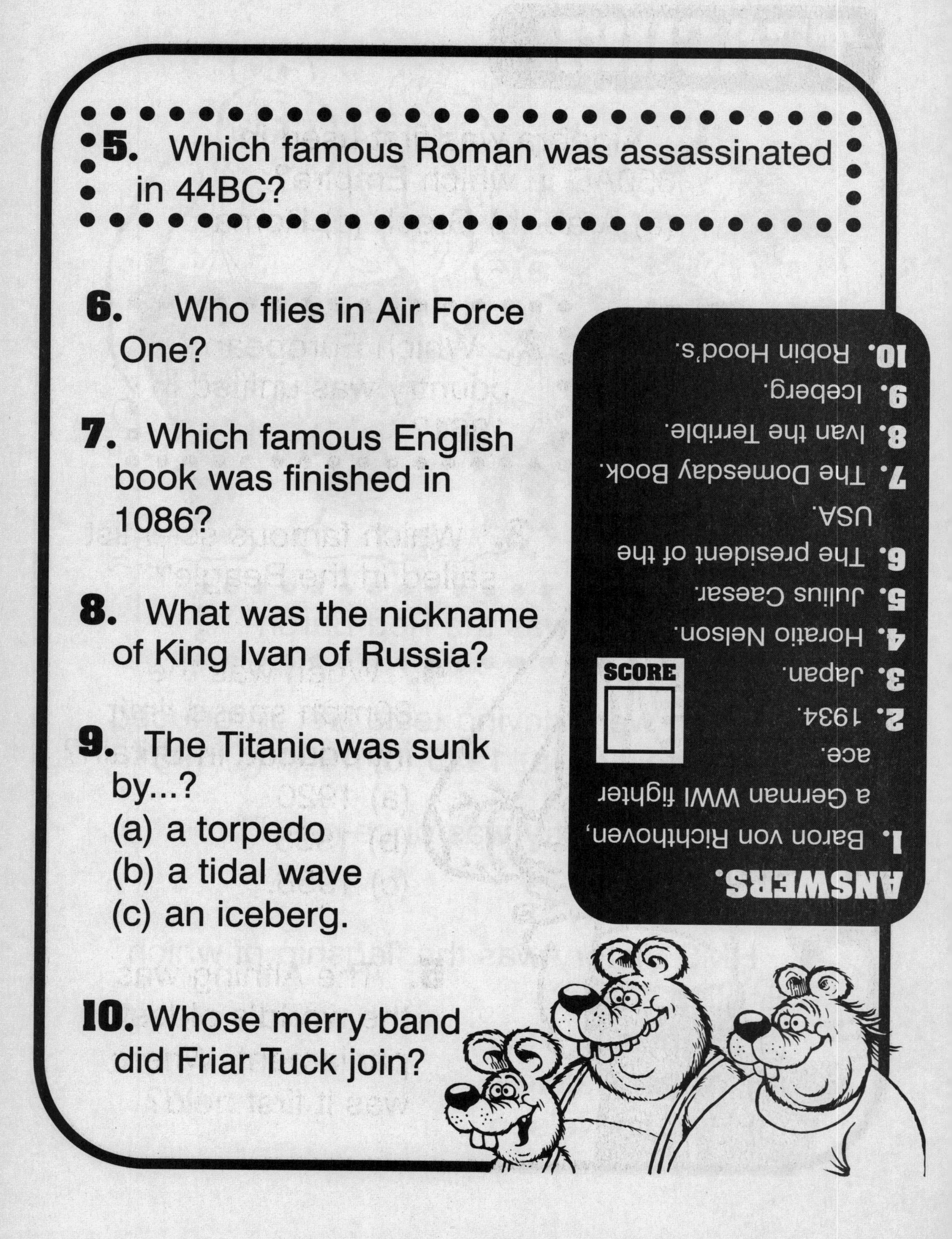

5. Which famous Roman was assassinated in 44BC?

6. Who flies in Air Force One?

7. Which famous English book was finished in 1086?

8. What was the nickname of King Ivan of Russia?

9. The Titanic was sunk by...?
(a) a torpedo
(b) a tidal wave
(c) an iceberg.

10. Whose merry band did Friar Tuck join?

ANSWERS.

1. Baron von Richthoven, a German WWI fighter ace.
2. 1934.
3. Japan.
4. Horatio Nelson.
5. Julius Caesar.
6. The president of the USA.
7. The Domesday Book.
8. Ivan the Terrible.
9. Iceberg.
10. Robin Hood's.

SCORE

TEACHER

1. Algebra was first used in 850AD in which Empire?
(a) Arab (b) Greek (c) Roman.

2. Which European country was unified in 1861?

3. Which famous scientist sailed in the Beagle?

4. When was the 30mph speed limit introduced in Britain?
(a) 1920
(b) 1935
(c) 1956.

5. The Althing was the world's oldest parliament. Where was it first held?

6. In which Civil War did the Union army fight the Confederates?

7. Who was the first king of a united Scotland?
(a) Kenneth I
(b) James I
(c) Malcolm I.

8. Which famous gold rush took place in 1847?

9. Where was the earliest known pottery produced?
(a) China (b) India (c) Japan.

10. Which country invaded Afghanistan in 1979...?
(a) Iran
(b) America
(c) USSR

ANSWERS.

1. Arab.
2. Italy.
3. Charles Darwin.
4. 1935.
5. Iceland.
6. American Civil War.
7. Kenneth I.
8. Californian.
9. Japan.
10. USSR.

SCORE

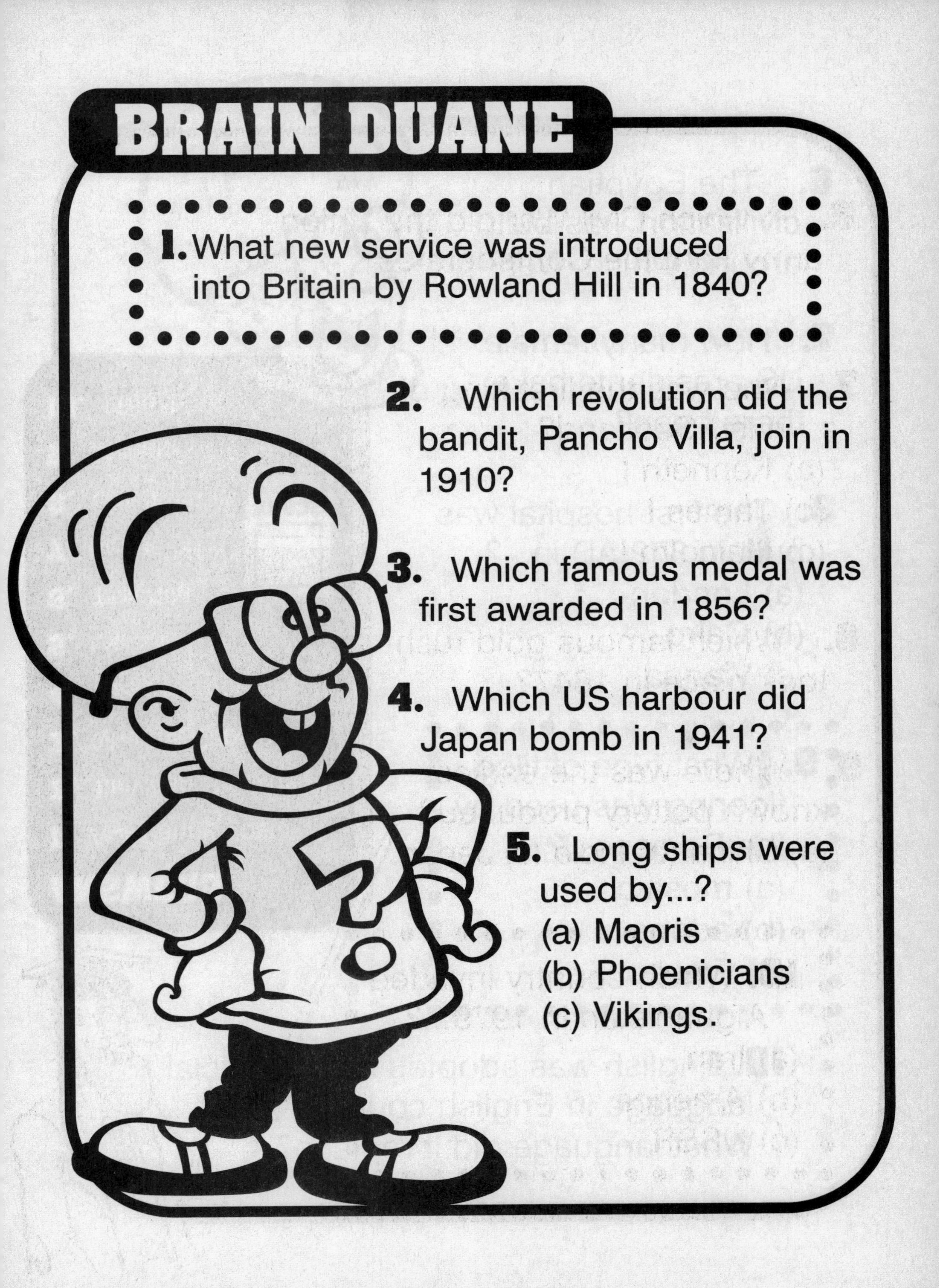
BRAIN DUANE
1. What new service was introduced into Britain by Rowland Hill in 1840?
2. Which revolution did the bandit, Pancho Villa, join in 1910?
3. Which famous medal was first awarded in 1856?
4. Which US harbour did Japan bomb in 1941?
5. Long ships were used by...?
(a) Maoris
(b) Phoenicians
(c) Vikings.

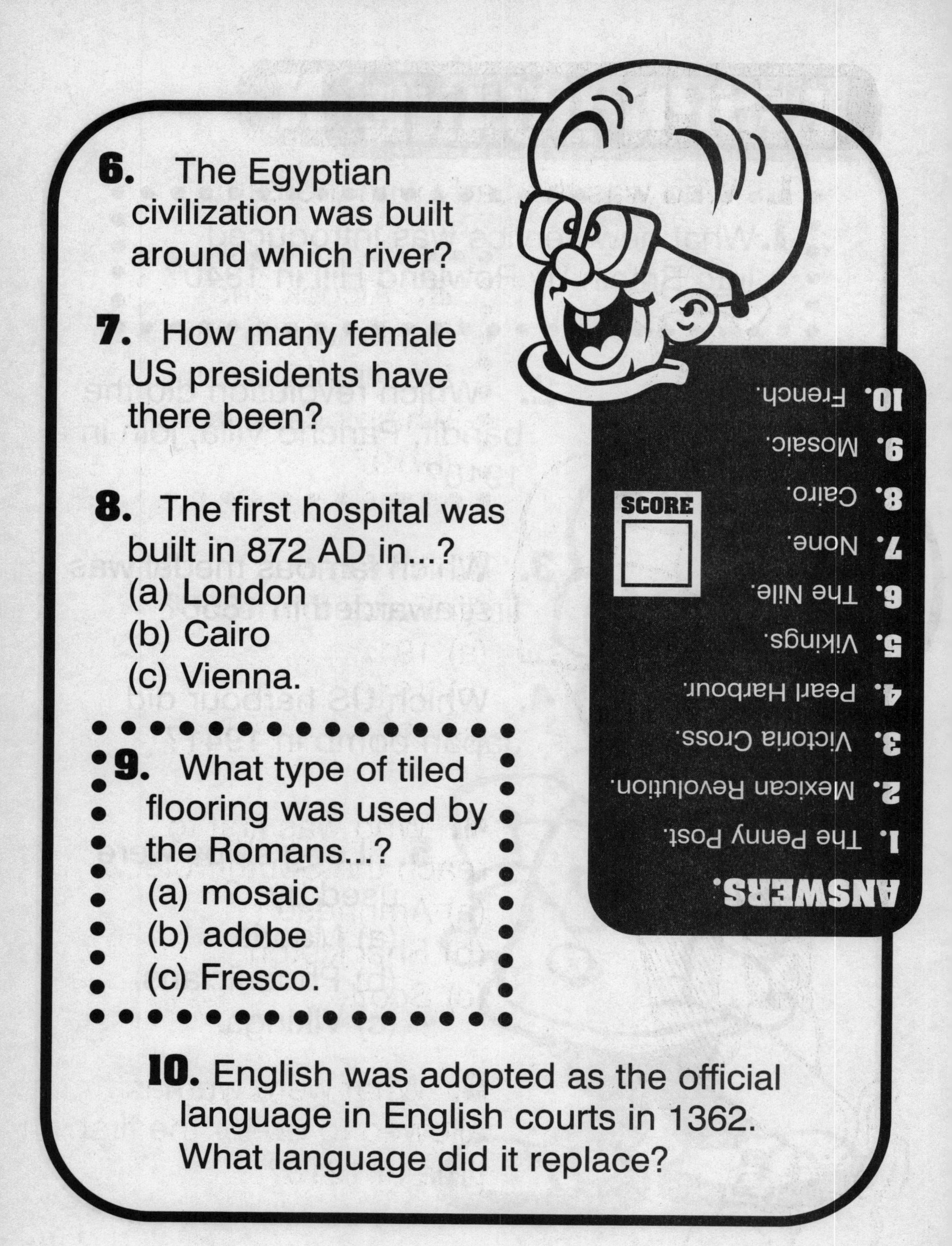

6. The Egyptian civilization was built around which river?

7. How many female US presidents have there been?

8. The first hospital was built in 872 AD in...?
(a) London
(b) Cairo
(c) Vienna.

9. What type of tiled flooring was used by the Romans...?
(a) mosaic
(b) adobe
(c) Fresco.

10. English was adopted as the official language in English courts in 1362. What language did it replace?

ANSWERS.

1. The Penny Post.
2. Mexican Revolution.
3. Victoria Cross.
4. Pearl Harbour.
5. Vikings.
6. The Nile.
7. None.
8. Cairo.
9. Mosaic.
10. French.

SCORE

DESPERATE DAN

1. Who was the Lady with the Lamp?

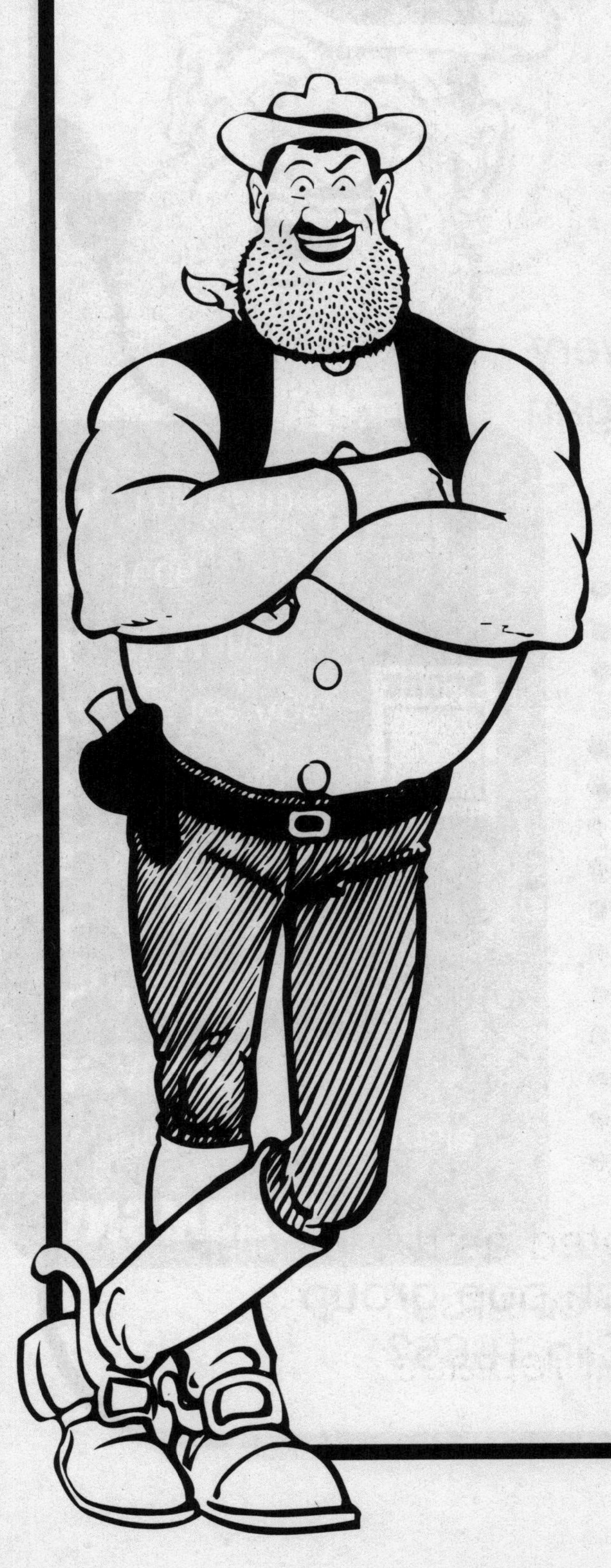

2. Alcock and Brown made the first flight across which ocean in 1919?

3. When was the Royal Air Force formed?
(a) 1912
(b) 1918
(c) 1939.

4. Who was first to reach the South Pole...?
(a) Amundsen
(b) Shackleton
(c) Scott.

5. What were woman allowed to do for the first time in 1918?

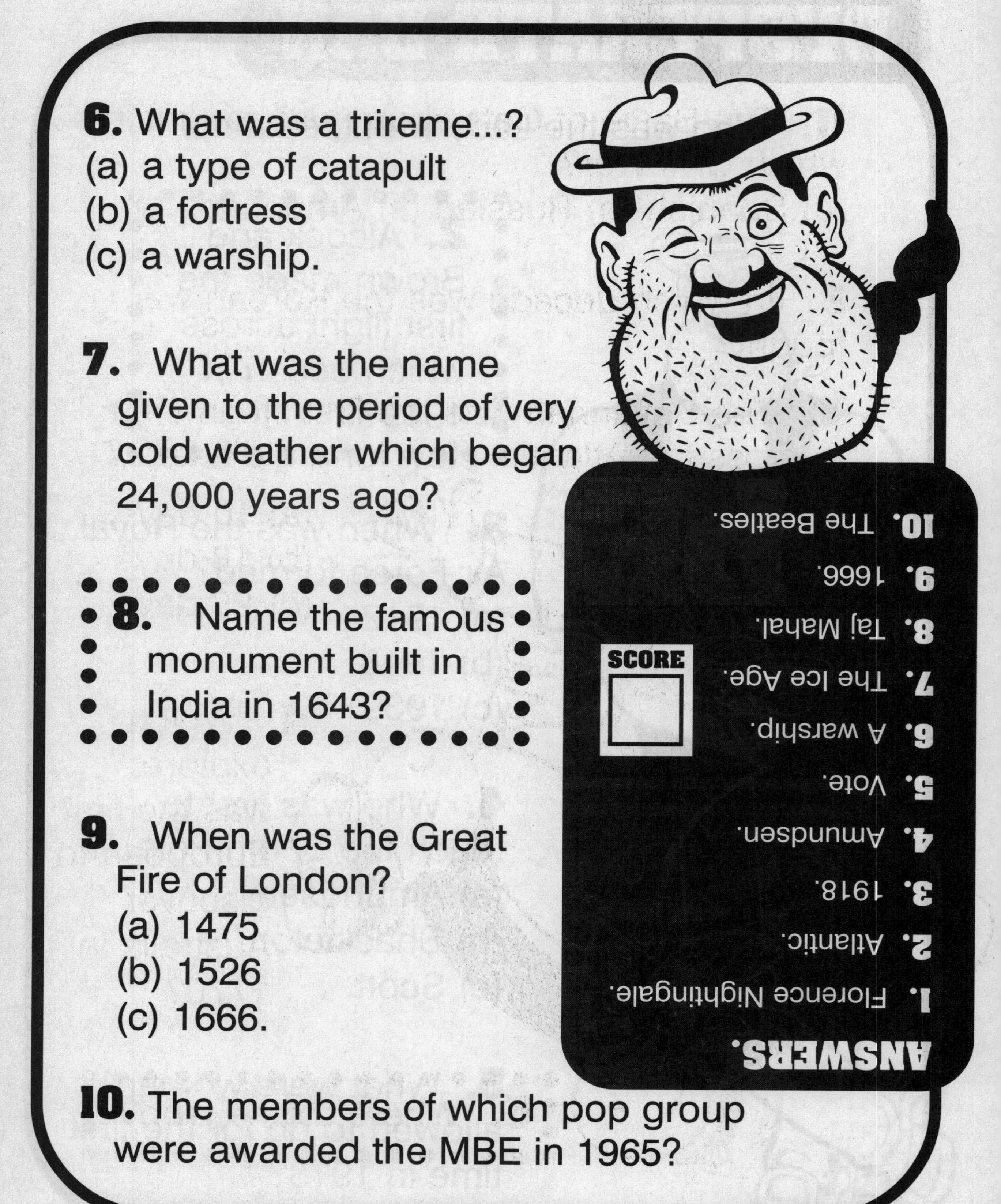

6. What was a trireme...?
(a) a type of catapult
(b) a fortress
(c) a warship.

7. What was the name given to the period of very cold weather which began 24,000 years ago?

8. Name the famous monument built in India in 1643?

9. When was the Great Fire of London?
(a) 1475
(b) 1526
(c) 1666.

10. The members of which pop group were awarded the MBE in 1965?

ANSWERS.
1. Florence Nightingale.
2. Atlantic.
3. 1918.
4. Amundsen.
5. Vote.
6. A warship.
7. The Ice Age.
8. Taj Mahal.
9. 1666.
10. The Beatles.

SCORE

FATTY

1. The Battle of Gettysburg was fought in which Civil War?
(a) Spanish (b) Russian (c) American.

2. In which decade was the Korean war fought?

3. The Savannah was the first steamship to cross the Atlantic. How long did it take?

(a) 10 days
(b) 18 days
(c) 26 days.

4. Which explorer was the first European to discover Australia in 1770?

5. Where did he land?

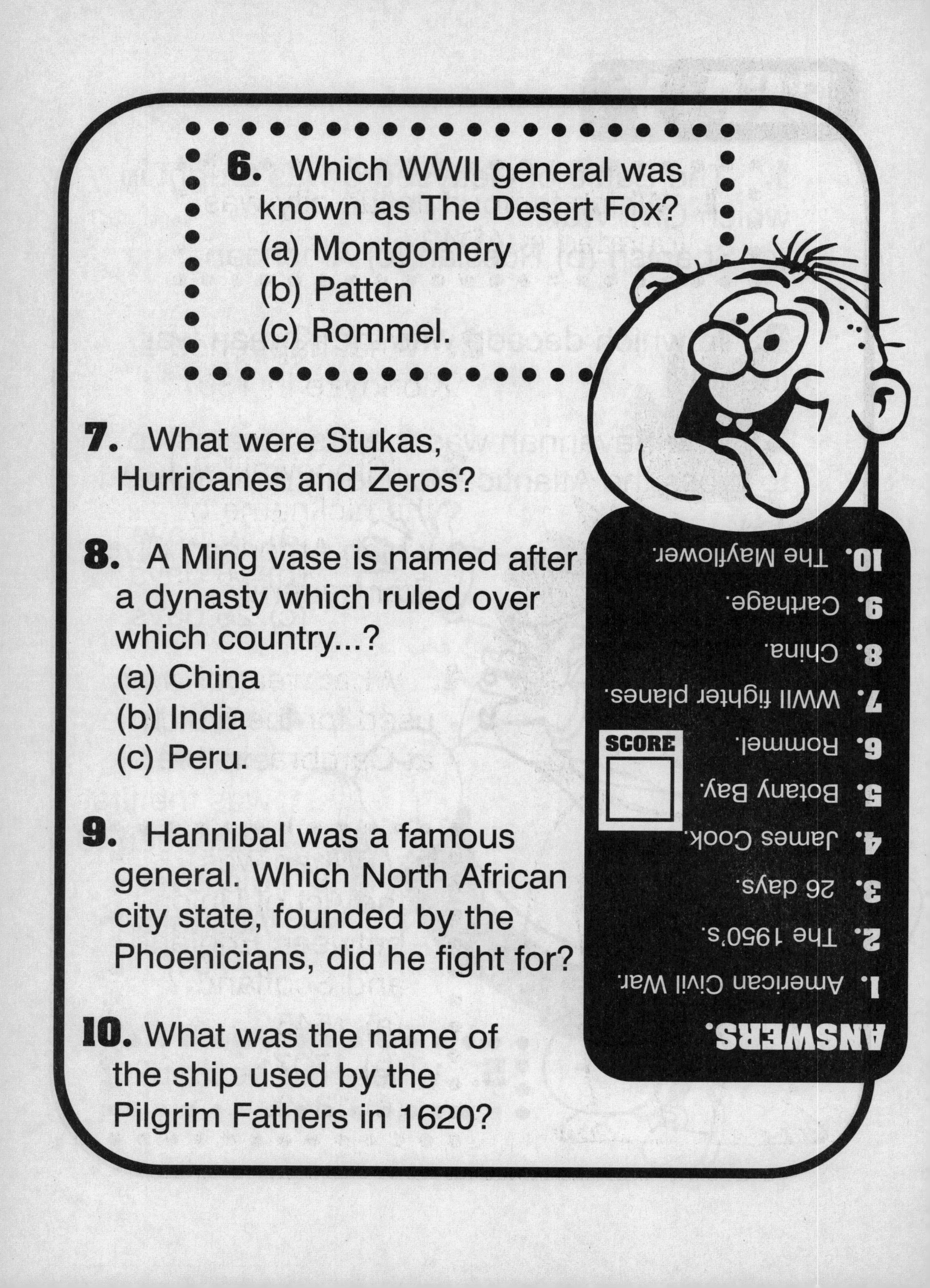

6. Which WWII general was known as The Desert Fox?
(a) Montgomery
(b) Patten
(c) Rommel.

7. What were Stukas, Hurricanes and Zeros?

8. A Ming vase is named after a dynasty which ruled over which country...?
(a) China
(b) India
(c) Peru.

9. Hannibal was a famous general. Which North African city state, founded by the Phoenicians, did he fight for?

10. What was the name of the ship used by the Pilgrim Fathers in 1620?

ANSWERS.

1. American Civil War.
2. The 1950's.
3. 26 days.
4. James Cook.
5. Botany Bay.
6. Rommel.
7. WWII fighter planes.
8. China.
9. Carthage.
10. The Mayflower.

SCORE

1. Which famous Italian city was founded in AD43?

2. What happened at Klondyke in 1897?

3. "Stonewall" was the nickname of which American Civil War general?

4. What weapon was used for the first time at Cambrai in 1916?

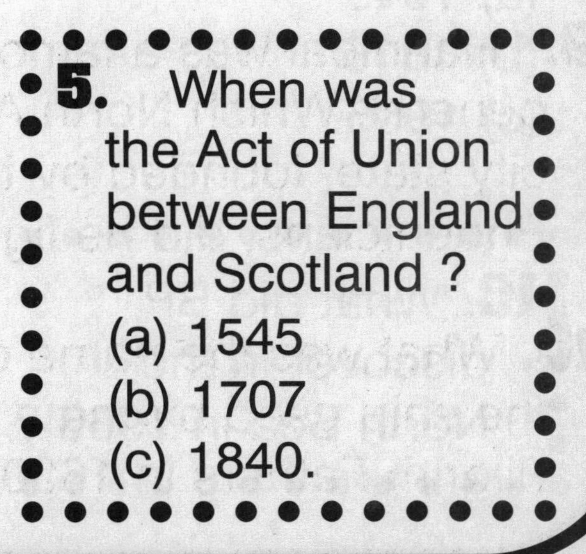

5. When was the Act of Union between England and Scotland ?
(a) 1545
(b) 1707
(c) 1840.

6. Peary was the first man to reach the pole in 1909. Was it the North or South Pole?

7. In which country did the Bolshevik Revolution take place in 1917?

8. The Gulf War began when which country was invaded?

9. Norway became an independent country in...?
(a) 1649
(b) 1816
(c) 1905.

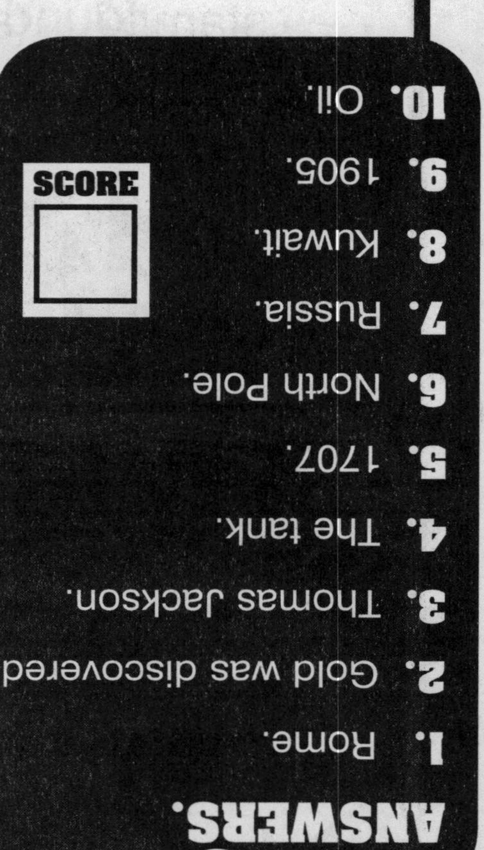

10. What did BP discover in the North Sea in 1965 ?

IVY

1. What was the colour of the first postage stamp?
(a) red
(b) brown
(c) black.

2. Who won the world Cup in 1966?

3. What kind of institution opened for the first time in Cairo in AD972?

4. Who wrote the Origin of the Species?

5. Which monastery was founded by St Columba in AD 563?

6. Who was the first English sailor to sail round the world, in 1580?

7. What was the Black Death?

8. Who left Britain in AD 407?

9. America acquired Florida in 1819. From which country?

10. Which African country did Italy invade in 1935?
(a) Tunisia
(b) Jordan
(c) Abyssinia.

ANSWERS.

1. Black.
2. England.
3. A university.
4. Charles Darwin.
5. Iona.
6. Francis Drake.
7. A terrible plague of the 14th Century.
8. The Romans.
9. Spain.
10. Abyssinia.

SCORE

SMIFFY

1. What first appeared on the streets of London in 1958?

2. Which country declared itself independent from Britain in 1776?

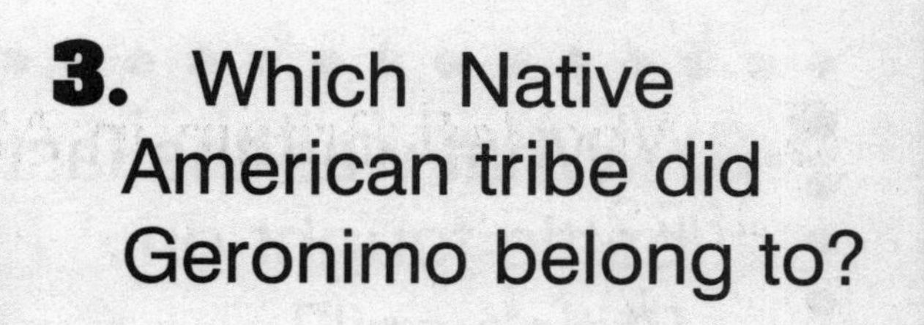

3. Which Native American tribe did Geronimo belong to?

4. Which wall was built in 1961 and knocked down in 1989?

5. Which famous English sailor was executed?
(a) Raleigh
(b) Frobisher
(c) Shackleton.

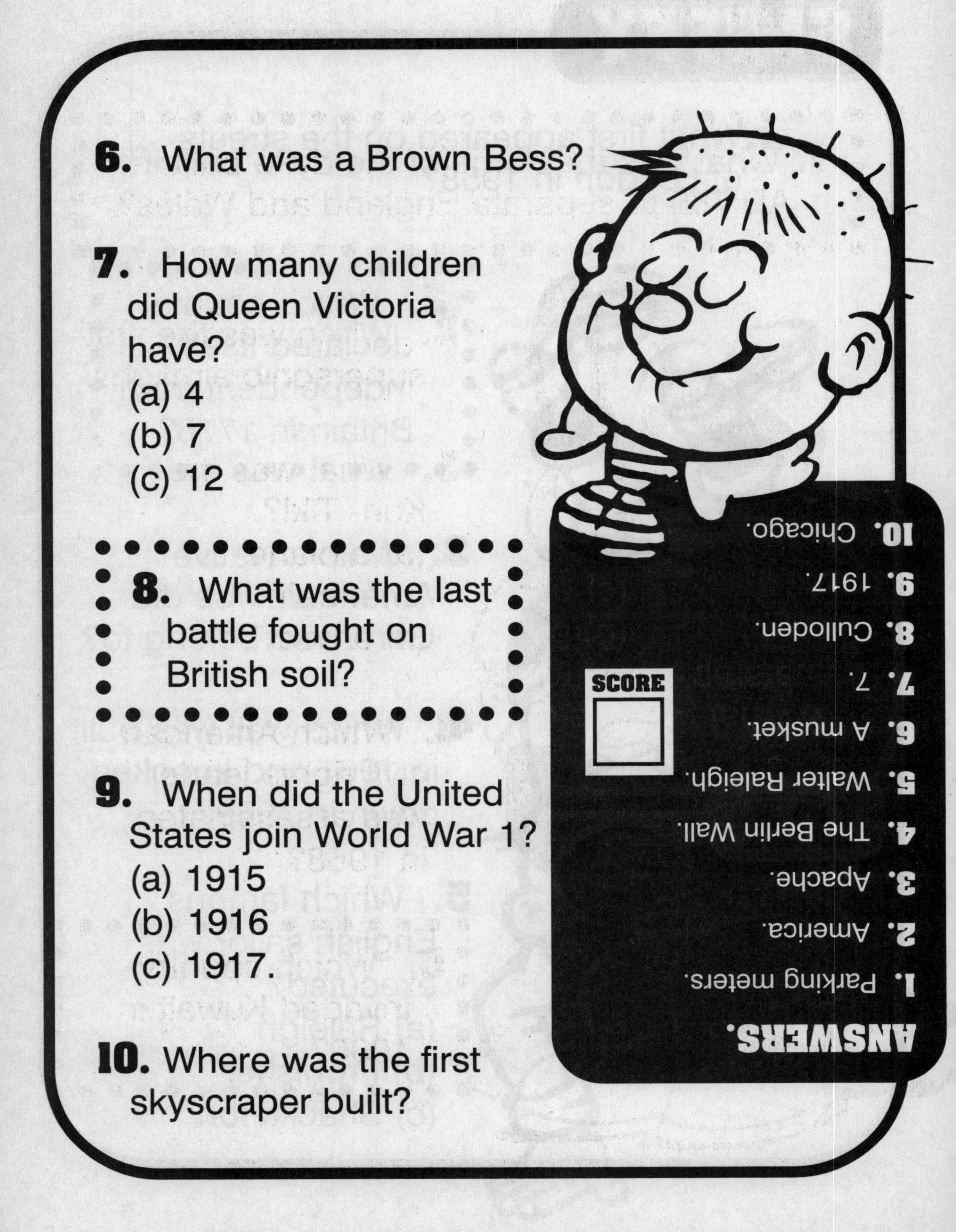

6. What was a Brown Bess?

7. How many children did Queen Victoria have?
(a) 4
(b) 7
(c) 12

8. What was the last battle fought on British soil?

9. When did the United States join World War 1?
(a) 1915
(b) 1916
(c) 1917.

10. Where was the first skyscraper built?

ANSWERS.
1. Parking meters.
2. America.
3. Apache.
4. The Berlin Wall.
5. Walter Raleigh.
6. A musket.
7. 7.
8. Culloden.
9. 1917.
10. Chicago.

SCORE

BLINKY

1. What was the name of the dyke built in AD 785 to separate England and Wales?

2. When was the first supersonic air flight?

3. What was the Kon- Tiki?
(a) a plane
(b) a train
(c) a boat.

4. Which American civil rights leader was assassinated in 1968?

5. Which country invaded Kuwait in 1990?

6. In 1381 there was a popular revolt against the Poll Tax. What was it called?

7. Which canal between the Atlantic and the Pacific was opened in 1914?

8. What kind of ship did Zeppelin build in 1898?

9. What was the name of the dictator who led Italy in the Second World War?

10. When was the first electric washing machine built?
(a) 1869
(b) 1910
(c) 1889.

ANSWERS.

1. Offa's Dyke.
2. 1947.
3. A bamboo boat built to sail across the Pacific.
4. Martin Luther King.
5. Iraq.
6. The Peasants' Revolt.
7. The Panama Canal.
8. An airship.
9. Mussolini.
10. 1869.

GNASHER

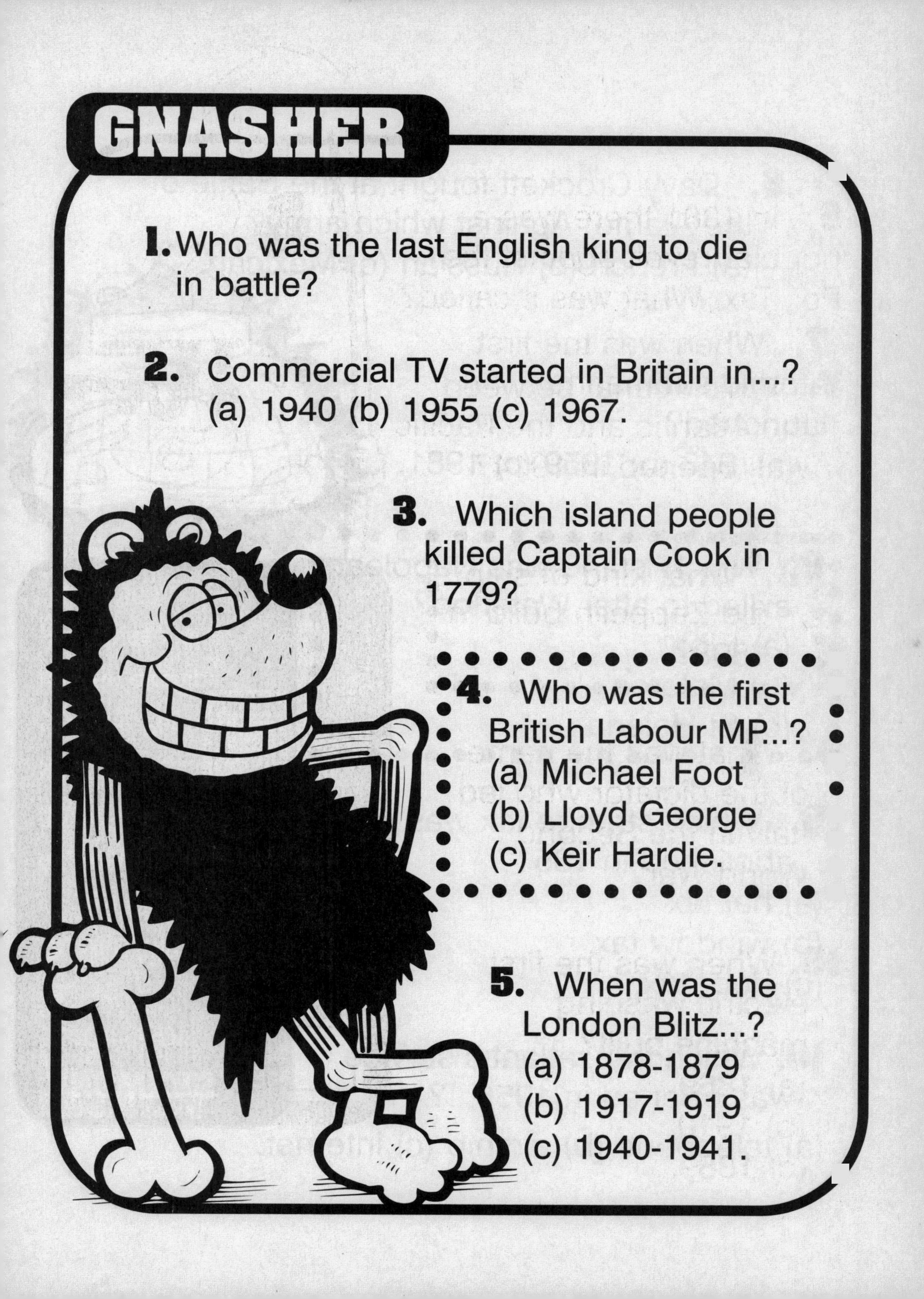

1. Who was the last English king to die in battle?

2. Commercial TV started in Britain in...? (a) 1940 (b) 1955 (c) 1967.

3. Which island people killed Captain Cook in 1779?

4. Who was the first British Labour MP...?
(a) Michael Foot
(b) Lloyd George
(c) Keir Hardie.

5. When was the London Blitz...?
(a) 1878-1879
(b) 1917-1919
(c) 1940-1941.

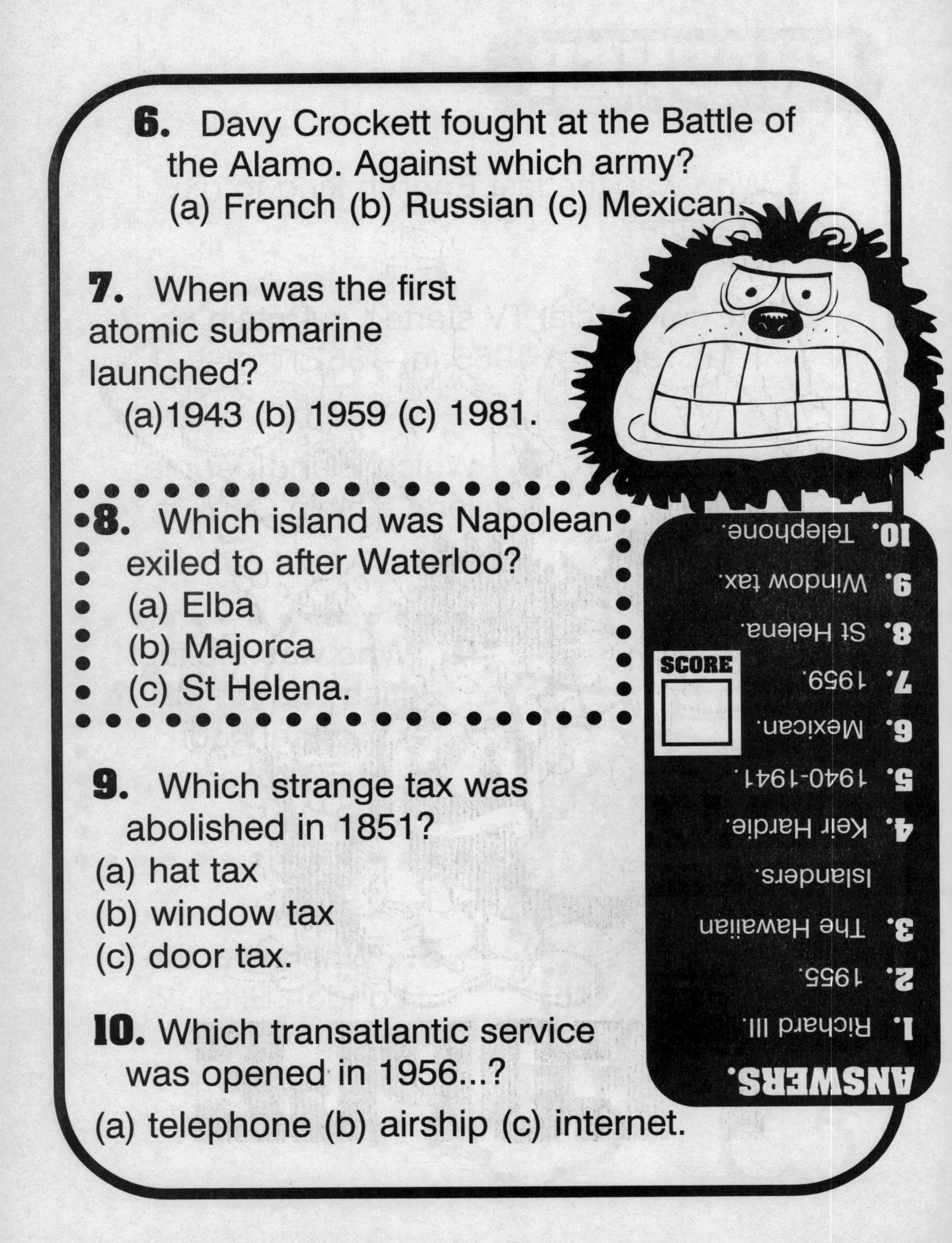

6. Davy Crockett fought at the Battle of the Alamo. Against which army?
(a) French (b) Russian (c) Mexican.

7. When was the first atomic submarine launched?
(a)1943 (b) 1959 (c) 1981.

8. Which island was Napolean exiled to after Waterloo?
(a) Elba
(b) Majorca
(c) St Helena.

9. Which strange tax was abolished in 1851?
(a) hat tax
(b) window tax
(c) door tax.

10. Which transatlantic service was opened in 1956...?
(a) telephone (b) airship (c) internet.

ANSWERS.
1. Richard III.
2. 1955.
3. The Hawaiian Islanders.
4. Keir Hardie.
5. 1940-1941.
6. Mexican.
7. 1959.
8. St Helena.
9. Window tax.
10. Telephone.

SCORE

PEOPLE

DENNIS

1. What was William Frederick Cody known as?

2. Which people used to hunt with the boomerang?

3. Who lives at 11 Downing Street?

4. Name a famous English sailor called ..er ...Walter?

5. Which famous pop group were Agnetha, Frida, Bjorn and Benny

6. Where was the Aztec Empire?
(a) Japan (b) Mexico (c) Peru.

7. What sport do you associate with Tim Henman?

8. A British politician is sometimes called "The Iron Lady". Can you name her?

9. If you used a scalpel, would you be...?
(a) a surgeon
(b) a carpenter
(c) a sculptor.

10. Which people believed they would go to Valhalla if they died in battle?
(a) Mongols
(b) Franks
(c) Vikings.

MINNIE

1. Which famous general had a boot named after him?

2. Can you name a composer with the initials JSB?

3. Who did Minnie Ha-Ha fall in love with?

4. Which singer was known as "The King"?

5. Who was the star of Mission Impossible?
(a) Tim Robbins
(b) Tom Cruise
(c) Clint Eastwood.

6. Who was Blackbeard?

7. Which American president was a well known film actor?

8. Was Amy Johnson
(a) a singer
(b) a politician
(c) an aviator?

9. What is the name of the native people of New Zealand?

10. Who began his diary aged thirteen and three-quarters?

ANSWERS.

1. Wellington.
2. Johann Sebastian Bach.
3. Hiawatha.
4. Elvis Presley.
5. Tom Cruise.

6. A pirate.
7. Ronald Reagan.
8. Aviator.
9. Maoris.
10. Adrian Mole.

BILLY WHIZZ

1. Was Billy the Kid...?
(a) a pirate
(b) a gunfighter
(c) a highwayman.

2. Who was killed at the Battle of Little Big Horn?

3. What is Gazza's real name?

4. Is Mike Atherton...?
(a) a jockey
(b) a singer
(c) a cricketer.

5. Which football team did Matt Busby manage?
(a) Tottenham Hotspur
(b) Liverpool
(c) Manchester United.

6. What language is spoken by people in Brazil?

7. The Victoria Falls were discovered by which explorer?

8. Who were the falls named after?

9. Is Mary Quant a model, a fashion designer or a singer?

10. What other name is used for the New Zealand rugby team?

ANSWERS.

1. Gunfighter.
2. General Custer.
3. Paul Gascoigne.
4. A cricketer.
5. Manchester United.
6. Portuguese.
7. David Livingstone.
8. Queen Victoria.
9. Fashion designer.
10. The All Blacks.

SCORE

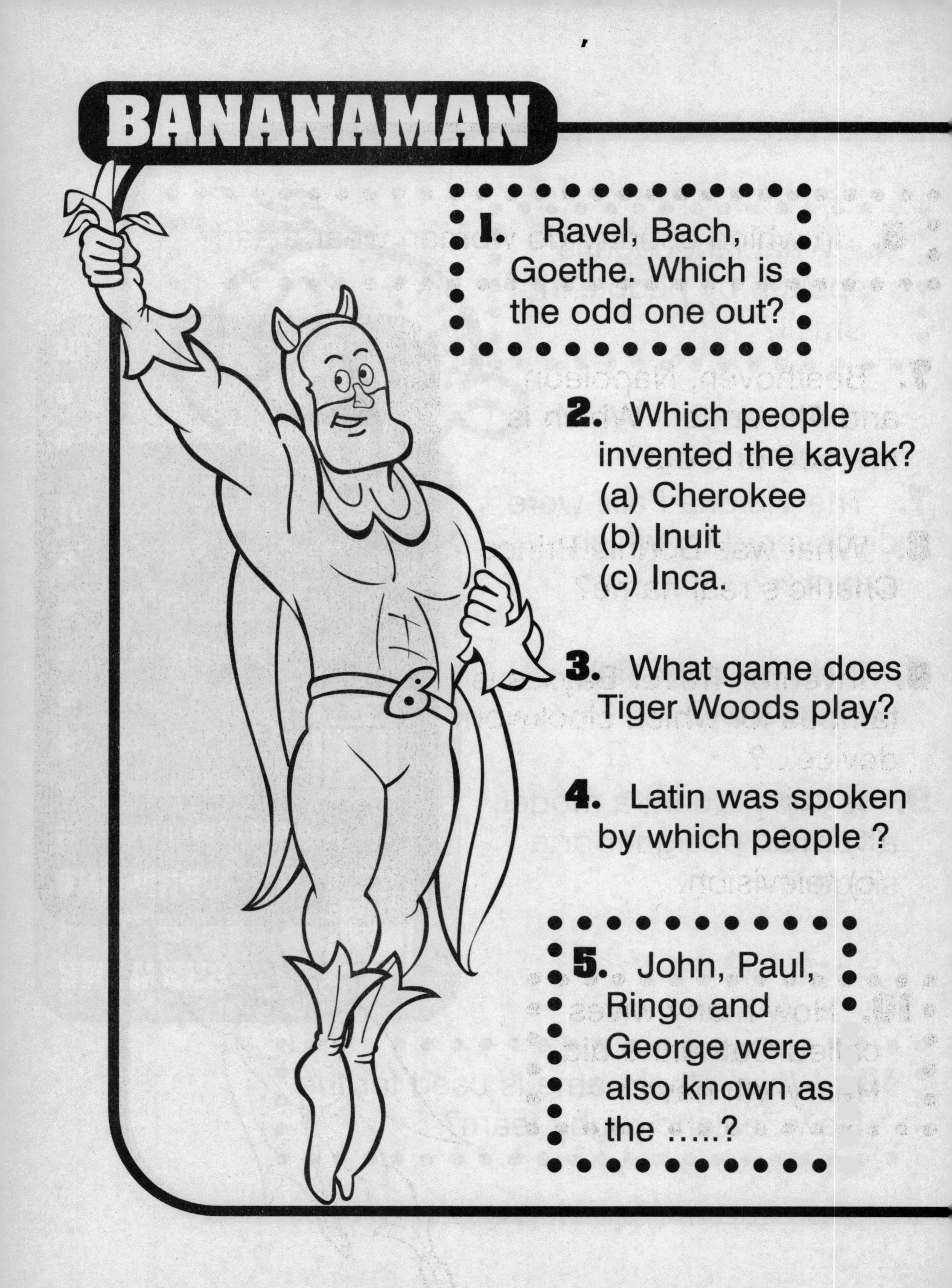
BANANAMAN
1. Ravel, Bach, Goethe. Which is the odd one out?
2. Which people invented the kayak?
(a) Cherokee
(b) Inuit
(c) Inca.
3. What game does Tiger Woods play?
4. Latin was spoken by which people ?
5. John, Paul, Ringo and George were also known as the …..?

6. In which country do woman wear a sari?

7. Beethoven, Napoleon and Alexander. Which is the odd one out?

8. What was Bonnie Prince Charlie's real name?

9. Inventor Trevor Bayliss is famous for which clockwork device...?
(a) train
(b) radio
(c) television.

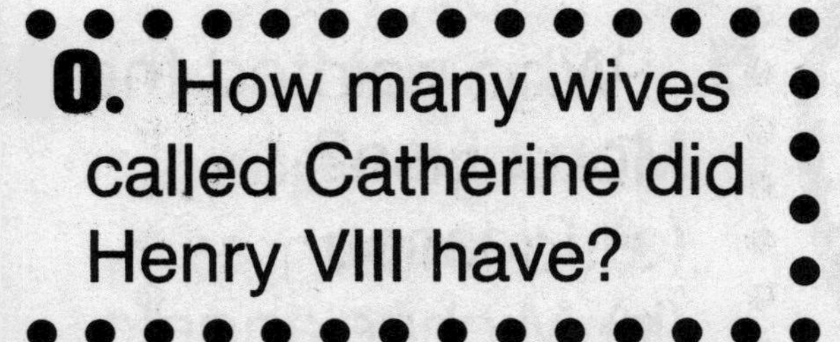

10. How many wives called Catherine did Henry VIII have?

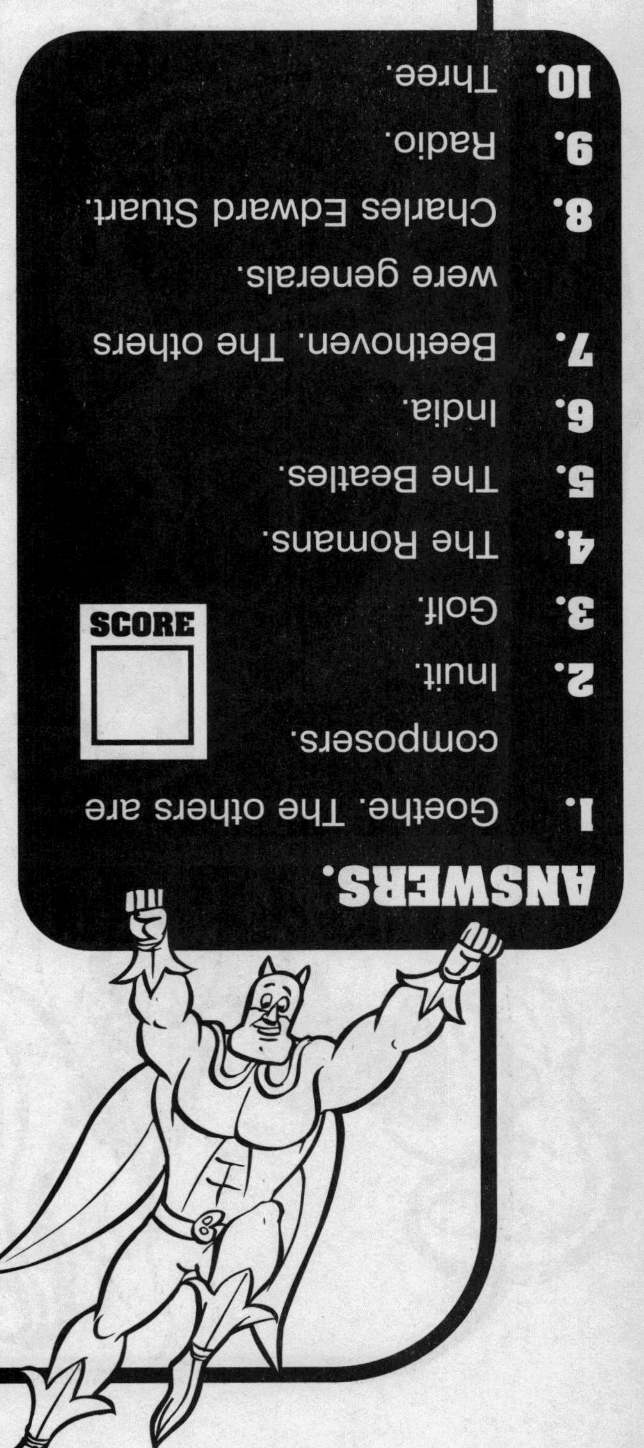

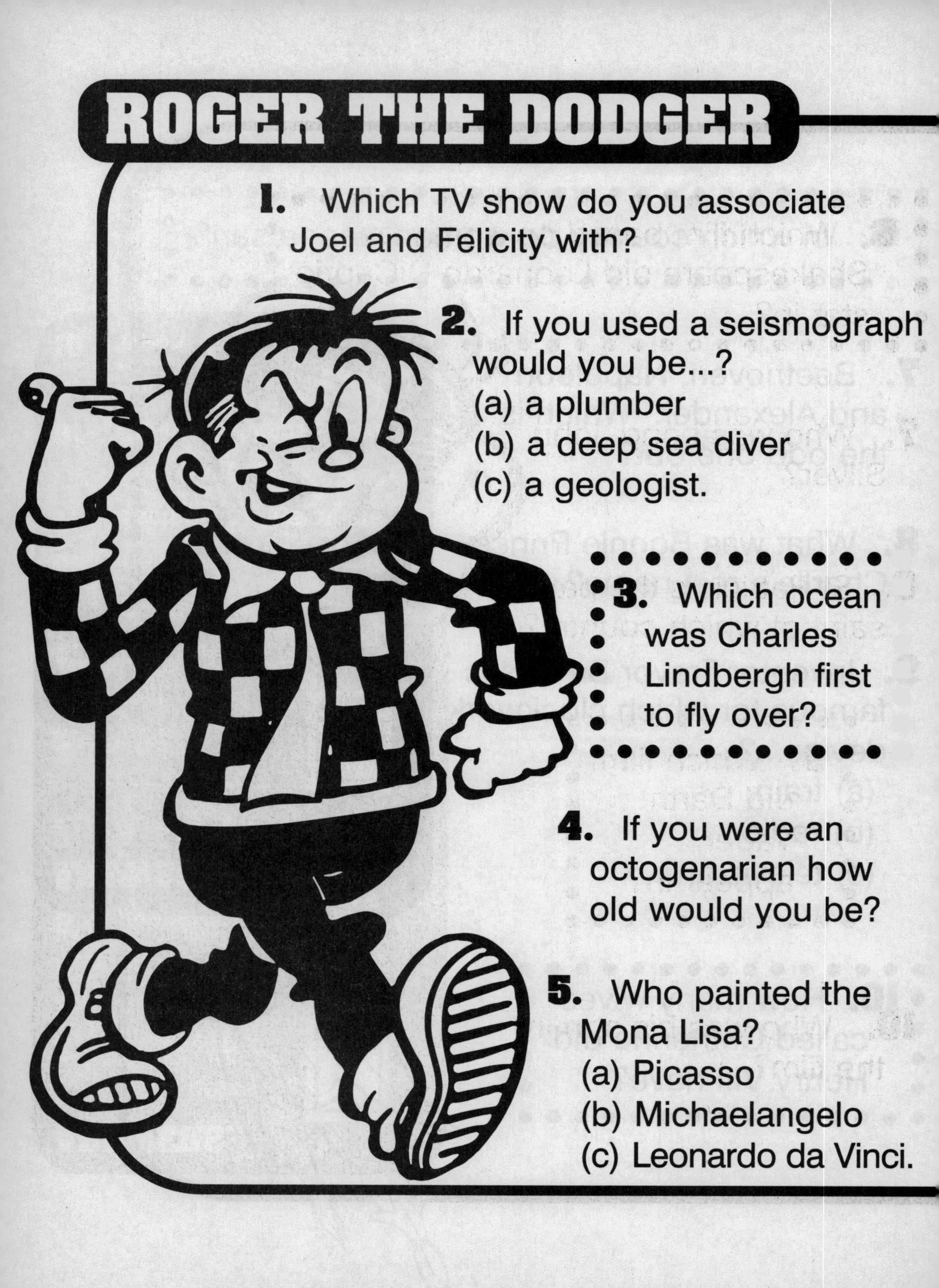

ROGER THE DODGER

1. Which TV show do you associate Joel and Felicity with?

2. If you used a seismograph would you be...?
(a) a plumber
(b) a deep sea diver
(c) a geologist.

3. Which ocean was Charles Lindbergh first to fly over?

4. If you were an octogenarian how old would you be?

5. Who painted the Mona Lisa?
(a) Picasso
(b) Michaelangelo
(c) Leonardo da Vinci.

6. Which film based on a play by Shakespeare did Leonardo DiCaprio star in?

7. Who was Long John Silver?

8. St Patrick is the patron saint of which country?

9. Which film did Darth Vader appear in?

10. Who was his son in the film?

ANSWERS.

1. Neighbours.
2. Geologist.
3. Atlantic.
4. 80.
5. Leonardo da Vinci.
6. Romeo and Juliet.
7. A pirate in the novel, Treasure Island.
8. Ireland.
9. Star Wars.
10. Luke Skywalker.

SCORE

BERYL THE PERIL

1. Is Michael Fish a game show host , a sports commentator or a weatherman?

2. What do the initials WHO stand for?

3. What language is spoken in the Netherlands?

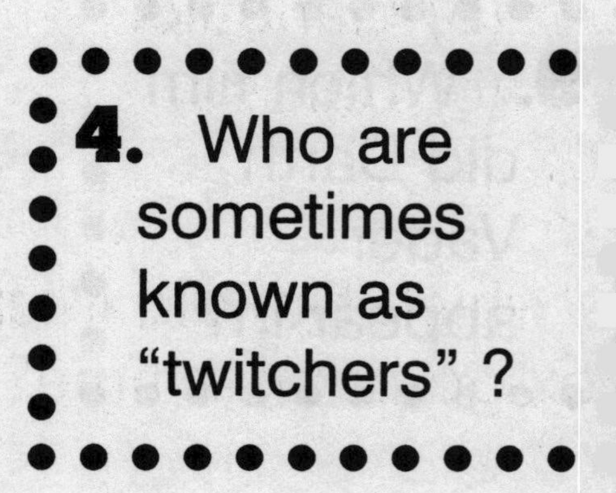

4. Who are sometimes known as "twitchers" ?

5. Which sport is Linford Christie associated with?

6. Who did Sophie Rhys-Jones marry in 1999?

7. Which pop group did Barry, Robin and Maurice Gibb form?

8. Who is the odd one out? (a) Pavorotti
(b) Garibaldi
(c) Caruso.

9. In which film did Michael J Fox go back in time?

10. Which well known singer introduces Blind Date?

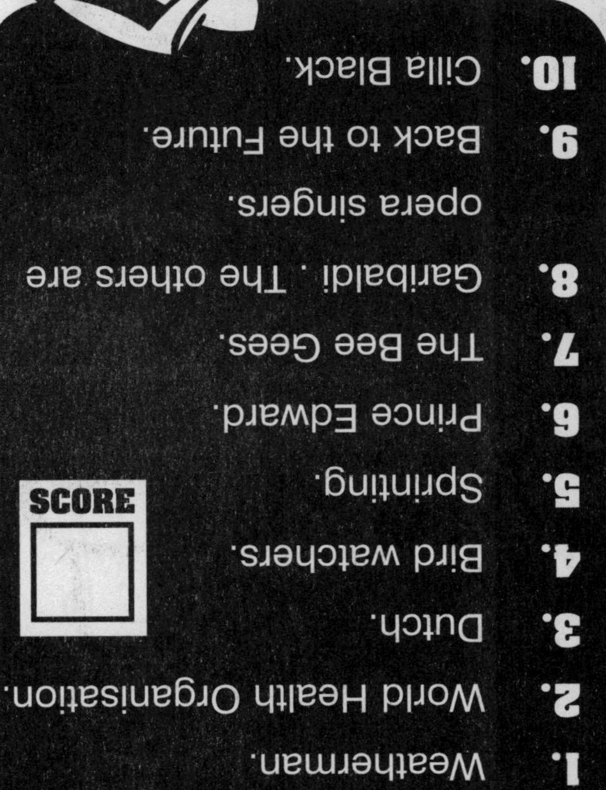

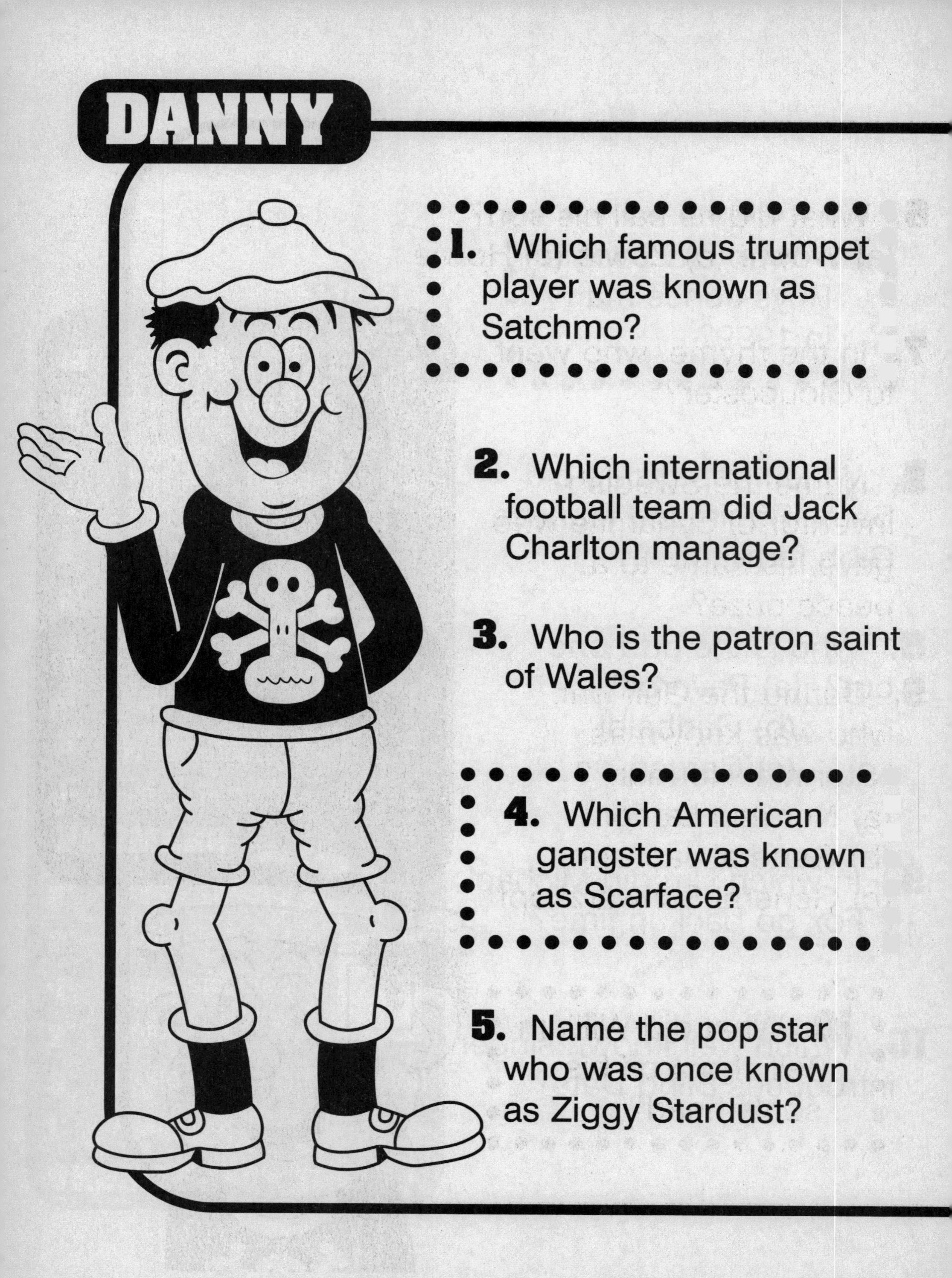
DANNY
1. Which famous trumpet player was known as Satchmo?
2. Which international football team did Jack Charlton manage?
3. Who is the patron saint of Wales?
4. Which American gangster was known as Scarface?
5. Name the pop star who was once known as Ziggy Stardust?

6. What did he call his son?
(a) Wowie (b) Zowie (c) Howie

7. In the rhyme, who went to Gloucester?

8. Name the Swedish inventor of dynamite who gave his name to a peace prize?

9. During the Gulf war, who was known as "Stormin' Norman"?
(a) Norman Lamont
(b) General Jackson
(c) General Schwarzkopf

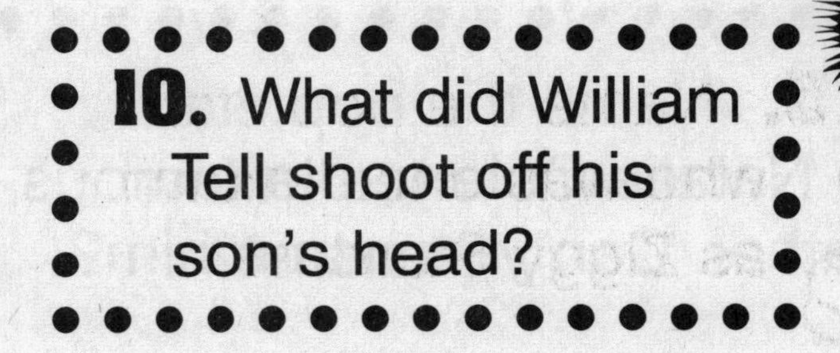

10. What did William Tell shoot off his son's head?

ANSWERS.

1. Louis Armstrong.
2. Republic of Ireland.
3. St David.
4. Al Capone.
5. David Bowie.
6. Zowie.
7. Dr Foster.
8. Nobel.
9. Gen. Schwarzkopf.
10. An apple.

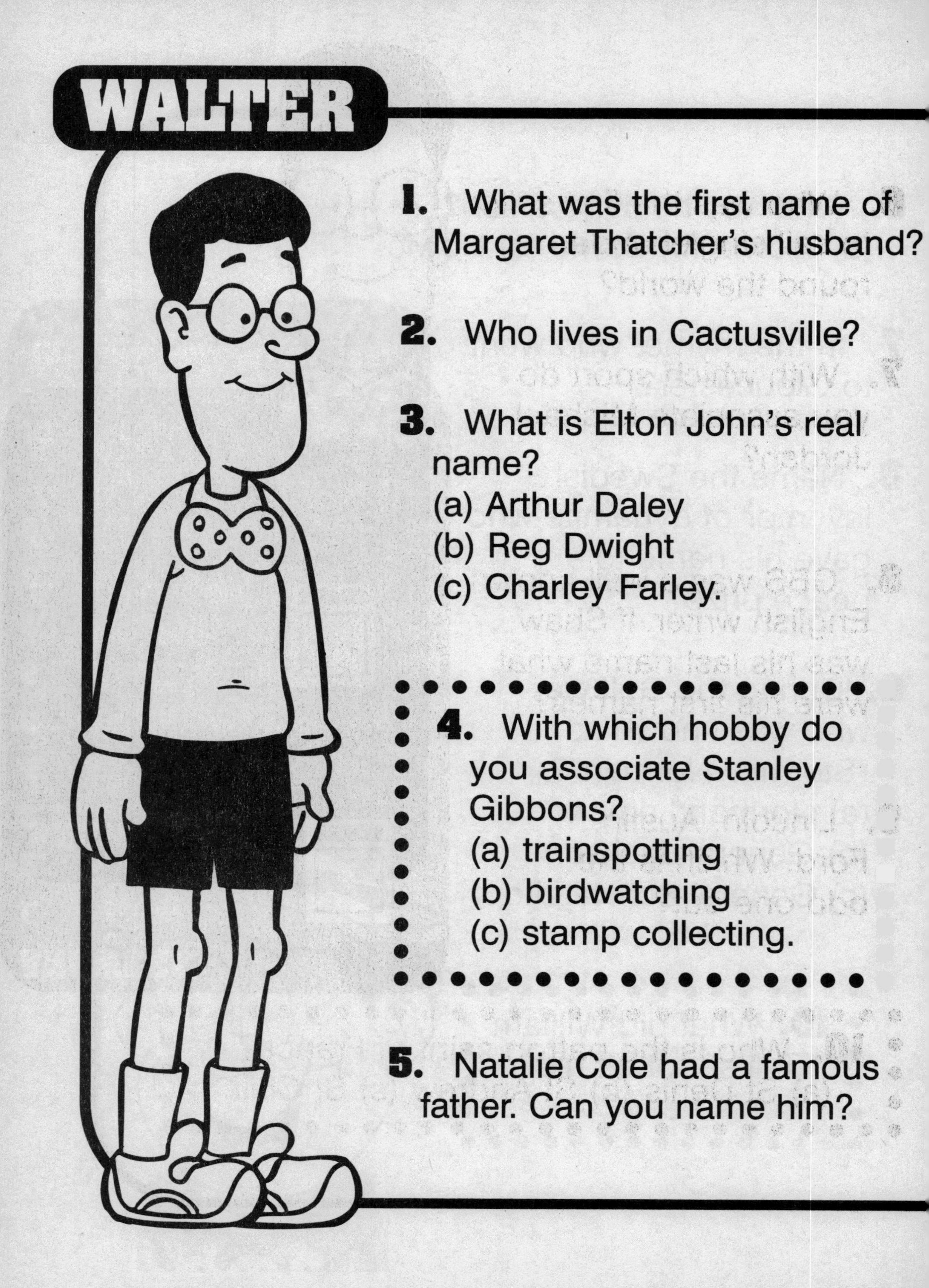

1. What was the first name of Margaret Thatcher's husband?

2. Who lives in Cactusville?

3. What is Elton John's real name?
(a) Arthur Daley
(b) Reg Dwight
(c) Charley Farley.

4. With which hobby do you associate Stanley Gibbons?
(a) trainspotting
(b) birdwatching
(c) stamp collecting.

5. Natalie Cole had a famous father. Can you name him?

6. Who was the first sailor to sail singlehanded round the world?

7. With which sport do you associate Michael Jordan?

8. GBS was a well known English writer. If Shaw was his last name what were his first names?

9. Lincoln, Austin, Ford. Which is the odd one out?

10. Who is the patron saint of France? (a) St Denis (b) St Andrew (c) St Clair.

ANSWERS.

1. Dennis.
2. Desperate Dan.
3. Reg Dwight.
4. Stamp collecting.
5. Nat King Cole.
6. Joshua Slocum.
7. Basketball.
8. George Bernard.
9. Austin. The others were American presidents.
10. St Denis.

SCORE

THE NUMSKULLS

1. General Blight is the enemy of which comic superhero?

2. Jakob, Guipetto and Jaques are all foreign versions of which popular name?

3. If you were an ornithologist what would you study?
(a) weather
(b) rocks
(c) birds.

4. Which of the Attenborough brothers is a famous naturalist?

5. Which writer created David Copperfield?

6. "Teddy" bears were named after?
(a) Edward Heath
(b) Theodore Roosevelt
(c) Eddy Izzard.

7. What was the gunfighter William Bonney also known as?

8. Edmund Hillary was the first man to climb which mountain?

9. What country was he from?
(a) Scotland
(b) South Africa
(c) New Zealand.

10. Which instrument did Jimi Hendrix play?

ANSWERS.
1. Bananaman.
2. James.
3. Birds.
4. David.
5. Charles Dickens.
6. Theodore Roosevelt.
7. Billy the Kid.
8. Mount Everest.
9. New Zealand.
10. Guitar.

SCORE

PLUG

1. Which TV detective was played by John Thaw?

2. Who defeated Goliath with a catapult?

3. Ian Hislop is the editor of Private Eye. Which TV programme does he appear in?

4. Which tennis star was known as superbrat?

5. Cortez conquered the Inca Empire. Was he Portuguese, Dutch or Spanish?

6. Barry Sheene is famous for riding...?
(a) horses
(b) motorcycles
(c) balloons.

7. Which country was Haile Selassie the Emperor of?
(a) Egypt
(b) Libya
(c) Ethiopia.

8. Which instrument did Dizzy Gillespie play?
(a) saxophone
(b) drums
(c) trumpet.

9. Which continent was named after Amerigo Vespucci?

10. What is Superman's other name?

ANSWERS.
1. Inspector Morse.
2. David.
3. Have I got news for you ?
4. John McEnroe.
5. Spanish.
6. Motorcycles.
7. Ethiopia.
8. Trumpet.
9. America.
10. Clark Kent.

SCORE

CUDDLES AND DIMPLES

1. Which TV show did Rik Mayall star in?
   (a) Only Fools And Horses
   (b) The Young Ones
   (c) Porridge.

2. What is Maurice Micklewhite's stage name?

3. What sport was Sebastian Coe associated with before he became a politician ?

4. Who lives in Buckingham Palace ?

5. What was the name of Tarzan's mate ?
   (a) Betty (b) Agnes (c) Jane.

6. Who was Good Queen Bess ?

7. Harpo, Zeppo and Groucho were brothers. What were they known as ?

8. Who was the last male British tennis player to win a Grand Slam title ?

9. Who invented the characters Wallace and Grommit?
(a) Walt Disney
(b) Nick Park
(c) Steven Spielberg.

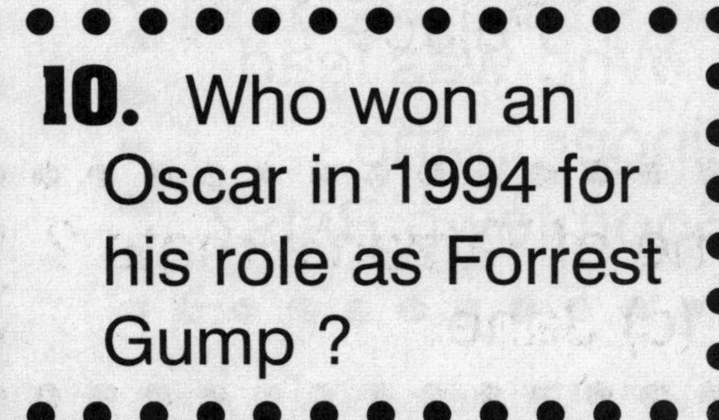

10. Who won an Oscar in 1994 for his role as Forrest Gump ?

ANSWERS.

1. The Young Ones.
2. Michael Caine.
3. Athletics.
4. The Queen.
5. Jane.
6. Queen Elizabeth I.
7. The Marx Brothers.
8. Fred Perry.
9. Nick Park.
10. Tom Hanks.

1. What name is the Brazilian sportsman, Edson Arantes do Nascimento better known by?

2. Who wrote the novel Kidnapped?

3. Who went to the Mad Hatters Tea Party?

4. El Cordobes was a famous?..
(a) pirate
(b) dancer
(c) bullfighter.

5. Who was lead singer in the Boomtown Rats?

6. With which sport do you associate Fred Trueman?

7. What nationality was Picasso?

8. If you were a centenarian, how old would you be?

9. Who led the charge of the Light Brigade at the Battle of Balaclava?
(a) Duke of Wellington
(b) Earl of Cardigan
(c) Duke of Cumberland

10. Is Jack Dee a golfer, singer or comedian?

ANSWERS.

1. Pele.
2. Robert Louis Stevenson.
3. Alice in Wonderland.
4. Bullfighter.
5. Sir Bob Geldof.
6. Cricket.
7. Spanish.
8. 100.
9. Earl of Cardigan.
10. Comedian.

MOLLY

1. Emil Zatopek was a famous?
(a) cyclist (b) swimmer (c) runner.

2. What name is Molly a version of?

3. In the Bible, what happened to Jonah?

4. Who wrote "The Pirates of Penzance"?
(a) Gilbert and George
(b) Gilbert and Grace
(c) Gilbert and Sullivan.

5. What was Glenda Jackson before she became an MP?

6. If you were a Grand Master, what game would you be playing?

7. Which famous comedian is known as the Big Yin?

8. Who was Montezuma?
(a) the last Aztec Emperor
(b) an Apache warchief
(c) a Spanish explorer.

9. Jane, Henry and Peter are all famous actors. What is their family name ?

10. Apache, Masai, Navaho. Which is the odd one out?

ANSWERS.

1. Runner.
2. Mary.
3. He was swallowed by a whale.
4. Gilbert and Sullivan.
5. An actress.
6. Chess.
7. Billy Connolly.
8. The last Aztec Emperor.
9. Fonda.
10. Masai. The other two are Native American tribes.

SCORE

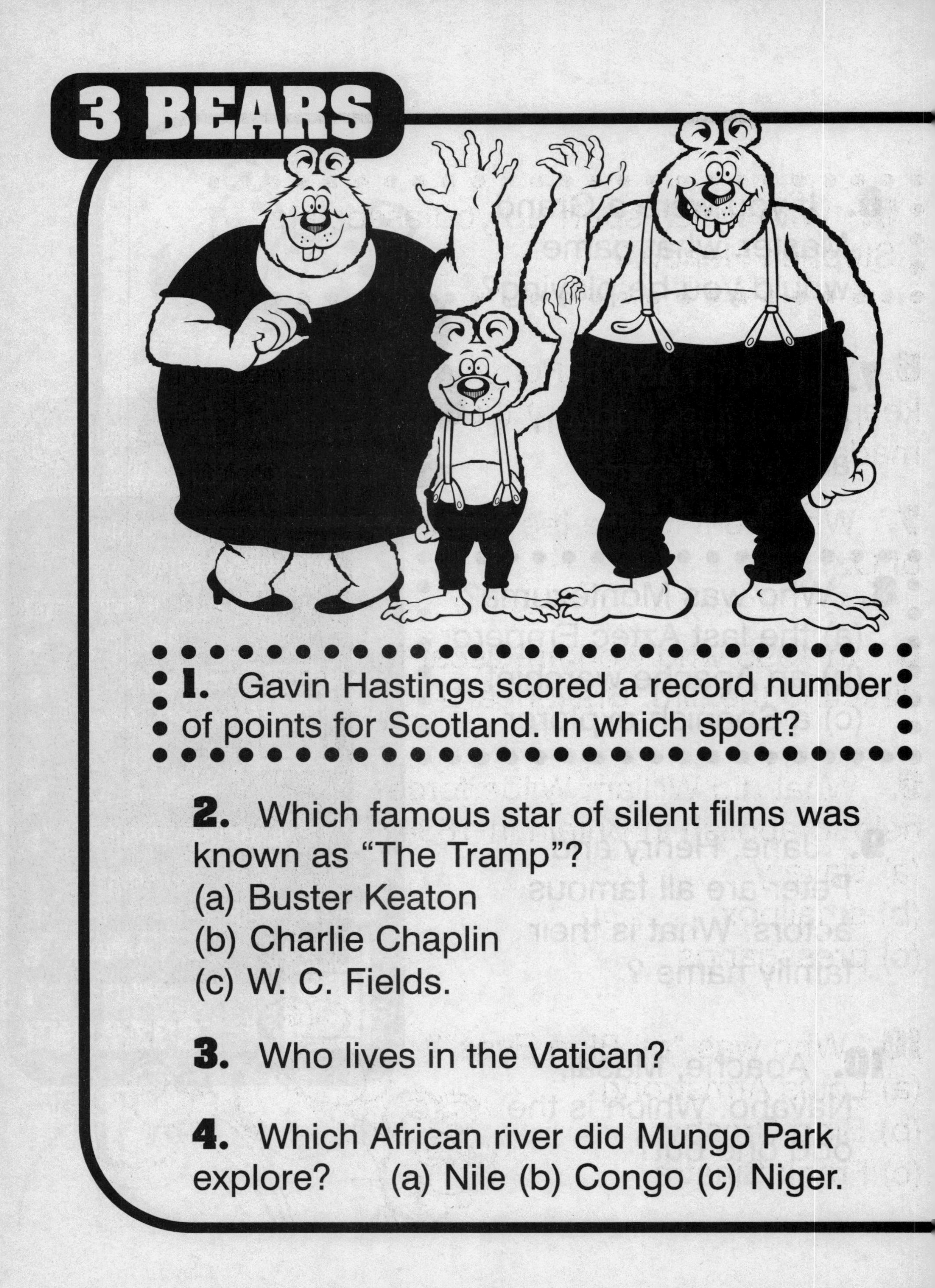

3 BEARS

1. Gavin Hastings scored a record number of points for Scotland. In which sport?

2. Which famous star of silent films was known as "The Tramp"?
(a) Buster Keaton
(b) Charlie Chaplin
(c) W. C. Fields.

3. Who lives in the Vatican?

4. Which African river did Mungo Park explore? (a) Nile (b) Congo (c) Niger.

5. With which sport do you associate Stephen Hendry?

6. What did Samuel Pepys keep in the 17th century that made him famous?

7. Who went to see the Wizard of Oz?

8. In 1995 who won an Oscar for directing the film, Braveheart?

9. What did William Wilberforce help to abolish in Britain in 1834?
(a) slavery
(b) smallpox
(c) pressgangs.

10. Who was "ol' Blue Eyes"?
(a) Louis Armstrong
(b) Bing Crosby
(c) Frank Sinatra.

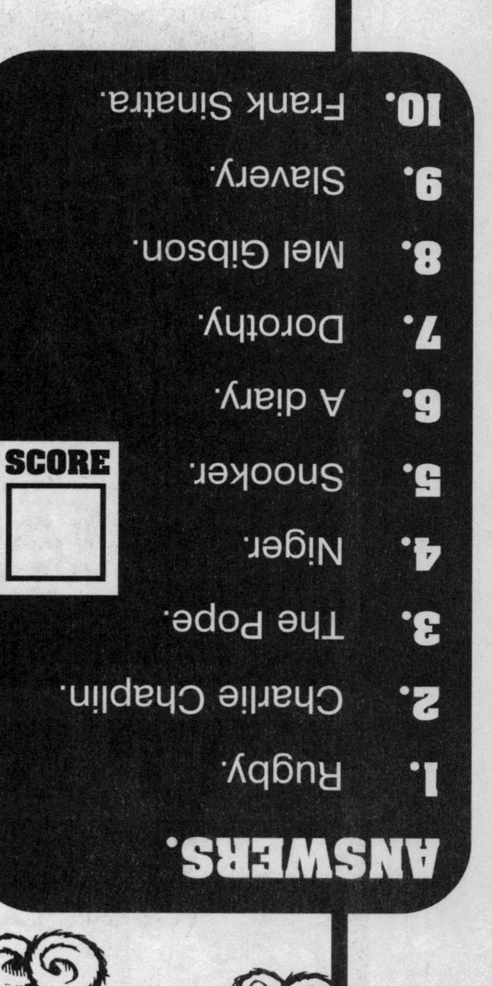

TEACHER

1. The United States bought Alaska in 1867. From which country? (a) Canada
(b) Japan
(c) Russia

2. Which film star played Maria in The Sound of Music?

3. What was the name of the real family, on whose adventures the film was based?

4. Stan Laurel was a famous comedian. Who was his partner?
(a) Oliver Hardy
(b) Buster Keaton
(c) Groucho Marx.

5. Who sailed in the Golden Hind?

6. What was named after William Halley?
(a) a telescope
(b) a concert hall
(c) a comet.

7. Which language is spoken in Majorca?

8. Who is Cherie Booth married to?

9. Which swimmer won 7 gold medals at the Munich Olympics in 1972?
(a) Ian Thorpe
(b) Aleksander Popov
(c) Mark Spitz.

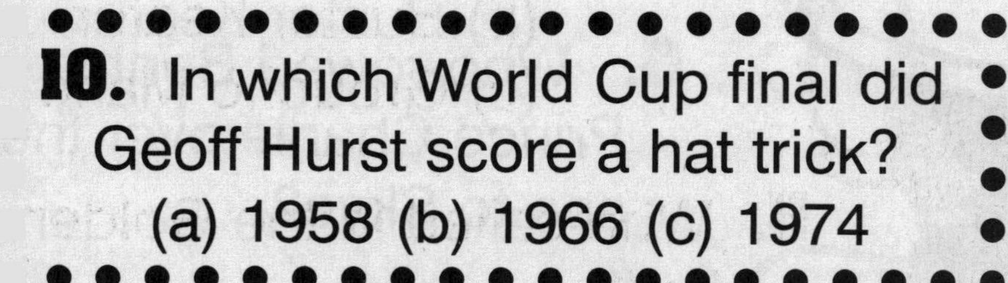

10. In which World Cup final did Geoff Hurst score a hat trick?
(a) 1958 (b) 1966 (c) 1974

ANSWERS.
1. Russia.
2. Julie Andrews.
3. The Von Trapp family.
4. Oliver Hardy.
5. Sir Francis Drake.
6. A comet.
7. Spanish.
8. Tony Blair.
9. Mark Spitz.
10. 1966.

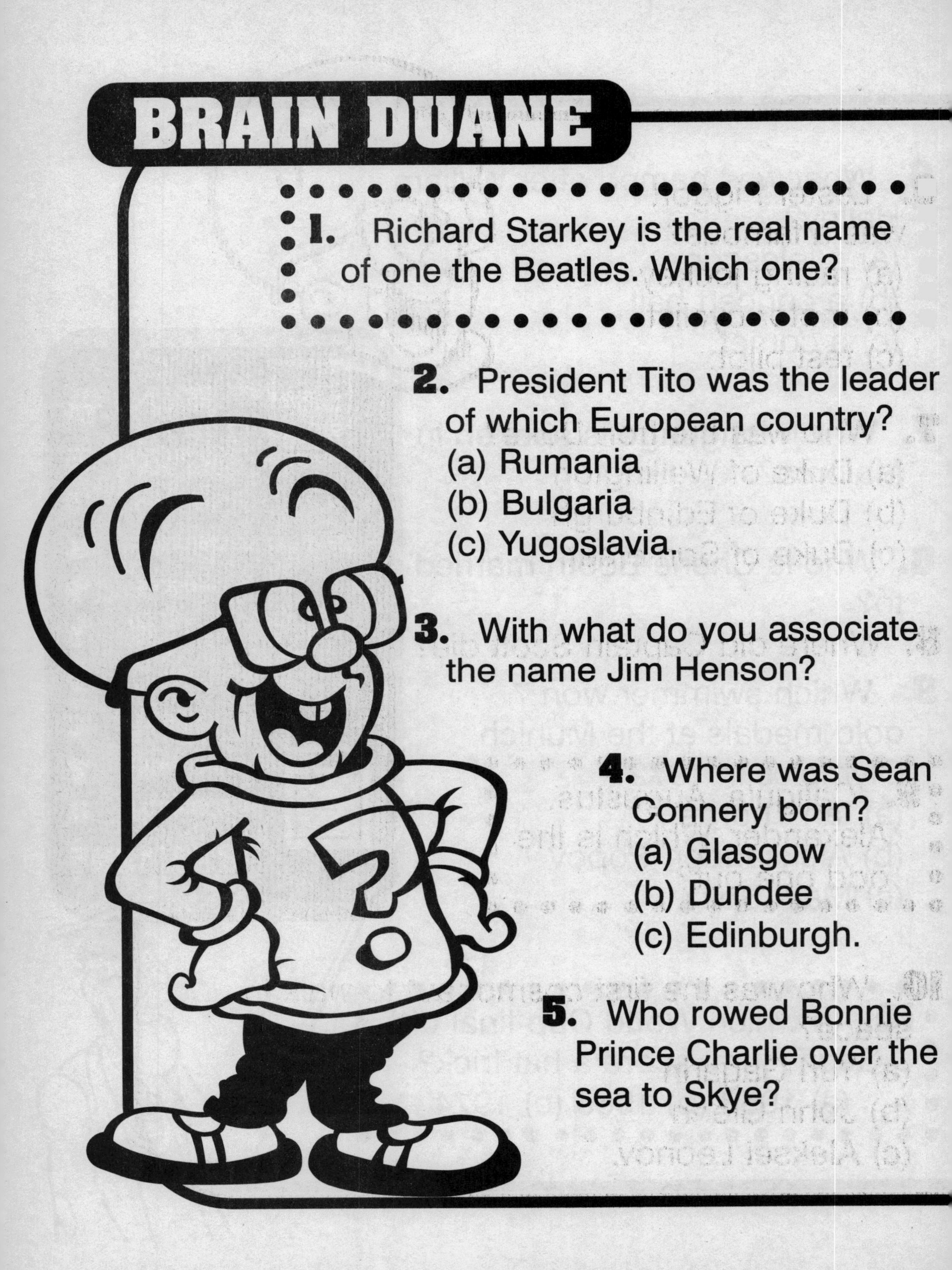

BRAIN DUANE

1. Richard Starkey is the real name of one the Beatles. Which one?

2. President Tito was the leader of which European country?
(a) Rumania
(b) Bulgaria
(c) Yugoslavia.

3. With what do you associate the name Jim Henson?

4. Where was Sean Connery born?
(a) Glasgow
(b) Dundee
(c) Edinburgh.

5. Who rowed Bonnie Prince Charlie over the sea to Skye?

6. Lester Piggott was a famous?
(a) racing jockey
(b) motor cyclist
(c) test pilot.

7. Who was the Iron Duke?
(a) Duke of Wellington
(b) Duke of Edinburgh
(c) Duke of Somerset.

. Where did Captain Scott die?

9. Caligula, Augustus, Alexander. Which is the odd one out?

0. Who was the first cosmonaut to walk in space?
(a) Yuri Gagarin
(b) John Glenn
(c) Aleksei Leonov.

ANSWERS.

1. Ringo Starr.
2. Yugoslavia.
3. Muppets.
4. Edinburgh.
5. Flora McDonald.
6. Racing jockey.
7. Duke of Wellington.
8. Antarctica.
9. Alexander. He was a Greek general. The others were Roman Emperors.
10. Aleksei Leonov.

SCORE

DESPERATE DAN

1. Which people live in the Canadian territory of Nunavuk?

2. For which sport did Nelson Mandela present the World Cup Trophy in 1999?
(a) football (b) golf (c) rugby.

3. Yasser Arafat is the leader of the PLO. What do these initials stand for?

4. Which famous slave led a revolt against the Roman Empire?
(a) Asterix
(b) Galactacus
(c) Spartacus.

5. Who played the lead in the film of the same name? (a) Kirk Douglas
(b) Charlton Heston
(c) John Wayne.

6. Which American general forced the British to surrender at the Battle of Yorktown?

7. Which sport is Pete Sampras associated with?
(a) golf
(b) baseball
(c) tennis.

8. St Andrew is the patron saint of?
(a) Norway
(b) Scotland
(c) Iceland.

9. In Hermann Melville's book, Captain Ahab pursued a white whale. What was its name?

10. Who is the Princess Royal?

ANSWERS.

1. Inuit.
2. Rugby.
3. Palestine Liberation Organisation.
4. Spartacus.
5. Kirk Douglas.
6. George Washington.
7. Tennis.
8. Scotland.
9. Moby Dick.
10. Princess Anne.

FATTY

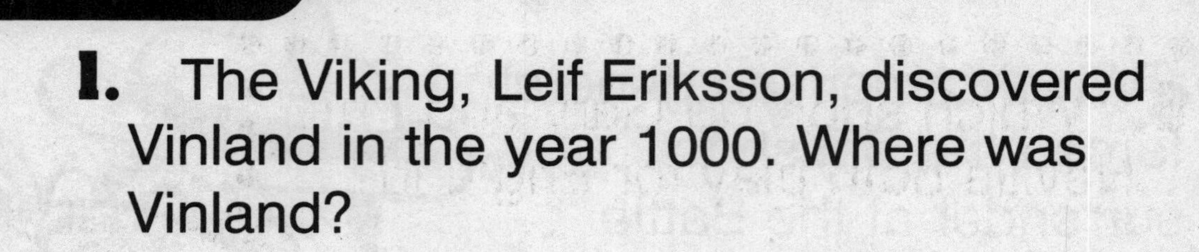

1. The Viking, Leif Eriksson, discovered Vinland in the year 1000. Where was Vinland?

2. What do Les Patterson and Dame Edna Everage have in common?

3. St Christopher is the patron saint of?
(a) actors
(b) gardeners
(c) travellers.

4. Sherlock Holmes was a famous detective invented by Agatha Christie. True or false?

5. Madonna was born in which US city?
(a) Detroit
(b) Washington
(c) Baltimore.

6. Which sport do Gary and Phil Neville both play for England?

7. Wordsworth, Elgar, Shelley. Which is the odd one out?

8. The singer, Robert Zimmerman is better known by another name, What is it?

9. Prince William was born in?
(a) 1979
(b) 1982
(c) 1986

10. Jim Davis draws a famous cartoon cat. What is its name?

ANSWERS.

1. North America.
2. They are both played by Barry Humphreys.
3. Travellers.
4. False . The Sherlock Holmes stories were written by Arthur Conan Doyle.
5. Detroit.
6. Football.
7. Elgar. He is a composer, the others are poets.
8. Bob Dylan.
9. 1982.
10. Garfield.

SCORE

1. Which American river was Henry Hudson the first European to sail up in 1609?

2. Paul Hewson is the real name of which Irish pop star?

3. Which Caribbean island did the Fugees originally come from?
(a) Haiti
(b) Jamaica
(c) Barbados.

4. Which opera singer had an ice cream dessert named after her?
(a) Maria Callas
(b) Margaret Sutherland
(c) Dame Nellie Melba.

5. Alec Salmond was the leader of which political party?

6. Who created the characters Donald Duck and Mickey Mouse?

7. With what do you associate the name John McAdam?
(a) railways (b) canals (c) roads.

8. Who is the Mayor of London?

9. Which Hollywood film star was the Terminator?

10. Celine Dion won the Eurovision Song Contest with "The Power of Love" in 1988. Which country did she represent?

ANSWERS.

1. The Hudson.
2. Bono.
3. Haiti.
4. Peach Melba was named after Dame Nellie Melba.
5. The Scottish National Party.
6. Walt Disney.
7. Roads.
8. Ken Livingstone.
9. Arnold Schwarzenegger.
10. Switzerland.

SCORE

1. Which famous character did Charles Schulz create?

2. What was the name of the character's dog?

3. Who is the patron saint of England?

4. Which musical was based on the life of the Argentinian, Eva Peron?

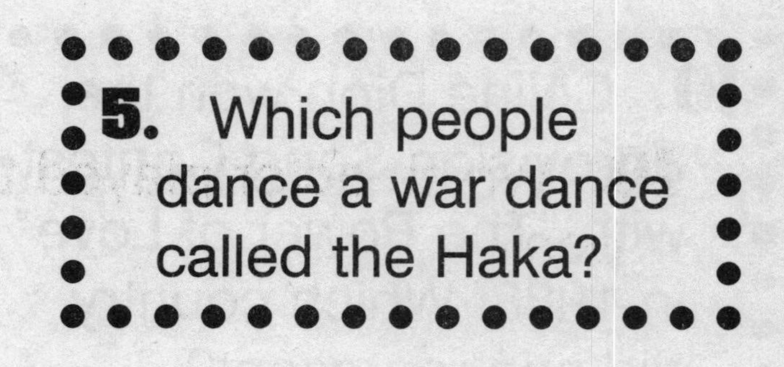

5. Which people dance a war dance called the Haka?

6. Which football team did Bobby Charlton play for?

7. Whose knights gathered at the Round Table?

8. What was John Wayne's nickname?
(a) Prince
(b) Count
(c) Duke.

9. Obi Wan Kenobe was a Jedi Knight in which films?

10. Which actor played the part?

1. Which inventor had a coat named after him?

2. With which sport do you associate Chris Bonnington?

3. In 1991 Helen Sharman was the first British woman to...?
(a) sail round the world
(b) go into space
(c) climb Mt. Everest.

4. The film star Shirley Maclaine's brother is also a film actor. Is he...?
(a) Charlton Heston
(b) Val Kilmer
(c) Warren Beatty.

5. If you worked alongside Claudia, Naomi and Elle, what would you be?

6. Whose nickname is Whirlwind?
(a) Stephen Hendry
(b) Steve Davis
(c) Jimmy White.

7. Which sport do they all play?

8. What is the name of Prince Andrew's elder daughter?

9. Robert Craig was better known as Evel Knievel. Why was he famous ?

10. Who was Britain's youngest ever Prime Minister?
(a) William Wilberforce
(b) William Hague
(c) William Pitt.

ANSWERS.

1. Mackintosh.
2. Mountain Climbing.
3. Go into space.
4. Warren Beatty.
5. A fashion model.
6. Jimmy White.
7. Snooker.
8. Beatrice.
9. He was a motor cycle daredevil rider.
10. William Pitt.

SCORE

BLINKY

1. Amy Johnson was the first woman to fly solo from England to...?
(a) Australia (b) America (c) France.

2. "Serpents of the sea" was the name given to the boats of which seafaring people?

3. What animal is herded by the Sami people of Lapland?

4. With which sport do you associate Lee Westwood?
(a) athletics
(b) darts
(c) golf.

5. Andrew Lloyd Webber wrote a famous musical based on poems by T.S. Eliot. What kind of animals was it about?

6. Which boxer said he could "float like a butterfly and sting like a bee"?
(a) Mike Tyson
(b) Henry Cooper
(c) Muhammad Ali.

7. Is Rio Ferdinand a singer, runner or footballer?

8. What do Eddie Izzard, Dylan Moran and Ardal Hanlon have in common?

9. Jacques Cousteau was a famous
(a) diver
(b) painter
(c) sculptor?

10. Which character first appeared in the Beano in 1951?

ANSWERS.
1. Australia.
2. The Vikings.
3. Reindeer.
4. Golf.
5. Cats.
6. Muhammed Ali.
7. Footballer.
8. They're all comedians.
9. Diver.
10. Dennis the Menace.

SCORE

GNASHER

1. With which sport do you associate the name Eddie Irvine?
(a) snooker
(b) darts
(c) motor racing.

2. Which well known footballer recently became a film star?

3. Lassie, Skippy and Rin Tin Tin. Which is the odd one out?

4. Sir Christopher Wren was...?
(a) an artist
(b) a poet
(c) an architect.

5. Who is the most successful member of the Jackson Five?

6. Jennifer Aniston is married to which Hollywood film star?

7. Who was the first European to sail around the globe?
(a) Vasco Da Gama
(b) Ferdinand Magellan
(c) Marco Polo.

8. Which US President was nicknamed "Ike"?

9. Michael, Lynn, Corin and Vanessa are all members of the same acting family. What is their surname?

10. In whose book of fables did The Hare and the Tortoise appear?

ANSWERS.

1. Motor racing.
2. Vinnie Jones.
3. Skippy the kangaroo. The other two are dogs.
4. An architect.
5. Michael Jackson.
6. Brad Pitt.
7. Ferdinand Magellan.
8. President Eisenhower.
9. Redgrave.
10. Aesop's.

9×9
81
4+7
=
SCIENCE & NUMBERS

DENNIS

1. How many centimetres are there in one metre?

2. What is the name of the Japanese unit of currency?

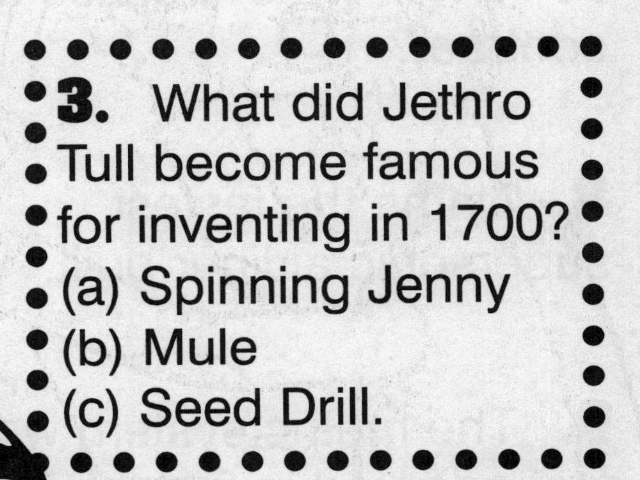

3. What did Jethro Tull become famous for inventing in 1700?
(a) Spinning Jenny
(b) Mule
(c) Seed Drill.

4. In which year did Concorde make its first flight?
(a) 1956
(b) 1969
(c) 1976.

5. How many fiddlers did Old King Cole have?

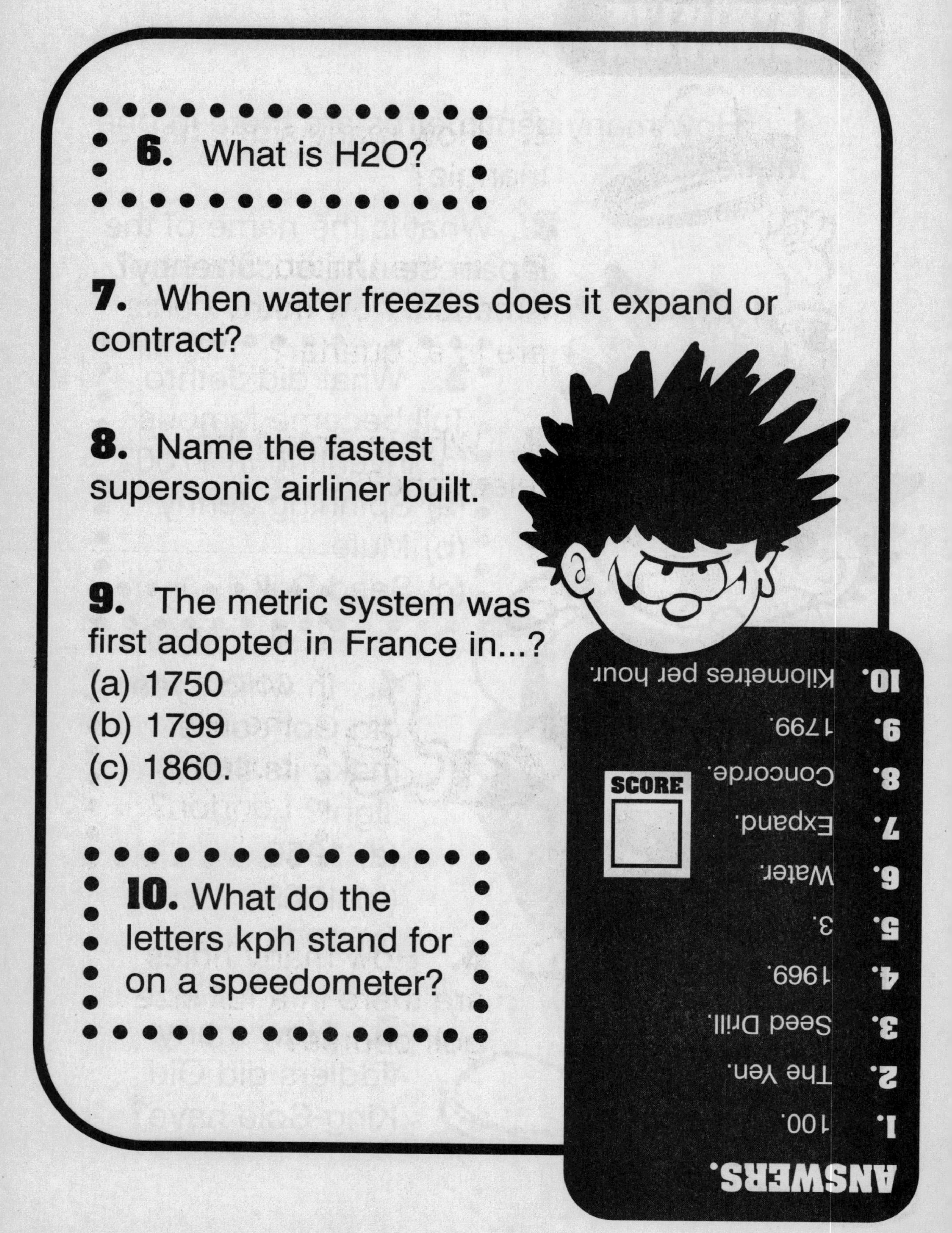

6. What is H_2O?

7. When water freezes does it expand or contract?

8. Name the fastest supersonic airliner built.

9. The metric system was first adopted in France in...?
(a) 1750
(b) 1799
(c) 1860.

10. What do the letters kph stand for on a speedometer?

ANSWERS.
1. 100.
2. The Yen.
3. Seed Drill.
4. 1969.
5. 3.
6. Water.
7. Expand.
8. Concorde.
9. 1799.
10. Kilometres per hour.

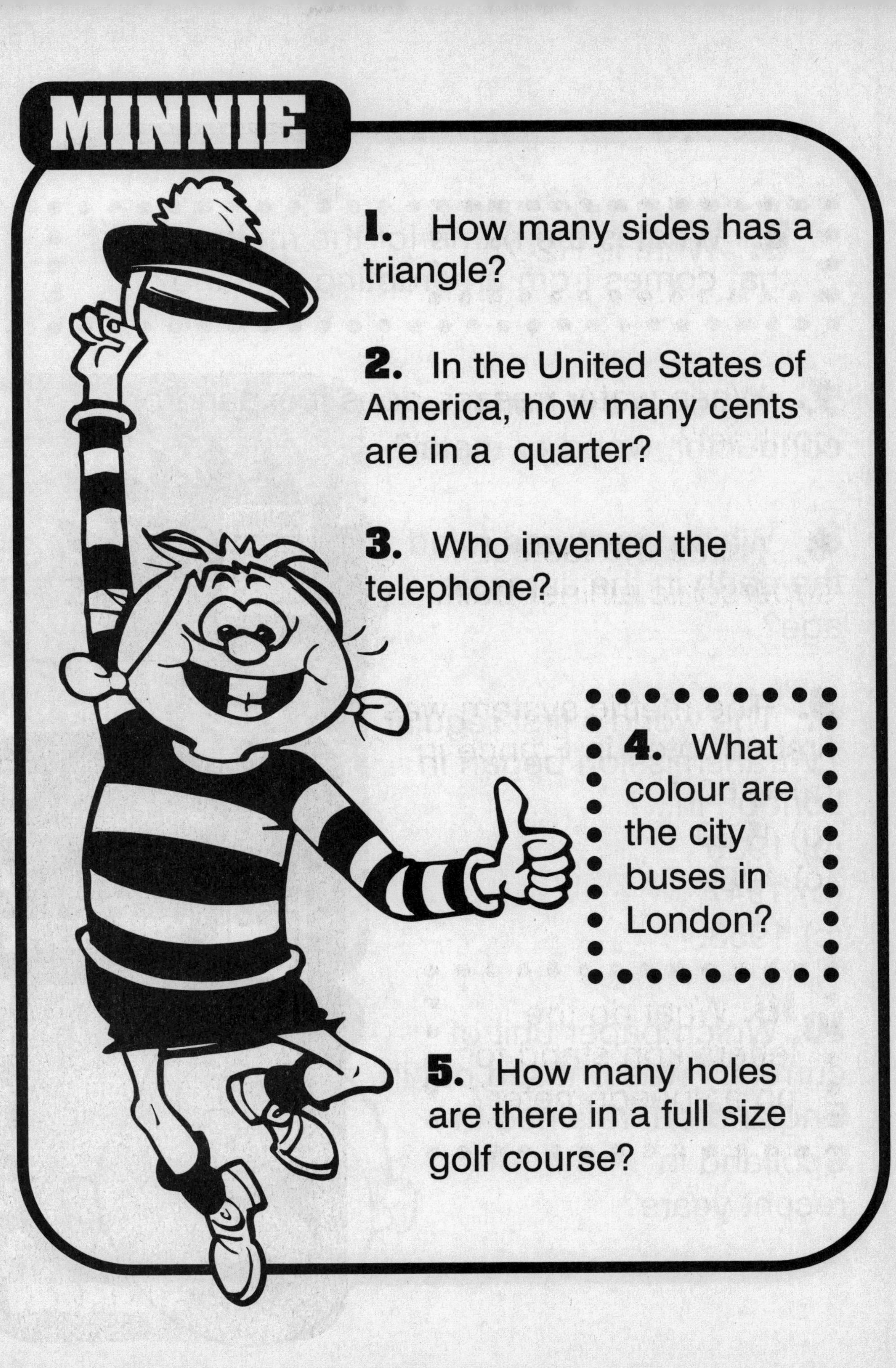
MINNIE
1. How many sides has a triangle?
2. In the United States of America, how many cents are in a quarter?
3. Who invented the telephone?
4. What colour are the city buses in London?
5. How many holes are there in a full size golf course?

6. What is the name for the molten rock that comes from an erupting volcano?

7. Which is the better conductor, wood or metal?

8. Which creatures ruled the earth in the Jurassic age?

9. The world's first regular TV transmission began in London in...?
(a) 1936
(b) 1947
(c) 1953.

10. Which paper unit of currency was phased out in England but retained in Scotland in recent years?

ANSWERS.

1. Three.
2. Twenty-five.
3. Alexander Graham Bell.
4. Red.
5. 18.
6. Lava.
7. Metal.
8. Dinosaurs.
9. 1936.
10. £1 note.

SCORE

BILLY WHIZZ

1. Which measurement is longer:- one yard or one metre?

2. At what centigrade temperature does water boil?

3. What did Johann Gutenberg invent?

4. Does a hydrofoil travel on land, water or in the air?

5. What is the name for an animal that has four legs?

6. It is hard, black and rich in carbon. It is a fossil fuel. What is it?

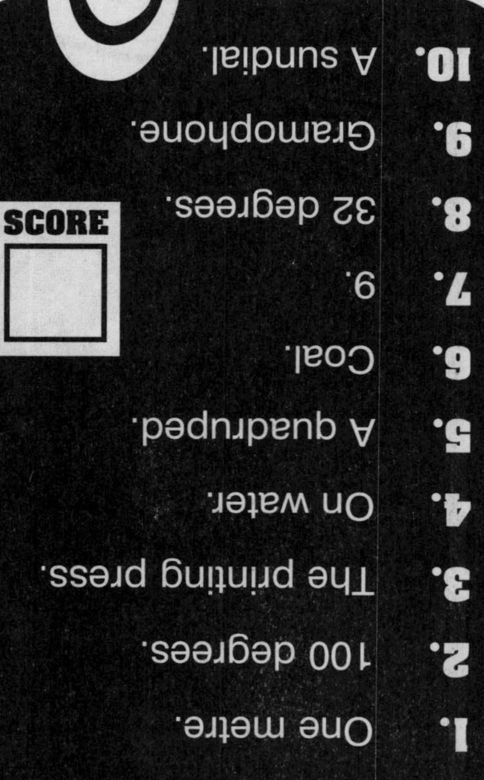

7. How many planets are there in the solar system?

8. At which Fahrenheit temperature does water freeze?

9. Which musical device was invented by Thomas Edison in 1878?

10. Which timekeeping device cannot be used at night, for it relies upon sunlight?

BANANAMAN

1. What number would a major earthquake register on the Richter scale? (a) 3 (b) 5 (c) 7.

2. In which European country is the deutschmark a unit of currency?

3. What was the name of the Italian scientist who sent the first radio signals?

4. Who invented the steam locomotive called the Rocket?

5. How many Horsemen of the Apocalypse are there?

6. What does NASA stand for?

7. Did the Brontosaurus eat meat or plants?

8. How many days in a leap year?

9. Which is the world's busiest airport?

10. For which company was the cruise liner the Queen Elizabeth II built?

ANSWERS.

1. 7.
2. Germany.
3. Marconi.
4. George Stephenson.
5. 4.
6. National Aeronautics & Space Administration.
7. Plants.
8. 366.
9. Chicago.
10. Cunard.

SCORE

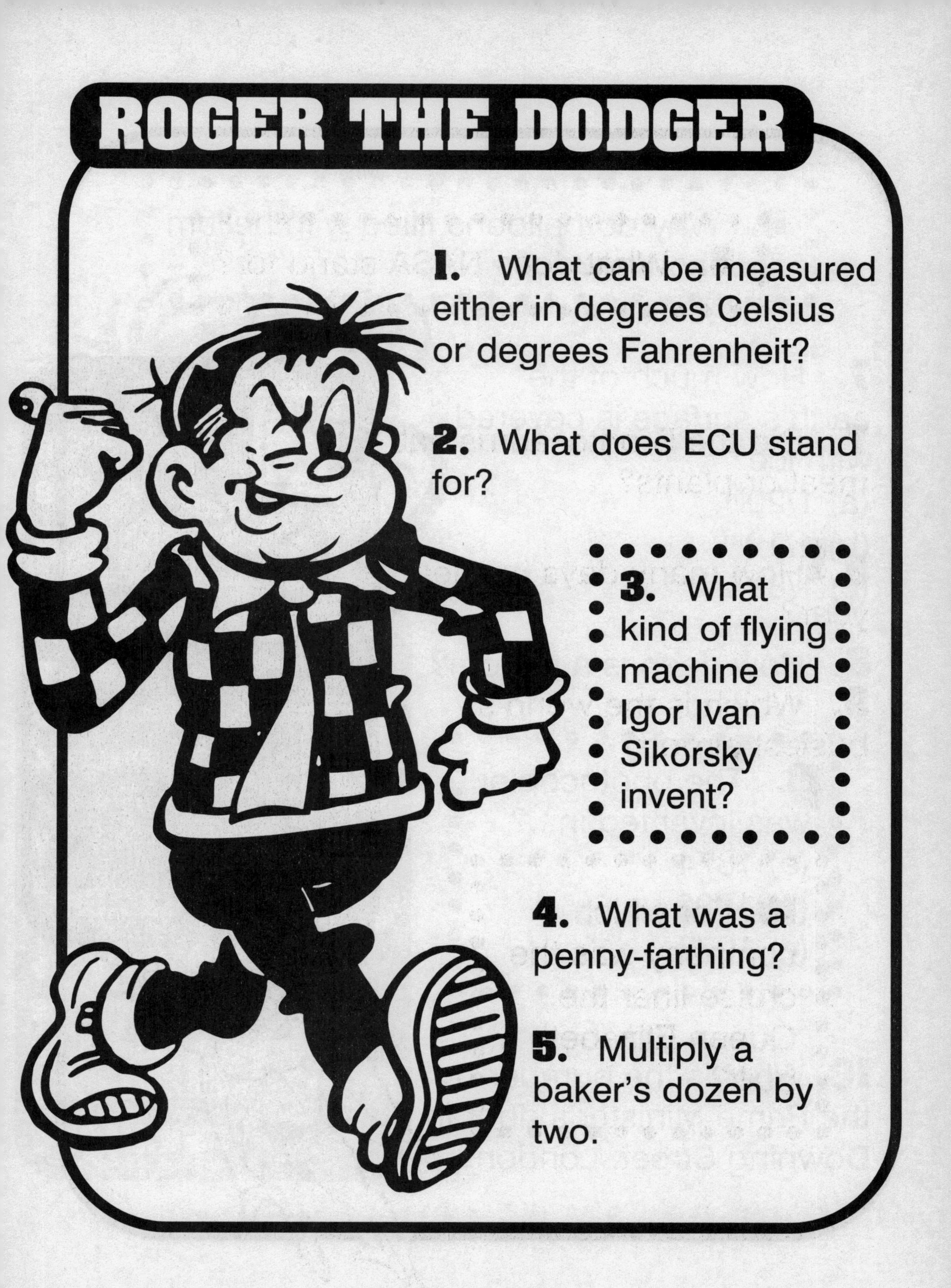
ROGER THE DODGER
1. What can be measured either in degrees Celsius or degrees Fahrenheit?
2. What does ECU stand for?
3. What kind of flying machine did Igor Ivan Sikorsky invent?
4. What was a penny-farthing?
5. Multiply a baker's dozen by two.

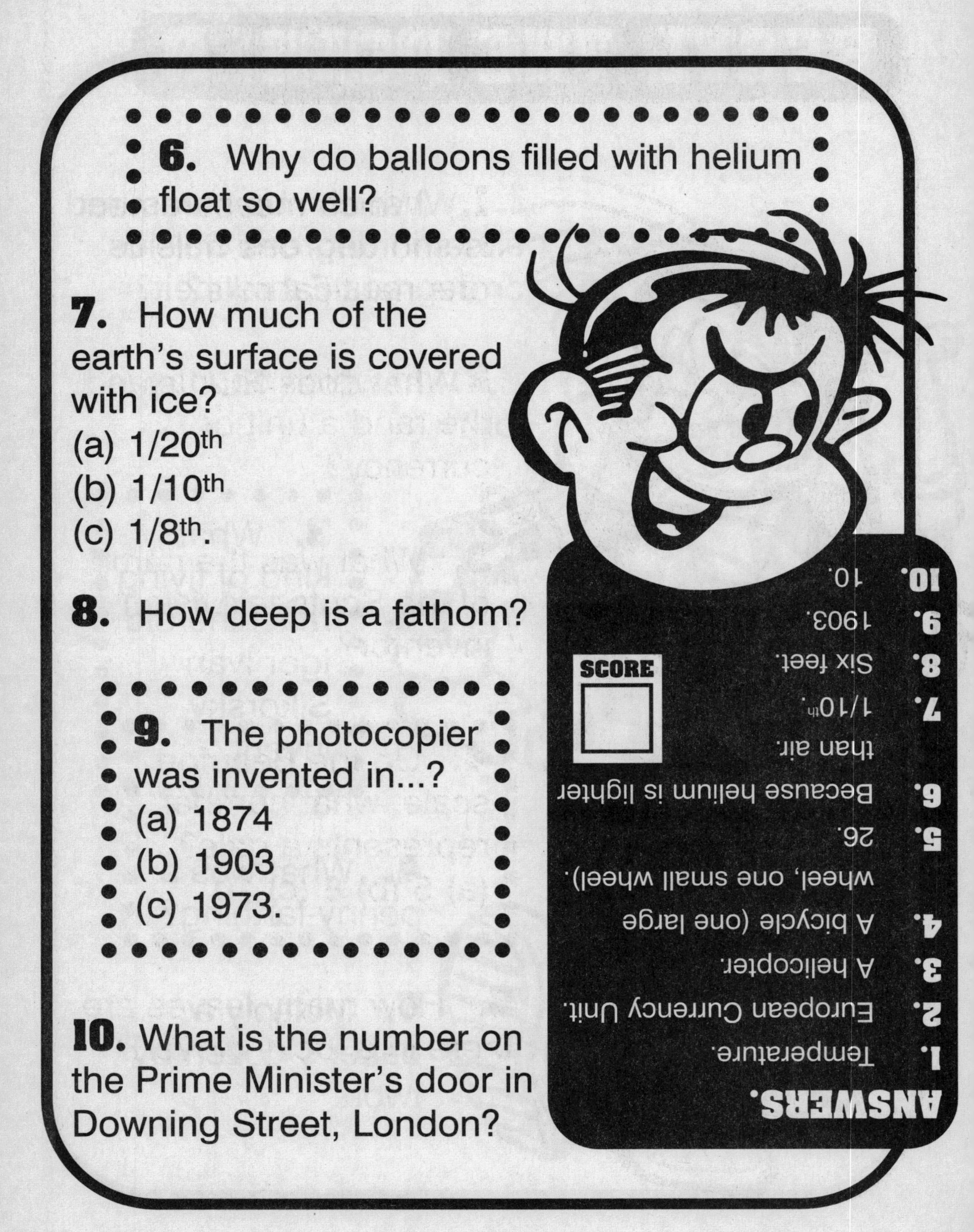

6. Why do balloons filled with helium float so well?

7. How much of the earth's surface is covered with ice?
(a) 1/20th
(b) 1/10th
(c) 1/8th.

8. How deep is a fathom?

9. The photocopier was invented in...?
(a) 1874
(b) 1903
(c) 1973.

10. What is the number on the Prime Minister's door in Downing Street, London?

ANSWERS.
1. Temperature.
2. European Currency Unit.
3. A helicopter.
4. A bicycle (one large wheel, one small wheel).
5. 26.
6. Because helium is lighter than air.
7. 1/10th.
8. Six feet.
9. 1903.
10. 10.

SCORE

BERYL THE PERIL

1. Which measurement is shorter:- one mile or one nautical mile?

2. In which country is the rand a unit of currency?

3. What was the name of the Scots television inventor?

4. On the Beaufort scale, what number represents a gale? (a) 5 (b) 8 (c) 10.

5. How many leaves are there in a lucky clover?

6. What kind of engine did James Watt design?

7. A number that can only be divided by itself or by one, is called...?
(a) an even number
(b) a true number
(c) a prime number.

8. What is permafrost?

9. The first aircraft flight around the world without refuelling lasted.?
(a) 3 days
(b) 6 days
(c) 9 days?

10. What is the word used to describe the change that a caterpillar undergoes to become a butterfly?

ANSWERS.

1. A nautical mile is shorter.
2. South Africa.
3. John Logie Baird.
4. 8.
5. 4.
6. Steam.
7. Prime number.
8. Ground that is always frozen.
9. 9 days.
10. Metamorphosis.

SCORE

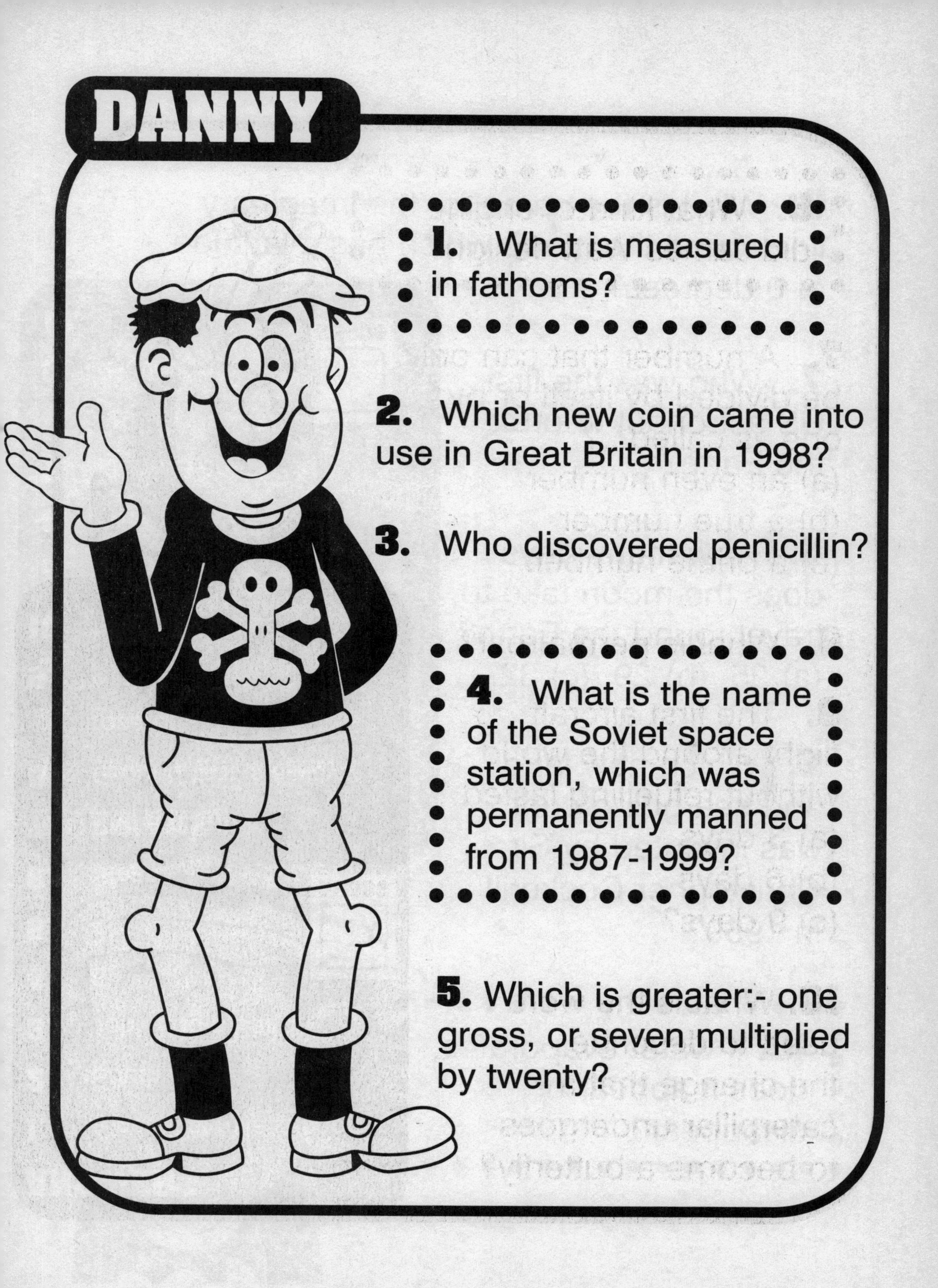
DANNY
1. What is measured in fathoms?
2. Which new coin came into use in Great Britain in 1998?
3. Who discovered penicillin?
4. What is the name of the Soviet space station, which was permanently manned from 1987-1999?
5. Which is greater:- one gross, or seven multiplied by twenty?

6. What is the name for the imaginary line round the globe which has a latitude of 0 degrees?

7. Who was the first US astronaut to orbit the Earth?

8. How many days does the moon take to travel round the Earth? (a) 25 (b) 29 (c) 32.

9. Which new land and sea-going craft was invented by Sir Christopher Cockerill in 1959?

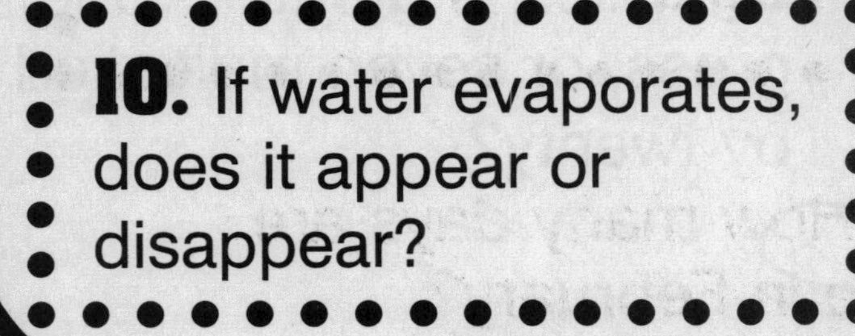

10. If water evaporates, does it appear or disappear?

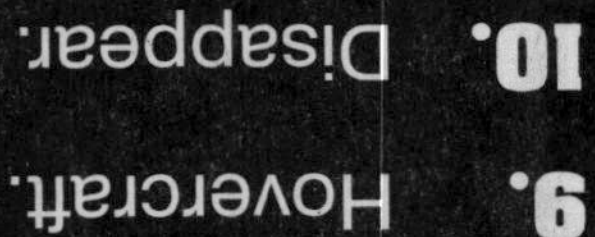

ANSWERS.

1. The depth of water.
2. The two pound piece.
3. Alexander Fleming.
4. Mir.
5. One gross.
6. The Equator.
7. John Glenn.
8. 29.
9. Hovercraft.
10. Disappear.

WALTER

1. Was Pythagoras...?
(a) Egyptian
(b) Roman
(c) Greek.

2. What do the currencies of New Zealand and the United States have in common?

3. Who won the Nobel prize in 1921 for his theory of relativity?

4. What was the name of the car in which Sir Donald Campbell broke the world land speed record in 1964?
(a) Swallow
(b) Bluebird
(c) Eagle.

5. How many days are there in February?

6. What is the solid form of water?

7. A, B, AB and O are four types of what?

8. Adobe houses are made with...?
(a) timber
(b) clay
(c) straw.

9. Where is the oldest underground railway system in the world?

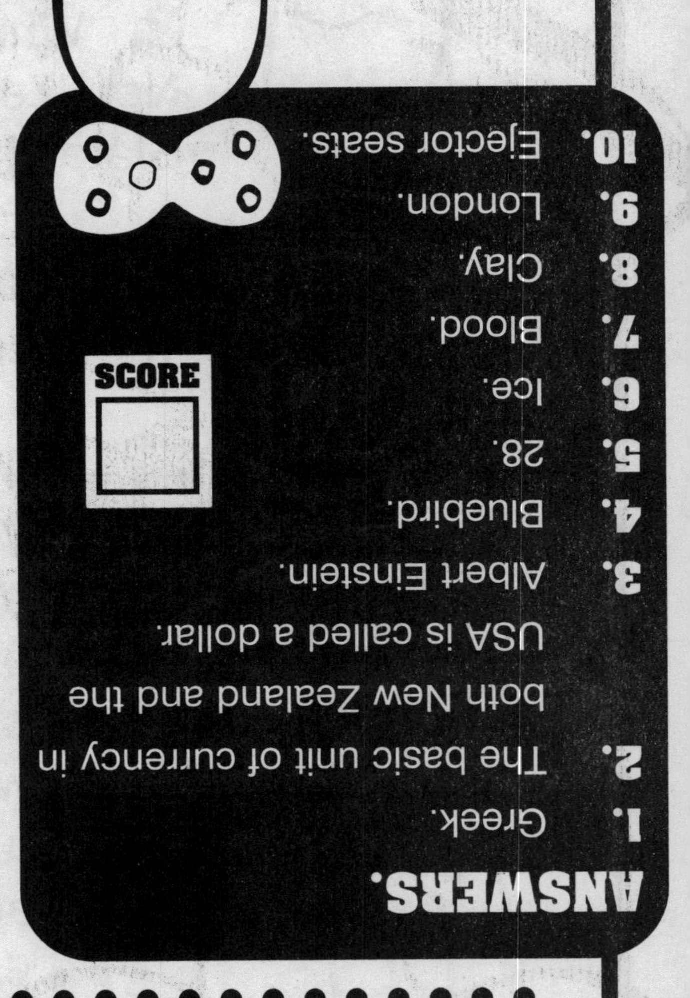

10. Which invention made the lives of jet pilots much safer?

THE NUMSKULLS

1. Name the Red Planet.

2. What number is represented by the Roman numeral X? (a) 5 (b) 8 (c) 10.

3. Who invented a code composed of dots and dashes for sending telegraph messages?

4. Which children's television programme has the same name as a famous steam locomotive?

5. There are two sisters in the family. Each of them has three times as many brothers as sisters. How many children are there altogether?

6. The percentage 50% is equal to which fraction?
(a) 1/4 (b) 1/5 (c) 1/2.

7. What was the first aircraft to break the sound barrier?
(a) Concorde
(b) B52
(c) Bell XI.

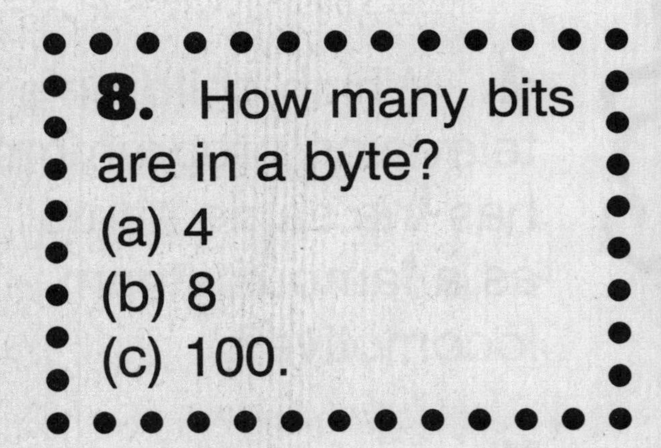

8. How many bits are in a byte?
(a) 4
(b) 8
(c) 100.

9. Who invented the jet engine?

10. Are there two, four or six musicians in a quartet?

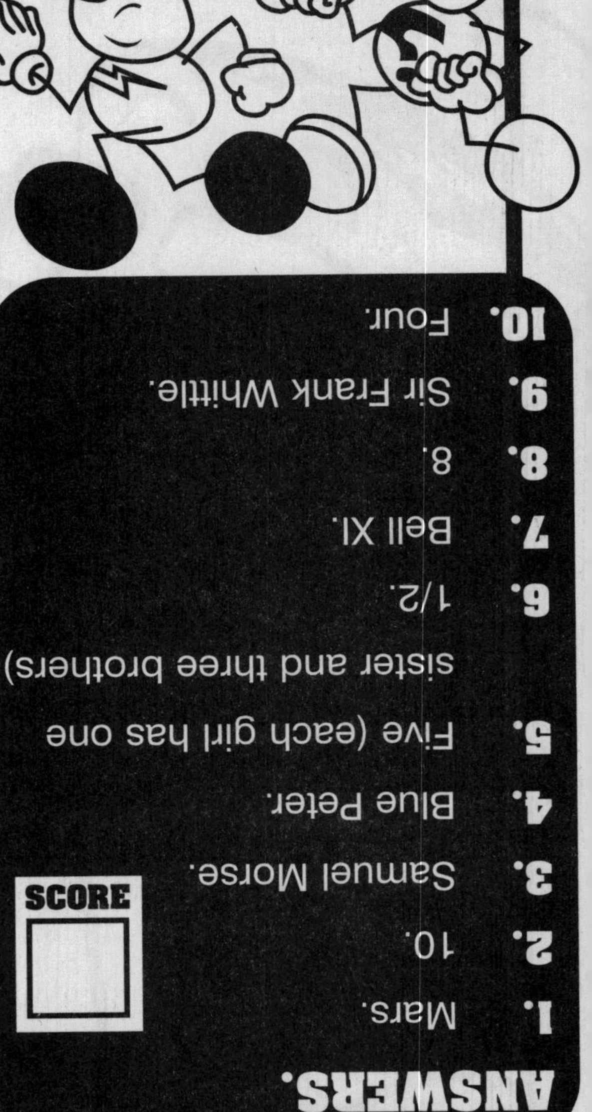

PLUG

1. To the nearest pound, how many pounds are in one kilogram?

2. How many sides does a British 50p piece have?

3. With which invention is the name of John Dunlop associated?

4. What did Hannibal use as transport when crossing the Alps in 218 B.C.?

5. How many days are there in September?

6. What is C02?

7. What is the boiling point of water on the Fahrenheit scale?

8. How many hours are there in a week?
(a) 120 (b) 142 (c) 168.

9. The St Lawrence Seaway is the longest in the world. Is it...?
(a) 100 miles long
(b) 148 miles long
(c) 189 miles long.

10. What was the name of the coin which had a value of one quarter of a penny in pre-decimal currency in Great Britain?

ANSWERS.

1. Two pounds.
2. Seven.
3. The pneumatic tyre.
4. Elephants.
5. 30.
6. Carbon dioxide.
7. 212 degrees.
8. 168.
9. 189.
10. A farthing.

SCORE

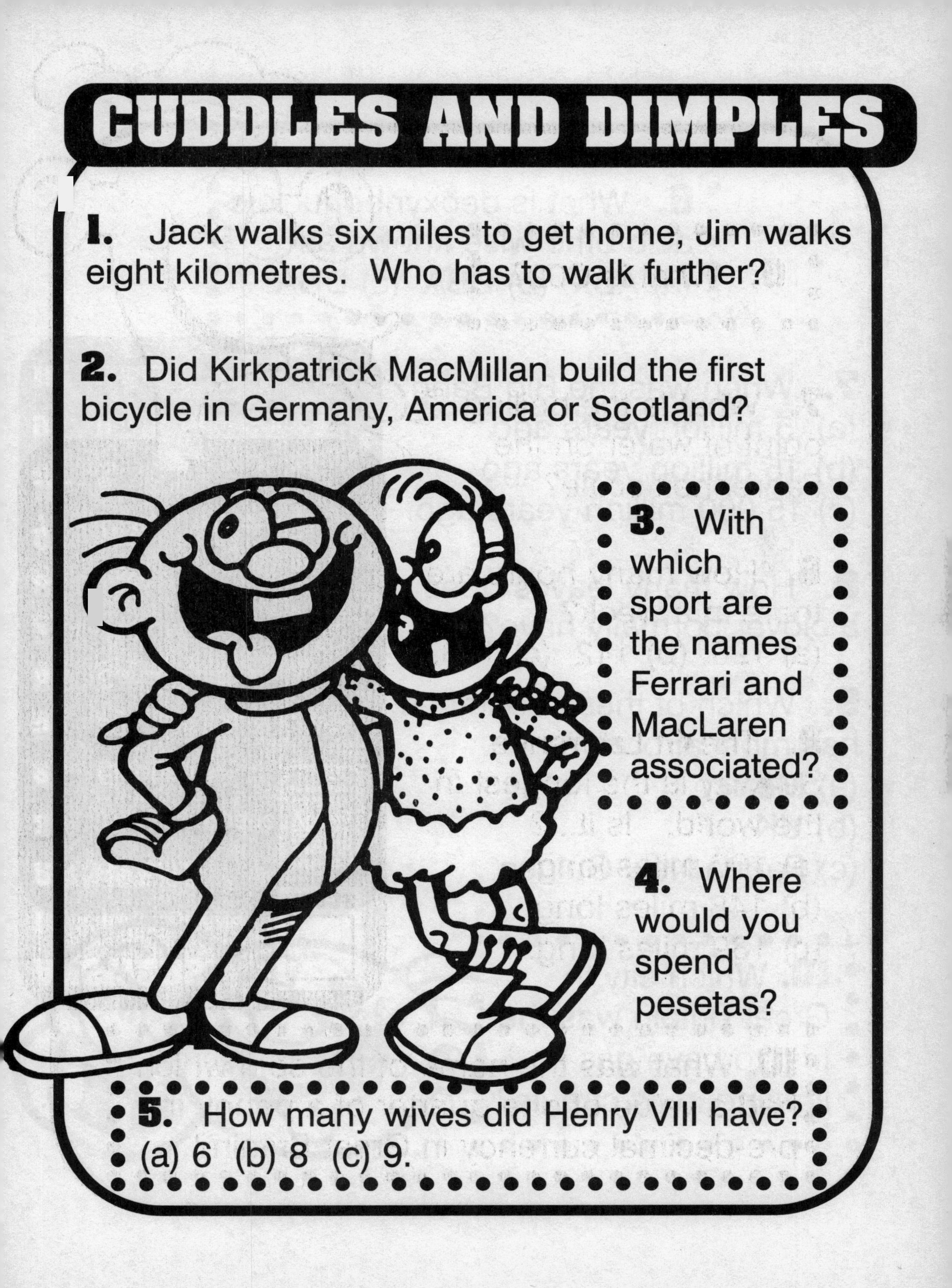
CUDDLES AND DIMPLES
1. Jack walks six miles to get home, Jim walks eight kilometres. Who has to walk further?
2. Did Kirkpatrick MacMillan build the first bicycle in Germany, America or Scotland?
3. With which sport are the names Ferrari and MacLaren associated?
4. Where would you spend pesetas?
5. How many wives did Henry VIII have? (a) 6 (b) 8 (c) 9.

6. What is deoxyribonucleic acid otherwise known as?
(a) ABX (b) DBA (c) DNA.

7. When was the Big Bang?
(a) 5 million years ago
(b) 15 million years ago
(c) 15,000 million years ago.

8. How many leaves does a clover normally have?

9. Which of these countries has most airports?
(a) Mexico
(b) UK
(c) Papua New Guinea.

10. Which city in Great Britain was the first to have gas lighting in its streets?

ANSWERS.

1. Jack.
2. Scotland.
3. Formula I motor racing.
4. Spain.
5. 6.
6. DNA.
7. 15,000 million.
8. 3.
9. Papua New Guinea.
10. London.

SCORE

BALL BOY

1. Is a Gatling a type of aircraft, motorcycle or gun?

2. What is the smallest coin (size, not value!) in circulation in Great Britain?

3. LCDs are found in many gadgets and machines that are used in and around the home every day. What do the letters LCD stand for?

4. How is a sedan chair powered?

5. If a couple celebrate their silver wedding anniversary, how many years have they been married?

6. Does an electron have a positive or a negative charge?

7. Who was the first pilot to break the sound barrier?
(a) Yuri Gagarin
(b) Douglas Bader
(c) Chuck Yeager.

8. When you walk, how many muscles do you use?
(a) 100
(b) 200
(c) 300.

9. When was the first railway line opened in Britain? (a) 1820 (b) 1830 (c) 1850

10. What was the name of the plane in which Charles Lindbergh made the first solo non-stop flight across the Atlantic?

ANSWERS.
1. Gun.
2. 5p piece.
3. Liquid crystal display.
4. By two people (the sedan chair is carried on poles).
5. 25.
6. Negative.
7. Chuck Yeager.
8. 200.
9. 1830.
10. The Spirit of St Louis.

SCORE

MOLLY

1. Worldwide, more people drive on the left side rather than the right side of the road. True or false?

2. How many kopecks are there in one rouble?
(a) 25 (b) 100 (c) 50.

3. Which people invented concrete?
(a) the British
(b) the Germans
(c) the Romans.

4. What is the name of the Grand Prix motor racing circuit in Great Britain?

5. Albert is an octogenarian. His wife Alice is three years younger. How old is she?

6. What is the name of the chemical compound that gives plants their green colour?

7. What is a Sea King?

8. If you mix red and yellow, which colour do you get?

9. How much of the Channel Tunnel runs underwater?
(a) 25k (b) 38k (c) 52k.

10. How many wonders of the Ancient World were there?

ANSWERS.

1. False.
2. One Hundred.
3. The Romans.
4. Silverstone.
5. 77.
6. Chlorophyll.
7. A helicopter.
8. Orange.
9. 38k.
10. 7.

SCORE

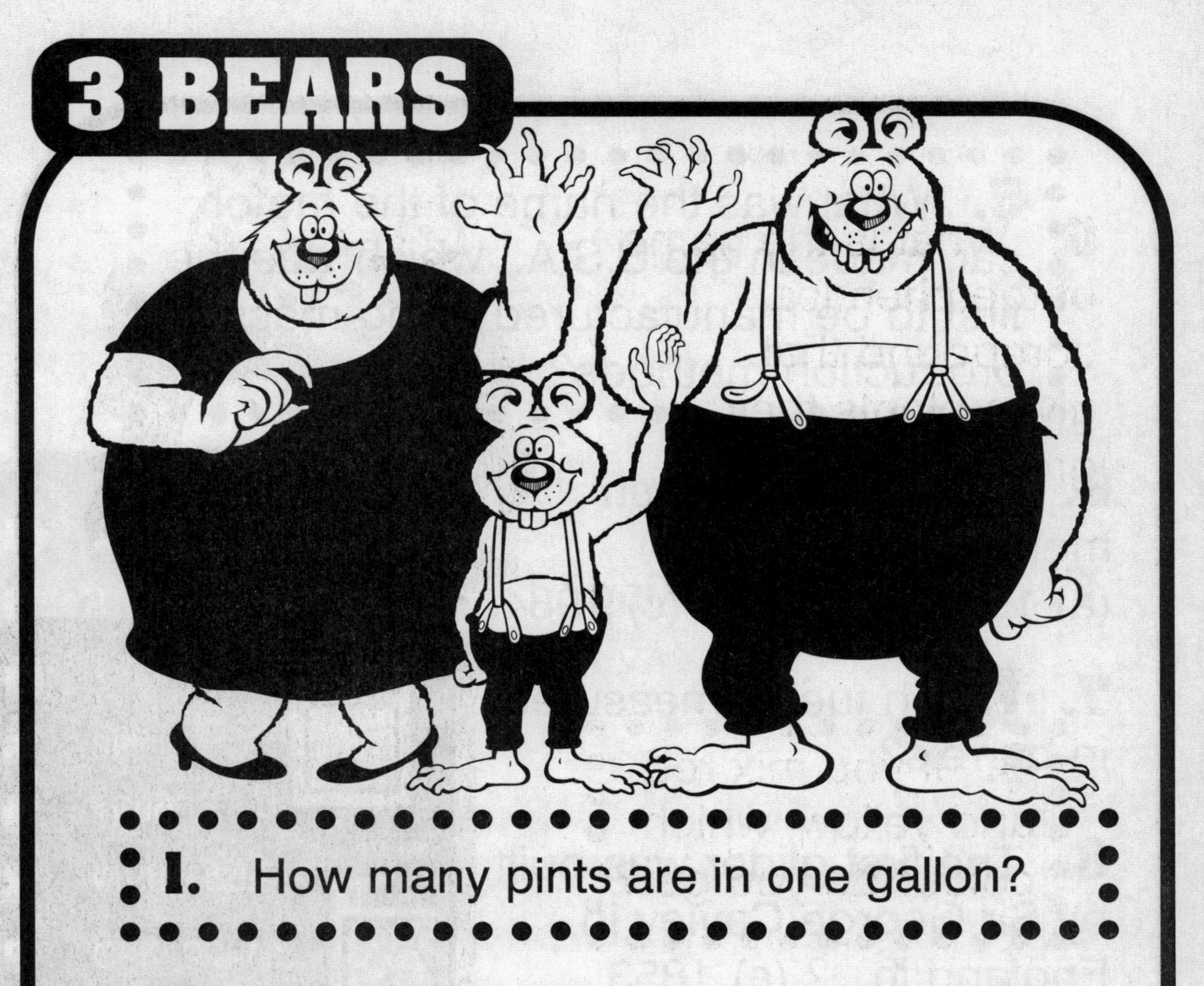

1. How many pints are in one gallon?

2. What is the name for one hundredth of a French franc?

3. What was discovered by Wilhelm Rontgen in 1895?
(a) X-Rays
(b) Gamma Rays
(c) Cathode Rays.

4. How many sides does a pentagon have?

5. What was the name of the motor car, made in the U.S.A., which was the first to be manufactured using mass production methods?

6. When was the first moon landing?
(a) 1953 (b) 1969 (c) 1984.

7. Which fuel is measured in barrels?

8. The first glider was built by Sir George Cayley in England in...? (a) 1853
(b) 1895
(c) 1910.

9. What did Gottfried Daimler invent in 1885?

10. Which body in the solar system is 330,000 times bigger than Earth but only 1/4 as dense?

ANSWERS.

1. Eight.
2. One centime.
3. The X-Ray.
4. 5.
5. Model T Ford.
6. 1969.
7. Oil.
8. 1853.
9. The motor cycle.
10. The sun.

SCORE

TEACHER

1. What is the unit of measurement used to describe speed when travelling over water?

2. What is the name for the standard unit of currency in Greece?

3. What do doctors place inside a person's chest to regulate heartbeat?

4. What is the name of the British steam locomotive which set a rail speed record of 125 mph/201 kph in 1926?

(a) Drake
(b) Seagull
(c) Mallard.

5. Which manufacturer produces the most cars?

(a) Toyota
(b) Fiat
(c) General Motors.

6. In Britain, does the clock go backwards or forwards in Autumn?

7. In which year did Louis Bleriot fly across the English Channel?
(a) 1895 (b) 1909 (c) 1919.

8. What was Skylab?

9. Where is the biggest pyramid in the world?
(a) Mexico
(b) Egypt
(c) China.

10. How long is the human gastro-intestinal tract?
(a) 15 ft (b) 25 ft (c) 30 ft.

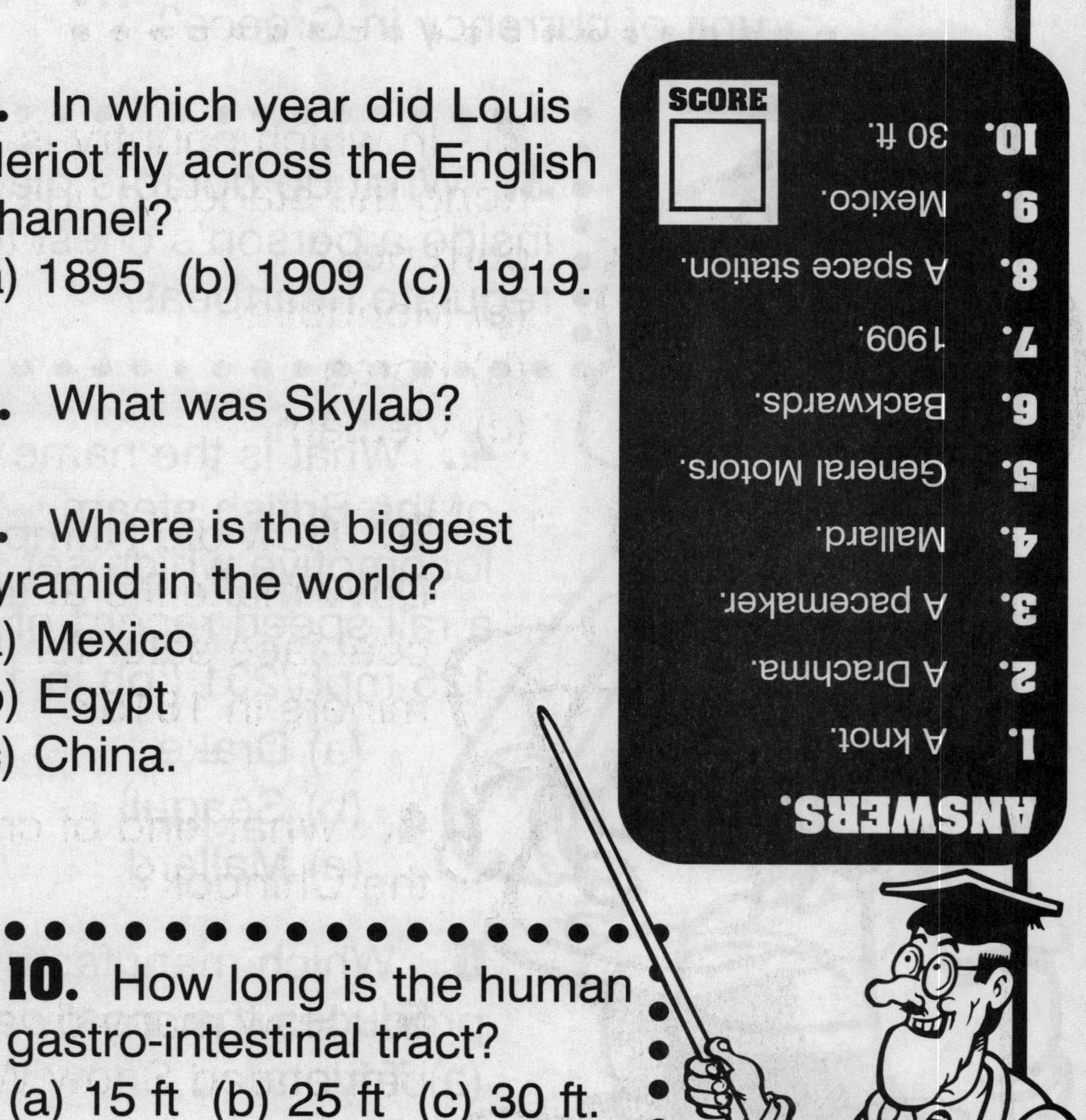

BRAIN DUANE

1. What is measured on the Richter Scale?

2. In which country is the dong the standard unit of currency?
(a) Mongolia
(b) Korea
(c) Vietnam.

3. How did Humphry Davy make life at the coal-face safer for miners in 1815?

4. What kind of craft is the Chinook?

5. How many dwarfs befriended Snow White?

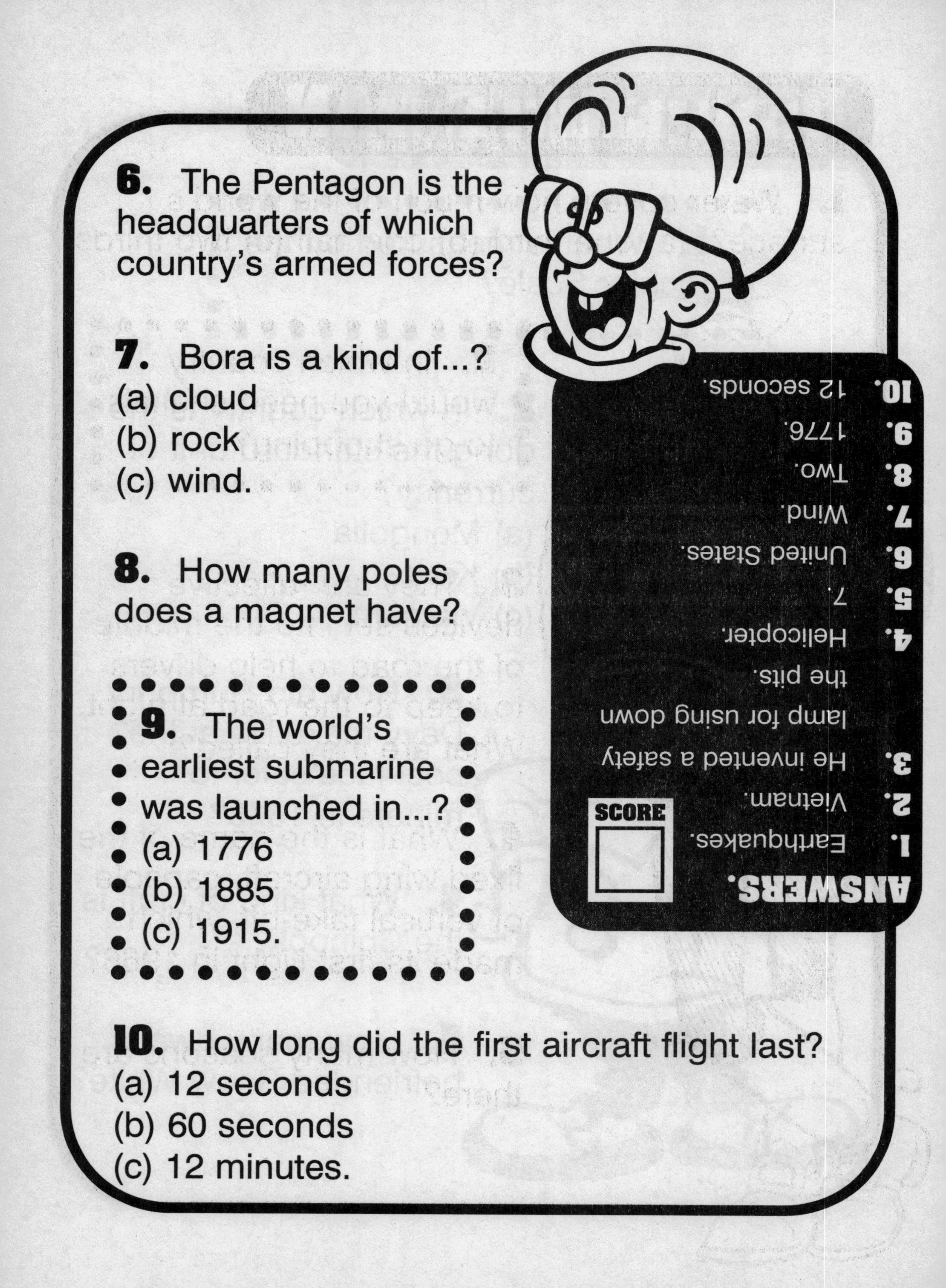

6. The Pentagon is the headquarters of which country's armed forces?

7. Bora is a kind of...?
(a) cloud
(b) rock
(c) wind.

8. How many poles does a magnet have?

9. The world's earliest submarine was launched in...?
(a) 1776
(b) 1885
(c) 1915.

10. How long did the first aircraft flight last?
(a) 12 seconds
(b) 60 seconds
(c) 12 minutes.

ANSWERS.
1. Earthquakes.
2. Vietnam.
3. He invented a safety lamp for using down the pits.
4. Helicopter.
5. 7.
6. United States.
7. Wind.
8. Two.
9. 1776.
10. 12 seconds.

SCORE

DESPERATE DAN

1. Water covers how much of the world's surface? (a) one third (b) one half (c) two thirds.

2. In which country would you need shekels to go shopping?

3. They are reflective devices set into the middle of the road to help drivers to keep to the road at night. What are they called?

4. What is the name of the fixed wing aircraft, capable of vertical take-off, which made its first flight in 1966?

5. How many seasons are there?

6. What was DDT used for?

7. Which of the Earth's atmospheres is the highest?
(a) Troposphere
(b) Stratosphere
(c) Exosphere.

8. Does a catalyst speed up or slow down chemical change?

9. What is the technique of healing with needles called?

10. The lowest land temperature ever recorded, at Vostok in Antarctica was...?
(a) -54oC (b) -73oC (c) -89oC

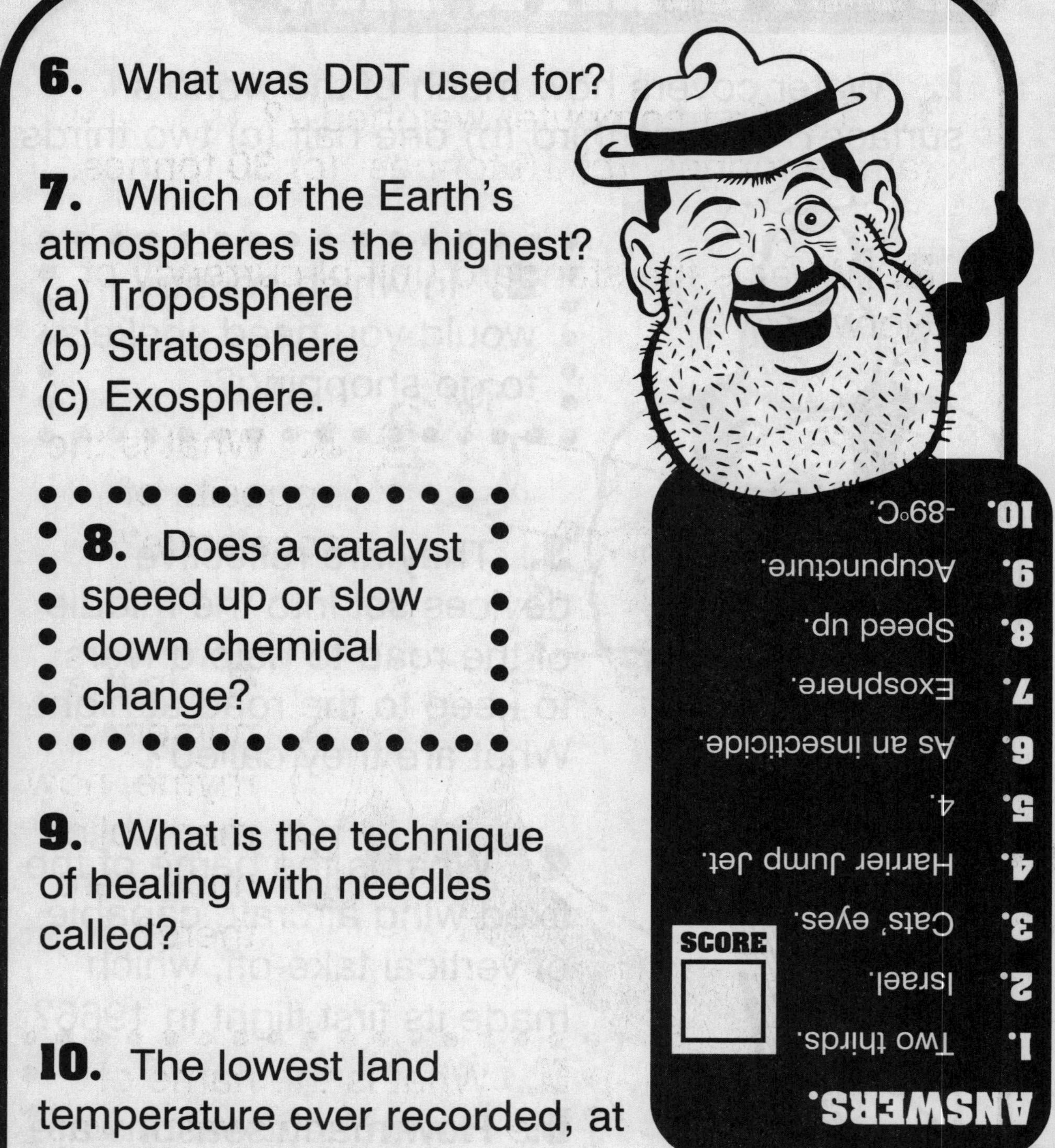

1. The first computer weighed...?
(a) five tonnes (b) 15 tonnes (c) 30 tonnes.

2. What is the standard unit of currency of Norway?

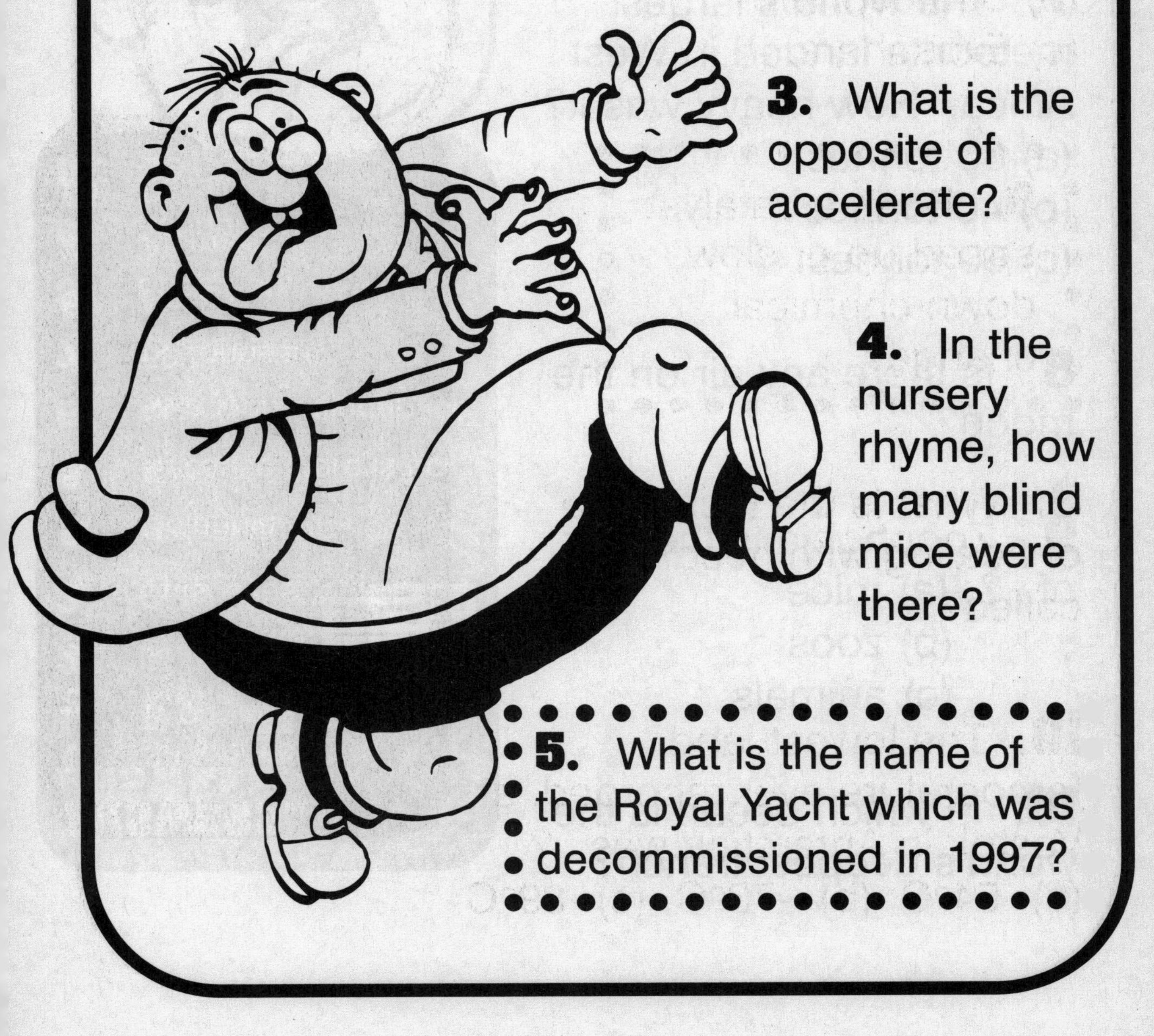

3. What is the opposite of accelerate?

4. In the nursery rhyme, how many blind mice were there?

5. What is the name of the Royal Yacht which was decommissioned in 1997?

6. Why do objects have no weight in outer space?

7. The world's largest meteorite landed in West Africa. How heavy was it?
(a) 30 tonnes
(b) 40 tonnes
(c) 60 tonnes.

8 Is there any air on the moon?

9. Zoophobia is the fear of...? (a) mice
(b) zoos
(c) animals.

10. In which ocean is the world's deepest trench?

ANSWERS.
1. 30 tonnes.
2. Krone.
3. Decelerate.
4. Three.
5. Britannia.
6. Because there is no gravity in outer space.
7. 60 tonnes.
8. No.
9. Animals.
10. Pacific.

SCORE

BEA
1. What instrument is used to measure radioactivity?
2. In which century are coins believed to have first been used?
(a) 1st Century A.D.
(b) 2nd Century B.C.
(c) 7th Century B.C.
3. How many grammes in a kilogram?
4. In which American city was the first public tram service put into operation?
(a) Boston
(b) San Francisco
(c) New York.

5. How many days of Christmas are there?

6. How many high tides are there every 24 hours?

7. If something is abridged, is it made shorter or longer?

8. When did the first space shuttle fly?
(a) 1963 (b) 1981 (c) 1990.

9. T'ai Chi is
(a) a game
(b) a type of meditation
(c) a form of self defence?

10. Who recorded the first million-selling CD in 1989?

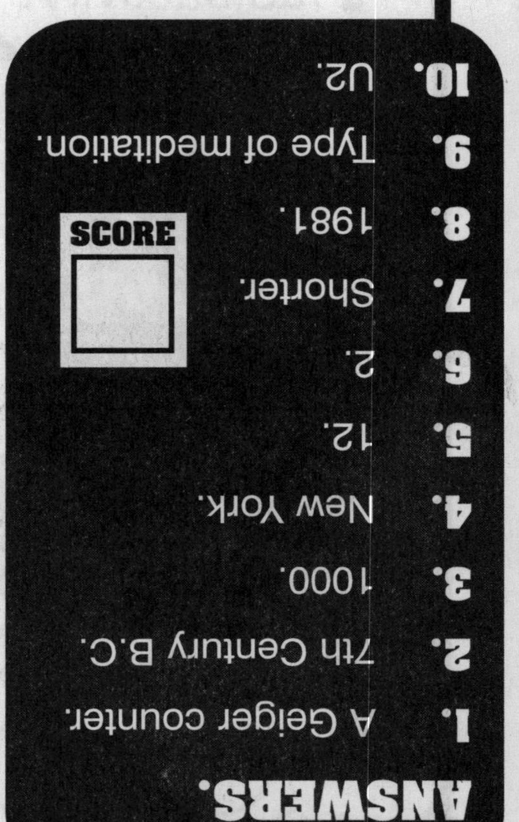

ANSWERS.

1. A Geiger counter.
2. 7th Century B.C.
3. 1000.
4. New York.
5. 12.
6. 2.
7. Shorter.
8. 1981.
9. Type of meditation.
10. U2.

SCORE

IVY

1. Which is greater:- one hectare or one acre?

2. What is the name of the government department that produces currency for use in The United Kingdom?

3. Which great Italian painter of the late fifteenth and early sixteenth century was also a gifted inventor?

4. When was the monorail invented?
(a) 1923 (b) 1925 (c) 1882.

5. How many steps were there in the famous thriller written by John Buchan?

6. How often can we see a full moon?

7. Who discovered the laws of gravity?

8. What is the value of pi?

9. What is the longest bone in the body?

10. Nyctophobia is fear of...?
(a) metal
(b) smoking
(c) darkness.

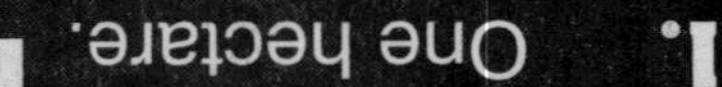

ANSWERS.

1. One hectare.
2. The Royal Mint.
3. Leonardo da Vinci.
4. 1882.
5. 39.
6. Once every month.
7. Sir Isaac Newton.
8. 3.142.
9. Femur or leg bone.
10. Darkness.

1. How many inches are there in one yard?

2. What metal was a dollar originally made from?

3. In which century was the electric light bulb invented?

4. Which company manufactured the car known as the 'Beetle'?

5. Divide the number of cards in a pack by four.

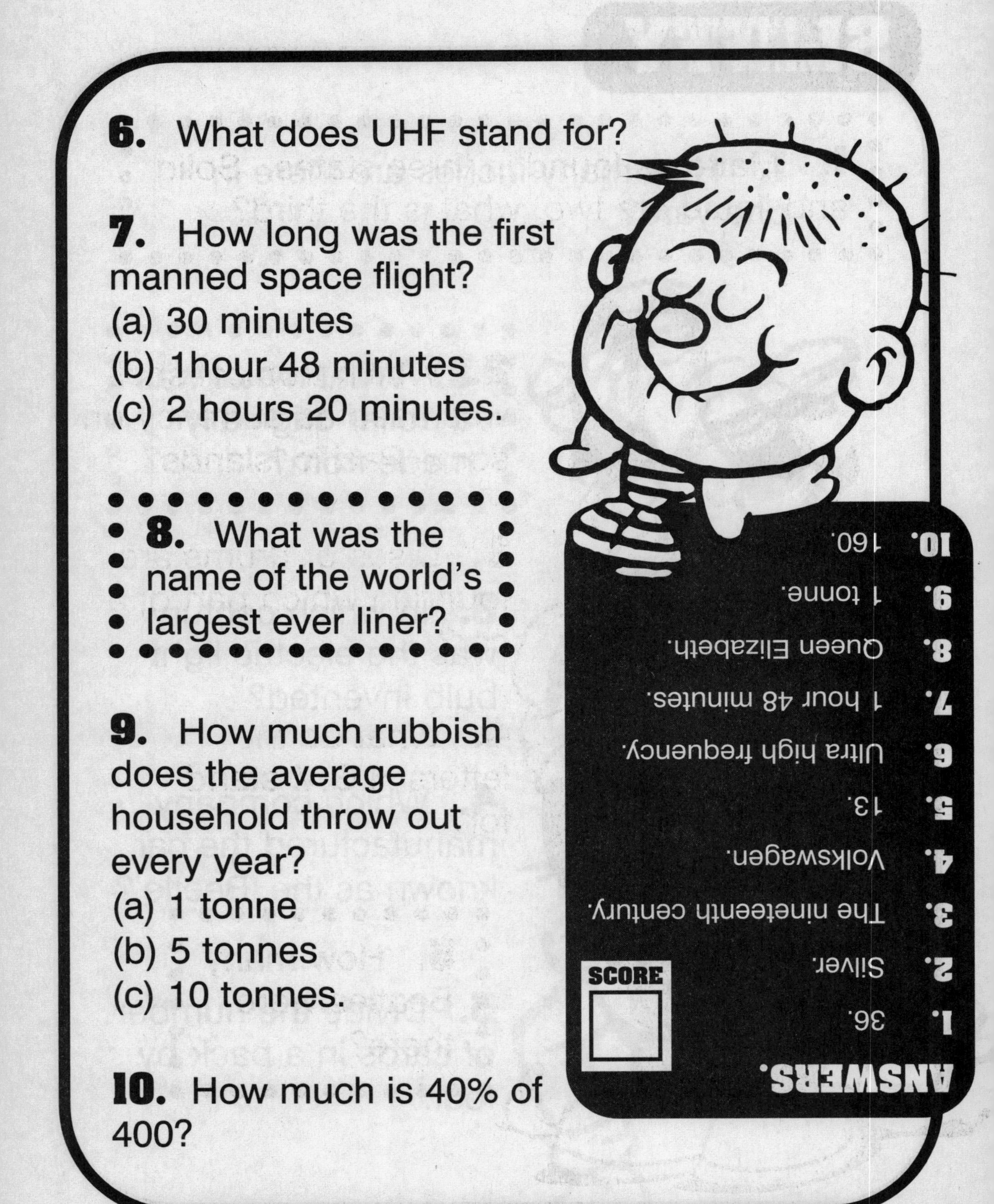

6. What does UHF stand for?

7. How long was the first manned space flight?
(a) 30 minutes
(b) 1hour 48 minutes
(c) 2 hours 20 minutes.

8. What was the name of the world's largest ever liner?

9. How much rubbish does the average household throw out every year?
(a) 1 tonne
(b) 5 tonnes
(c) 10 tonnes.

10. How much is 40% of 400?

ANSWERS.

1. 36.
2. Silver.
3. The nineteenth century.
4. Volkswagen.
5. 13.
6. Ultra high frequency.
7. 1 hour 48 minutes.
8. Queen Elizabeth.
9. 1 tonne.
10. 160.

SCORE

BLINKY

1. Matter is found in three states. Solid and liquid are two, what is the third?

2. Which tropical shell was used as currency on some Pacific Islands?

3. Discs or drums are found in which part of a car?

4. What do the letters H.G.V. stand for?

5. How many Beatles were there?

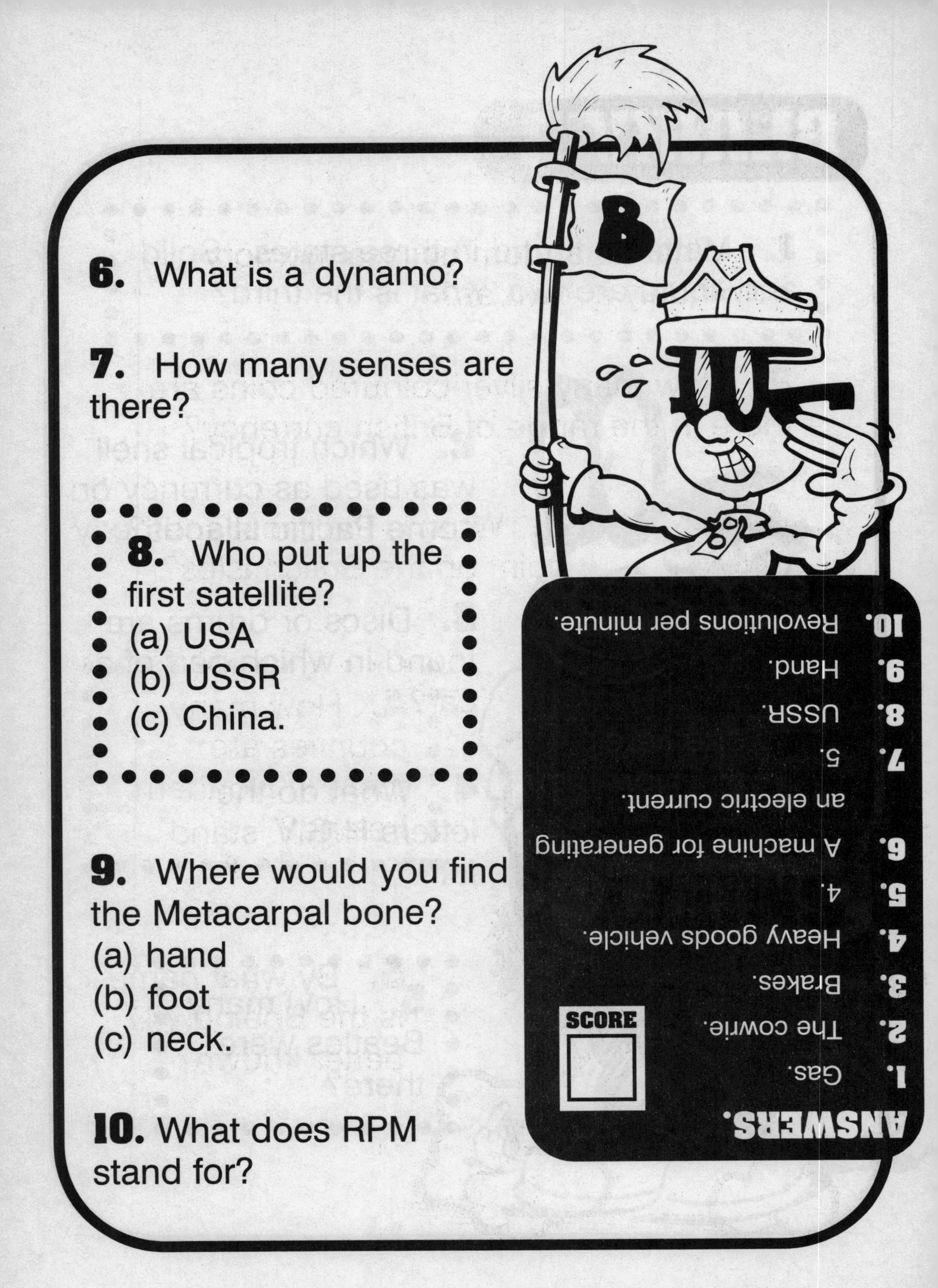

6. What is a dynamo?

7. How many senses are there?

8. Who put up the first satellite?
(a) USA
(b) USSR
(c) China.

9. Where would you find the Metacarpal bone?
(a) hand
(b) foot
(c) neck.

10. What does RPM stand for?

ANSWERS.

1. Gas.
2. The cowrie.
3. Brakes.
4. Heavy goods vehicle.
5. 4.
6. A machine for generating an electric current.
7. 5.
8. USSR.
9. Hand.
10. Revolutions per minute.

SCORE

GNASHER

1. What is random access memory commonly known as?

2. How many silver-coloured coins are there in the range of British currency?

3. What is the most southerly point on the British Isles?

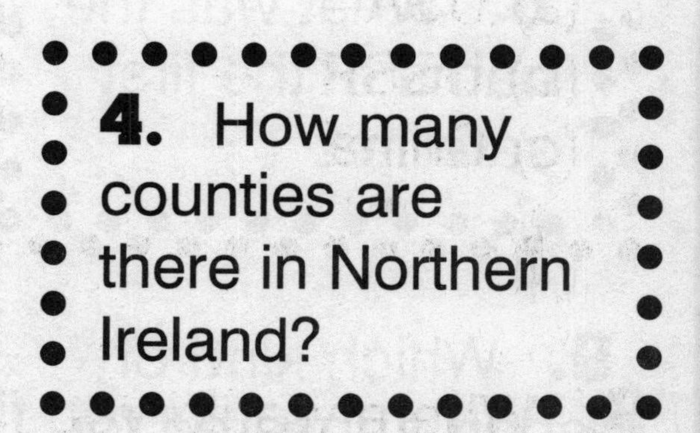

4. How many counties are there in Northern Ireland?

5. By what name is the Boeing 747 better known?

6. What is the only metal that is liquid at room temperature?

7. Which of the Seven Wonders of the World can still be seen?

8. What was the name of the first satellite?

9. Which kind of report appeared for the first time in the London Daily News in 1848?

10. Which inventor created the three wheeled electric car?

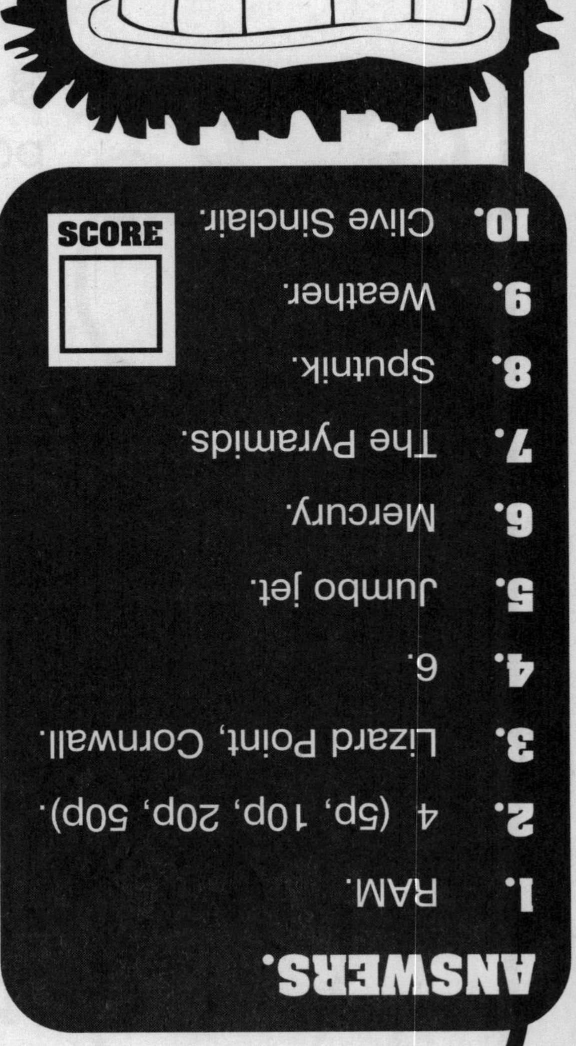

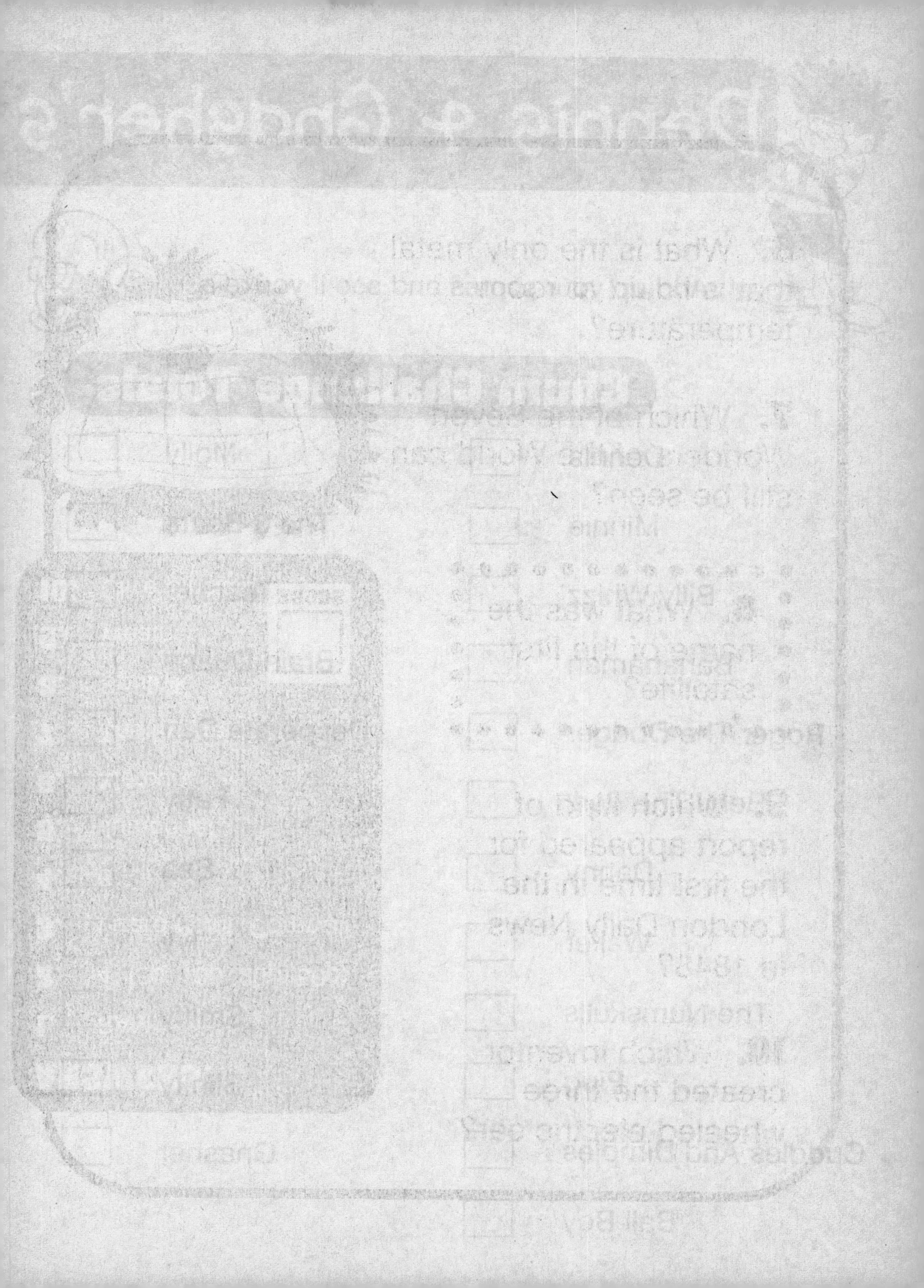

Dennis & Gnasher's

Add up your scores and see if you're a....

Chum Challenge Totals

Dennis		Molly	
Minnie		The 3 Bears	
Billy Whizz		Teacher	
Bananaman		Brain Duane	
Roger The Dodger		Desperate Dan	
Beryl The Peril		Fatty	
Danny		Bea	
Walter		Ivy	
The Numskulls		Smiffy	
Plug		Blinky	
Cuddles And Dimples		Gnasher	
Ball Boy			

Super Scoreboard

or a....

Topic Totals

Topic	Total	Topic	Total
Geography		Natural World	
General Knowledge		History	
Books/Films/TV		People	
Sport & Music		Science & Numbers	

	Best Ever Scores		Worst Ever Scores	
	Challenge	Topic	Challenge	Topic
You				
Mum				
Dad				
Brother				
Sister				
Pals....				
....				
....				
....				

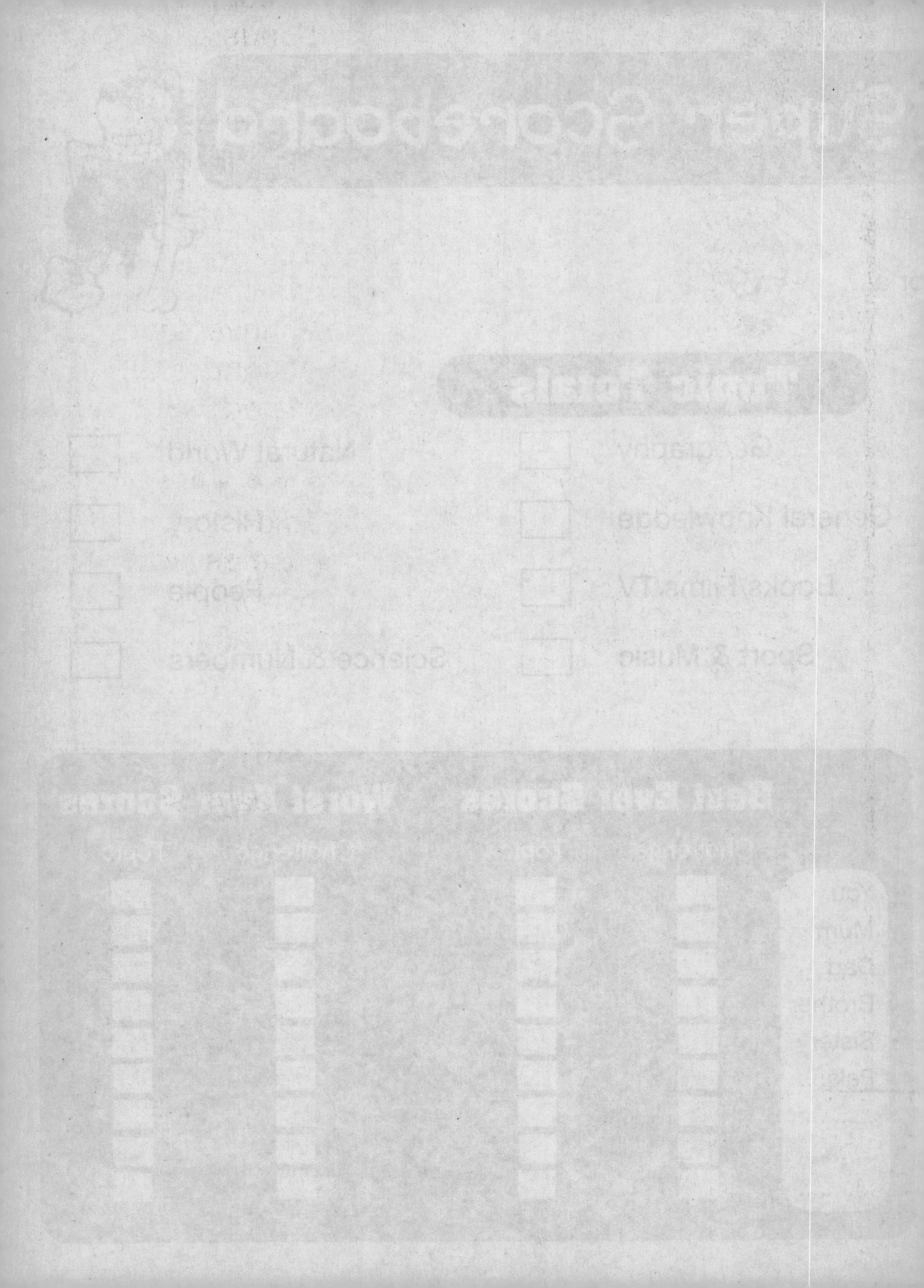